THIS BOOK HAS BEEN SENT TO YOU
AT THE SUGGESTION OF

JOHN T. MALONEY

Please accept it with our compliments

McGRAW-HILL BOOK COMPANY, Inc.

Ex Libris: _Robert L. Martin_

Classical
Electromagnetic
Theory

Classical Electromagnetic Theory

Nunzio Tralli

Professor of Physics
C. W. Post College
Long Island University

McGraw-Hill Book Company, Inc.

New York
San Francisco
Toronto
London

Classical
Electromagnetic
Theory

Copyright © 1963 by the McGraw-Hill Book Company, Inc.   All Rights
Reserved.   Printed in the United States of America.   This book, or
parts thereof, may not be reproduced in any form without permission
of the publishers.   *Library of Congress Catalog Card Number* 62-20730

65135

To My Wife Eva

Preface

This book is based on the author's lecture notes for a graduate course in electricity and magnetism which he gave at Hofstra College in the years 1954 to 1961. It is intended to serve as a textbook explaining the physical concepts of electricity and magnetism, describing the mathematical formalism, and presenting examples of both the ideas and methods involved.

An effort was made to keep the book self-contained. For this reason much of the material usually covered in an advanced undergraduate course in electrostatics has been included. Chapter 1 deals with the fundamentals of vector and tensor analysis. The reader is assumed to have no more mathematical background than that provided by undergraduate courses in advanced calculus and ordinary differential equations. More sophisticated mathematical methods are developed in the text as required. In this way it is hoped that the text will also prove suitable for both the ambitious undergraduate senior and the inadequately prepared graduate student.

As stated above, Chap. 1 treats the elements of vector and tensor analysis. The next five chapters deal with the fundamental ideas of electrostatics. Chapter 7 treats the special theory of relativity. Its main purpose is to lay the foundation for an introduction to the concept of the magnetic field in such a manner as to stress its origin in the motion of charges. The properties of the magnetic field are treated in Chap. 8. Chapter 9 deals with the derivation of Maxwell's equations and the wave equations. Chapters 10 to 13 are concerned with the propagation of plane, spherical, and cylindrical electromagnetic waves. Cavity resonators and wave guides are treated in Chaps. 14 and 15, respectively. Chapter 16 deals with the Lagrangian and Hamiltonian formulation of the electromagnetic field. Electron theory is treated in Chap. 17.

Rationalized mks units are used throughout the text. Tables for the conversion of units and equations to other unit systems are given in Appendixes IV and V.

Problems are listed at the end of each chapter. They are sometimes used to treat material omitted from the text because of space limitations. References are also listed at the end of each chapter.

The author wishes to express his gratitude to Mrs. Claudia Quickel, who typed the manuscript. He is indebted to his former students and his colleagues for encouragement and suggestions. He is especially indebted to Professor Lawrence A. Wills of the City College of New York for his careful perusal and criticism of the manuscript.

The author welcomes all suggestions for the improvement of the text.

Nunzio Tralli

Contents

CHAPTER 1

Scalars, Vectors, and Tensors

1-1. INTRODUCTION

In this chapter are presented those elements of vector and tensor analysis which will be found useful in the development of the subject matter in the remaining chapters of the text. No attempt at mathematical rigor has been made. It is hoped that the presentation will serve as a refreshing review for those who have already studied vector and tensor analysis and as a pleasant introduction for the novice.

1-2. VECTORS

A *vector* is a physical quantity which possesses both a magnitude and a direction. Such a quantity can be described mathematically by means of a *representative* in a cartesian coordinate system. In each cartesian coordinate system there is a unique representative of the vector.

To be specific, let **A** denote a vector. In the $OXYZ$ cartesian coordinate system its representative is the line segment $\vec{A}$ with components $A_x,\ A_y,\ A_z$. In another coordinate system, say $O'X'Y'Z'$, the representative of **A** is $\vec{A}'$ with components $A'_x,\ A'_y,\ A'_z$. The components of $\vec{A}$ and $\vec{A}'$ are related by

$$
\begin{aligned}
A'_x &= a_{xx}A_x + a_{xy}A_y + a_{xz}A_z \\
A'_y &= a_{yx}A_x + a_{yy}A_y + a_{yz}A_z \\
A'_z &= a_{zx}A_x + a_{zy}A_y + a_{zz}A_z
\end{aligned}
\tag{1-1}
$$

and

$$
\begin{aligned}
A_x &= a_{xx}A'_x + a_{yx}A'_y + a_{zx}A'_z \\
A_y &= a_{xy}A'_x + a_{yy}A'_y + a_{zy}A'_z \\
A_z &= a_{xz}A'_x + a_{yz}A'_y + a_{zz}A'_z
\end{aligned}
\tag{1-2}
$$

where the a's are direction cosines. For example, a_{xy} is the cosine of the angle between $O'X'$ and OY.

The transformation laws (1-1) and (1-2) define a vector quantity. That is, if the representative of a physical quantity in any cartesian

1

coordinate system has three components and these components transform according to the laws (1-1) and (1-2), the physical quantity is a vector.

Before proceeding further, it is convenient to introduce a more concise notation. Denote the OX axis by OX_1, the OY axis by OX_2, and the OZ axis by OX_3 with a like notation in the primed coordinate system. Then a_{xx} is denoted by a_{11}, a_{xy} by a_{12}, a_{xz} by a_{13}, etc., and Eqs. (1-1) and (1-2) can be written

$$A_i' = \sum_{j=1}^{3} a_{ij} A_j \qquad i = 1, 2, 3 \qquad (1\text{-}1a)$$

$$A_i = \sum_{j=1}^{3} a_{ji} A_j' \qquad i = 1, 2, 3 \qquad (1\text{-}2a)$$

The notation can be further simplified to

$$A_i' = a_{ij} A_j \qquad (1\text{-}1b)$$
$$A_i = a_{ji} A_j' \qquad (1\text{-}2b)$$

where it is to be understood that, whenever a literal suffix or index appears twice in a term, that term is to be summed for values of the suffix 1, 2, 3. Hence, since j appears twice, the summation $\sum\limits_{j=1}^{3}$ is indicated.

Furthermore, since a repeated index, often called a dummy index, indicates summation, another letter can be substituted for it at will.

Substitution for A_j in (1-1b) by means of (1-2b) yields

$$A_i' = a_{ij} a_{kj} A_k'$$

while substitution for A_j' in (1-2b) by means of (1-1b) yields

$$A_i = a_{ji} a_{jk} A_k$$

Hence the direction cosines satisfy the relations

$$a_{ij} a_{kj} = \delta_{ik} \qquad (1\text{-}3)$$
and
$$a_{ji} a_{jk} = \delta_{ik} \qquad (1\text{-}4)$$

where δ_{ik} is known as the *Kronecker delta* and has the values

$$\delta_{ik} = 1 \qquad \text{when } i = k$$
$$= 0 \qquad \text{when } i \neq k$$

Another much-used notation is the matrix notation. In this notation Eq. (1-1a) or (1-1b) is written

$$\begin{pmatrix} A_1' \\ A_2' \\ A_3' \end{pmatrix} = \begin{pmatrix} a_{11} & a_{12} & a_{13} \\ a_{21} & a_{22} & a_{23} \\ a_{31} & a_{32} & a_{33} \end{pmatrix} \begin{pmatrix} A_1 \\ A_2 \\ A_3 \end{pmatrix} \qquad (1\text{-}1c)$$

The 3×3 array

$$a \equiv \begin{pmatrix} a_{11} & a_{12} & a_{13} \\ a_{21} & a_{22} & a_{23} \\ a_{31} & a_{32} & a_{33} \end{pmatrix} \tag{1-5}$$

is known as a 3×3 *matrix* or as a square matrix of order 3^2. The quantities a_{ij} are called the *elements* of the matrix. The quantity

$$A \equiv \begin{pmatrix} A_1 \\ A_2 \\ A_3 \end{pmatrix} \tag{1-6}$$

is called a 3-*column* or a 3×1 matrix. Its elements A_i are the components of $\vec{A}$, the representative of the vector **A** in the $OX_1X_2X_3$ coordinate system. The multiplication of a 3-column by a 3×3 matrix from the left is defined by Eqs. (1-1a) and (1-1c).

In this matrix notation Eqs. (1-1a) and (1-2a) can be written

$$A' = aA \tag{1-1d}$$
$$A = a^T A' \tag{1-2c}$$

where the matrix

$$a^T = \begin{pmatrix} a_{11} & a_{21} & a_{31} \\ a_{12} & a_{22} & a_{32} \\ a_{13} & a_{23} & a_{33} \end{pmatrix} \tag{1-7}$$

which is formed from the matrix a by interchanging rows and columns, is known as the *transpose* of the matrix a.

The relations (1-3) and (1-4) can then be written[†]

$$aa^T = 1 \tag{1-3a}$$
$$a^T a = 1 \tag{1-4a}$$

or

$$\begin{pmatrix} a_{11} & a_{12} & a_{13} \\ a_{21} & a_{22} & a_{23} \\ a_{31} & a_{32} & a_{33} \end{pmatrix} \begin{pmatrix} a_{11} & a_{21} & a_{31} \\ a_{12} & a_{22} & a_{32} \\ a_{13} & a_{23} & a_{33} \end{pmatrix} = \begin{pmatrix} 1 & 0 & 0 \\ 0 & 1 & 0 \\ 0 & 0 & 1 \end{pmatrix} \tag{1-3b}$$

$$\begin{pmatrix} a_{11} & a_{21} & a_{31} \\ a_{12} & a_{22} & a_{32} \\ a_{13} & a_{23} & a_{33} \end{pmatrix} \begin{pmatrix} a_{11} & a_{12} & a_{13} \\ a_{21} & a_{22} & a_{23} \\ a_{31} & a_{32} & a_{33} \end{pmatrix} = \begin{pmatrix} 1 & 0 & 0 \\ 0 & 1 & 0 \\ 0 & 0 & 1 \end{pmatrix} \tag{1-4b}$$

† Any matrix b which satisfies the relations $ab = ba = 1$ is called the reciprocal of the matrix a and denoted by a^{-1}. Then, according to (1-3a) and (1-4a), $a^T = a^{-1}$. Such a matrix whose transpose is equal to its reciprocal is known as an *orthogonal* matrix.

Equations (1-3) and (1-3b) or (1-4) and (1-4b) define the multiplication of two matrices. The matrix

$$\underline{1} = \begin{pmatrix} 1 & 0 & 0 \\ 0 & 1 & 0 \\ 0 & 0 & 1 \end{pmatrix} \tag{1-8}$$

is known as the *unit matrix*. Its elements are the Kronecker deltas δ_{ij}.

In recapitulation, if the representative of a physical quantity in any cartesian coordinate system has three components and these components transform according to the laws (1-1) and (1-2), the physical quantity is a vector. In what follows we shall usually consider the representation of a vector **A** in only a single coordinate system. In such a case we shall not distinguish between the vector **A** and its representative and use the notation **A** for both. Furthermore, we shall refer to the components of the representative as the components of **A**.

Consider two vectors **A** and **B** whose representatives in a given coordinate system, $\vec{A}$ and $\vec{B}$, have components A_1, A_2, A_3 and B_1, B_2, B_3, respectively. The vector **A** + **B** has for representative $\vec{A} + \vec{B}$ with components $A_1 + B_1$, $A_2 + B_2$, $A_3 + B_3$, while the vector **B** + **A** has for representative $\vec{B} + \vec{A}$ with components $B_1 + A_1$, $B_2 + A_2$, $B_3 + A_3$. Since the A_i and B_i are numbers, $B_i + A_i = A_i + B_i$. Hence

$$\vec{B} + \vec{A} = \vec{A} + \vec{B}$$

and **B** + **A** = **A** + **B**. This result expresses the *commutative law of vector addition;* namely, the sum of two vectors is independent of the order of addition.

In a like manner, it can be shown that

$$\vec{A} + \vec{B} + \vec{C} = (\vec{A} + \vec{B}) + \vec{C} = \vec{A} + (\vec{B} + \vec{C}) = \vec{B} + (\vec{C} + \vec{A})$$

so that

$$\mathbf{A} + \mathbf{B} + \mathbf{C} = (\mathbf{A} + \mathbf{B}) + \mathbf{C} = \mathbf{A} + (\mathbf{B} + \mathbf{C}) = \mathbf{B} + (\mathbf{C} + \mathbf{A})$$

which expresses the *associative law of vector addition.*

1-3. VECTOR COMPONENTS

If we restrict ourselves to orthogonal coordinate systems, the component of a vector in a given direction is simply the projection of the vector along a line in that direction. The magnitude of the component is equal to the magnitude of the vector multiplied by the cosine of the angle between the vector and the given direction.

The component of $\mathbf{A}$ along the x_1 axis, for example, is A_1 where

$$A_1 = |\mathbf{A}| \cos (\mathbf{A},x_1) = A \cos (\mathbf{A},x_1) \tag{1-9}$$

where
$$A = |\mathbf{A}| = \sqrt{A_1{}^2 + A_2{}^2 + A_3{}^2} \tag{1-10}$$

denotes the magnitude of $\mathbf{A}$, $(\mathbf{A},x_1)$ is the positive angle between $\mathbf{A}$ and the x_1 axis, and

$$\cos (\mathbf{A},x_1) = \frac{A_1}{A} \tag{1-11}$$

If $\mathbf{i}_1$, $\mathbf{i}_2$, and $\mathbf{i}_3$ denote unit vectors along the x_1, x_2, and x_3 axes, respectively, then

$$\mathbf{A} = A_1\mathbf{i}_1 + A_2\mathbf{i}_2 + A_3\mathbf{i}_3 \tag{1-12}$$

The component of $\mathbf{A}$ in any arbitrary direction $\mathbf{s}$ is

$$A_s = A \cos (\mathbf{A},\mathbf{s})$$

or, using (1-12),

$$\begin{aligned} A_s &= |A_1\mathbf{i}_1| \cos (\mathbf{i}_1,\mathbf{s}) + |A_2\mathbf{i}_2| \cos (\mathbf{i}_2,\mathbf{s}) + |A_3\mathbf{i}_3| \cos (\mathbf{i}_3,\mathbf{s}) \\ &= A_1 \cos (x_1,\mathbf{s}) + A_2 \cos (x_2,\mathbf{s}) + A_3 \cos (x_3,\mathbf{s}) \end{aligned} \tag{1-13}$$

1-4. THE SCALAR PRODUCT

It was demonstrated in the preceding section that the direction cosines of any vector $\mathbf{A}$ are given by A_1/A, A_2/A, A_3/A. Let the direction cosines of any other vector $\mathbf{B}$ be B_1/B, B_2/B, B_3/B. Then the cosine of the angle between $\mathbf{A}$ and $\mathbf{B}$, $\theta = (\mathbf{A},\mathbf{B})$, is given by (see any text on analytic geometry)

$$\cos \theta = \frac{A_1}{A}\frac{B_1}{B} + \frac{A_2}{A}\frac{B_2}{B} + \frac{A_3}{A}\frac{B_3}{B}$$

Therefore
$$AB \cos \theta = A_1B_1 + A_2B_2 + A_3B_3 \tag{1-14}$$

The quantity $AB \cos \theta$ is known as the scalar product of the vectors $\mathbf{A}$ and $\mathbf{B}$ and is denoted by $\mathbf{A} \cdot \mathbf{B}$. Because of this notation the scalar product is also known as the dot product.

It follows from (1-14) that

$$\mathbf{A} \cdot \mathbf{B} = \mathbf{B} \cdot \mathbf{A} = AB \cos (\mathbf{A},\mathbf{B}) \tag{1-15}$$

which shows that the scalar product obeys the commutative law of multiplication.

Application of (1-15) to the unit vectors $\mathbf{i}_1$, $\mathbf{i}_2$, and $\mathbf{i}_3$ yields

$$\mathbf{i}_1 \cdot \mathbf{i}_1 = \mathbf{i}_2 \cdot \mathbf{i}_2 = \mathbf{i}_3 \cdot \mathbf{i}_3 = 1$$
$$\mathbf{i}_1 \cdot \mathbf{i}_2 = \mathbf{i}_2 \cdot \mathbf{i}_1 = \mathbf{i}_2 \cdot \mathbf{i}_3 = \mathbf{i}_3 \cdot \mathbf{i}_2 = \mathbf{i}_3 \cdot \mathbf{i}_1 = \mathbf{i}_1 \cdot \mathbf{i}_3 = 0 \qquad (1\text{-}16)$$

It is left as an exercise for the reader to verify that

$$(\mathbf{C} + \mathbf{D}) \cdot \mathbf{B} = \mathbf{C} \cdot \mathbf{B} + \mathbf{D} \cdot \mathbf{B}$$

which states that the distributive law holds for the scalar product.

The scalar product of two vectors is an example of the physical quantity called a *scalar*. By definition, a scalar quantity is one whose representative in any cartesian coordinate system is a single number which remains invariant in a transformation of coordinates. In order to verify that the scalar product is, indeed, a scalar quantity, consider two vectors $\mathbf{A}$ and $\mathbf{B}$ whose representatives in two cartesian coordinate systems are $\vec{A}$, $\vec{B}$ and $\vec{A}'$, $\vec{B}'$, respectively. Then, using (1-2a),

$$\begin{aligned}
\vec{A} \cdot \vec{B} &= \sum_i A_i B_i = \sum_i \left(\sum_j a_{ji} A'_j \right) \left(\sum_k a_{ki} B'_k \right) \\
&= \sum_{j,k} \left(\sum_i a_{ji} a_{ki} \right) A'_j B'_k = \sum_{j,k} \delta_{jk} A'_j B'_k \\
&= \sum_j A'_j B'_j = \vec{A}' \cdot \vec{B}'
\end{aligned}$$

Thus, the scalar product of two vectors remains invariant in the transformation of coordinates and, therefore, is a scalar quantity.

1-5. THE VECTOR PRODUCT

The vector product of any two vectors $\mathbf{A}$ and $\mathbf{B}$ is denoted by $\mathbf{A} \times \mathbf{B}$. Because of this notation it is also known as the cross product. By definition, it is a vector perpendicular to the plane of the vectors $\mathbf{A}$ and $\mathbf{B}$ whose magnitude is equal to the product of the magnitudes of $\mathbf{A}$ and $\mathbf{B}$ by the sine of the angle between them and whose direction is that of the advance of a right-hand screw rotating from the first vector to the second through the smaller angle between their positive directions. Thus

$$|\mathbf{A} \times \mathbf{B}| = AB \sin (\mathbf{A},\mathbf{B}) \qquad (1\text{-}17)$$

and
$$\mathbf{A} \times \mathbf{B} = -\mathbf{B} \times \mathbf{A} \qquad (1\text{-}18)$$

Equation (1-18) illustrates the failure of the commutative law of multiplication in the case of the vector product.

Application of the definition of the vector product to the unit vectors i_1, i_2, and i_3 yields

$$i_1 \times i_2 = -i_2 \times i_1 = i_3 \qquad i_2 \times i_3 = -i_3 \times i_2 = i_1$$
$$i_3 \times i_1 = -i_1 \times i_3 = i_2 \qquad i_1 \times i_1 = i_2 \times i_2 = i_3 \times i_3 = 0 \qquad (1\text{-}19)$$

It is left as an exercise for the reader to verify that

$$(C + D) \times B = C \times B + D \times B$$

which states that the distributive law holds for the vector product. It then follows, using (1-19), that

$$A \times B = (A_1 i_1 + A_2 i_2 + A_3 i_3) \times (B_1 i_1 + B_2 i_2 + B_3 i_3)$$
$$= i_1(A_2 B_3 - A_3 B_2) + i_2(A_3 B_1 - A_1 B_3) + i_3(A_1 B_2 - A_2 B_1)$$

which can be expressed in the more compact determinant form

$$A \times B = \begin{vmatrix} i_1 & i_2 & i_3 \\ A_1 & A_2 & A_3 \\ B_1 & B_2 & B_3 \end{vmatrix} \qquad (1\text{-}20)$$

It is interesting to note that the failure of the commutative law of multiplication in the case of the vector product now appears as a consequence of the fact that interchanging two rows of a determinant changes its sign. The vanishing of the vector product of two vectors in the same direction now appears as a consequence of the fact that a determinant vanishes if one of its rows is a multiple of another.

Because the vector product of two vectors differs from the vectors which we have considered thus far in one important respect, it is sometimes called a *pseudovector*. Consider two vectors A and B. Let $\vec{A}$ and $\vec{B}$ denote their representatives in one cartesian coordinate system and $\vec{A}'$ and $\vec{B}'$ their representatives in another system. Then, using (1-1a) and (1-2a),

$$(\vec{A} \times \vec{B})_1 = A_2 B_3 - A_3 B_2 = \sum_{j,k} (a_{j2} a_{k3} - a_{j3} a_{k2}) A_j' B_k'$$
$$= \sum_{j>k} (a_{j2} a_{k3} - a_{j3} a_{k2})(A_j' B_k' - A_k' B_j')$$
$$= \pm \sum_{j} a_{j1} (\vec{A}' \times \vec{B}')_j$$

Thus, in general

$$(\vec{A} \times \vec{B})_i = \pm \sum_{j} a_{ji} (\vec{A}' \times \vec{B}')_j$$

The plus and minus signs arise from the sign of the determinant of the matrix of the direction cosines [cf. Eq. (1-5)]. The plus sign holds if the coordinate systems are both right-handed or both left-handed; the minus sign holds if one is right-handed and the other left-handed.

Clearly, the representatives of vectors and pseudovectors obey different laws for transformations between right-handed and left-handed systems. The inversion $x_1' = -x_1$, $x_2' = -x_2$, $x_3' = -x_3$ is an example of such transformations. It can be used in a simple method for distinguishing between vectors and pseudovectors. Consider any vector **A**. Let its representative in a given cartesian coordinate system be $\vec{A}$ with components (A_1, A_2, A_3). In the inverse coordinate system its representative is $\vec{A}'$ with components $(-A_1, -A_2, -A_3)$. The components of the representative of a vector change sign in an inversion of coordinates. Consider now two vectors **A** and **B**. Let their representatives in the given coordinate system and the inverse coordinate system be $\vec{A}$, $\vec{B}$ and $\vec{A}'$, $\vec{B}'$, respectively. Then

$$(\vec{A}' \times \vec{B}')_1 = A_2' B_3' - A_3' B_2' = A_2 B_3 - A_3 B_2 = (\vec{A} \times \vec{B})_1$$

with similar expressions for the other two components. Thus, the components of the representative of a vector product do not change sign on an inversion of coordinates.

1-6. THE TRIPLE SCALAR PRODUCT

Consider three arbitrary vectors **A**, **B**, and **C**. By definition, the triple scalar product is **A · B ✕ C**. Application of the results of the last two sections then yields

$$\mathbf{A \cdot B \times C} = \begin{vmatrix} A_1 & A_2 & A_3 \\ B_1 & B_2 & B_3 \\ C_1 & C_2 & C_3 \end{vmatrix} \tag{1-21}$$

It follows at once on interchanging the position of the rows of the determinant that

$$\mathbf{A \cdot B \times C = B \cdot C \times A = C \cdot A \times B} \tag{1-22}$$

There is then no ambiguity in writing the triple scalar product as **ABC**; i.e., the positions of the dot and cross are immaterial, and the three factors can be permuted cyclically without changing the product.

It should be noted that, while the scalar product of two vectors has the same representative in all cartesian coordinate systems, the representative of the triple scalar product (which is the scalar product of a vector and a pseudovector) changes sign in transformations between right-handed and left-handed coordinate systems. For this reason the triple scalar product is sometimes called a *pseudoscalar*.

1-7. THE TRIPLE VECTOR PRODUCT

This product is defined as $\mathbf{A} \times (\mathbf{B} \times \mathbf{C})$, where the parentheses indicate that one first performs the vector product of $\mathbf{B}$ with $\mathbf{C}$ and then the vector product of $\mathbf{A}$ with the resulting vector. In general

$$(\mathbf{A} \times \mathbf{B}) \times \mathbf{C} \neq \mathbf{A} \times (\mathbf{B} \times \mathbf{C})$$

i.e., the triple vector product does not obey the associative law.

Let $\mathbf{F} = \mathbf{A} \times (\mathbf{B} \times \mathbf{C})$. Then from the definition of vector product, $\mathbf{F}$ is perpendicular to $(\mathbf{B} \times \mathbf{C})$ and must lie in the plane of $\mathbf{B}$ and $\mathbf{C}$. Consequently

$$\mathbf{F} = \alpha\mathbf{B} + \beta\mathbf{C} \tag{1-23}$$

where α and β are scalar multipliers to be determined. The scalar product of $\mathbf{A}$ and $\mathbf{F}$ yields

$$\mathbf{A} \cdot \mathbf{F} = \alpha\mathbf{A} \cdot \mathbf{B} + \beta\mathbf{A} \cdot \mathbf{C} = 0$$

or

$$\frac{\alpha}{\mathbf{A} \cdot \mathbf{C}} = -\frac{\beta}{\mathbf{A} \cdot \mathbf{B}} \tag{1-24}$$

since $\mathbf{F}$ is perpendicular to $\mathbf{A}$. Then

$$\alpha = n(\mathbf{A} \cdot \mathbf{C}) \qquad \text{and} \qquad \beta = -n(\mathbf{A} \cdot \mathbf{B}) \tag{1-25}$$

where n is some constant scalar to be determined.

Substitution of (1-25) into (1-23) yields

$$\mathbf{F} = n[(\mathbf{A} \cdot \mathbf{C})\mathbf{B} - (\mathbf{A} \cdot \mathbf{B})\mathbf{C}] \tag{1-26}$$

the x_1 component of which is

$$F_1 = n[(A_1C_1 + A_2C_2 + A_3C_3)B_1 - (A_1B_1 + A_2B_2 + A_3B_3)C_1] \tag{1-27}$$

The x_1 component of $\mathbf{F} = \mathbf{A} \times (\mathbf{B} \times \mathbf{C})$ is given by

$$\begin{aligned}
F_1 &= A_2(\mathbf{B} \times \mathbf{C})_3 - A_3(\mathbf{B} \times \mathbf{C})_2 \\
&= A_2(B_1C_2 - B_2C_1) - A_3(B_3C_1 - B_1C_3) \\
&= (A_1C_1 + A_2C_2 + A_3C_3)B_1 - (A_1B_1 + A_2B_2 + A_3B_3)C_1
\end{aligned} \tag{1-28}$$

Comparison of Eqs. (1-27) and (1-28) shows that $n = 1$ and, consequently, that

$$\mathbf{A} \times (\mathbf{B} \times \mathbf{C}) = (\mathbf{A} \cdot \mathbf{C})\mathbf{B} - (\mathbf{A} \cdot \mathbf{B})\mathbf{C} \tag{1-29}$$

1-8. THE GRADIENT

Let a scalar ϕ be associated with every point (x_1,x_2,x_3) of space in such a way that $\phi(x_1,x_2,x_3)$ is a continuous and differentiable function of position. In the transition from the point (x_1,x_2,x_3) to the point $(x_1 + dx_1,\ x_2 + dx_2,\ x_3 + dx_3)$ the scalar ϕ undergoes a change

$$d\phi = \frac{\partial \phi}{\partial x_1}\, dx_1 + \frac{\partial \phi}{\partial x_2}\, dx_2 + \frac{\partial \phi}{\partial x_3}\, dx_3 \tag{1-30}$$

corresponding to the change

$$d\mathbf{s} = dx_1\, \mathbf{i}_1 + dx_2\, \mathbf{i}_2 + dx_3\, \mathbf{i}_3 \tag{1-31}$$

in the position vector $\mathbf{s}$.

The right-hand member of Eq. (1-30) may be considered as the scalar product of $d\mathbf{s}$ with the vector

$$\text{grad } \phi = \frac{\partial \phi}{\partial x_1}\, \mathbf{i}_1 + \frac{\partial \phi}{\partial x_2}\, \mathbf{i}_2 + \frac{\partial \phi}{\partial x_3}\, \mathbf{i}_3 \tag{1-32}$$

where grad ϕ is read "gradient of ϕ." Thus

$$d\phi = \text{grad } \phi \cdot d\mathbf{s} \tag{1-33}$$

Since the scalar product of grad ϕ and $d\mathbf{s}$ is zero when $d\mathbf{s}$ lies in the surface $\phi = $ constant, it follows that grad ϕ is perpendicular to this surface. Such a surface for which ϕ is a constant is known as an *equipotential surface*.

The directional derivative of the scalar ϕ in any direction $\mathbf{s}$ is

$$\frac{d\phi}{ds} = \frac{\text{grad } \phi \cdot d\mathbf{s}}{ds} = \text{grad } \phi \cdot \mathbf{i}_s \tag{1-34}$$

where $\mathbf{i}_s$ is a unit vector in the direction of $\mathbf{s}$. Clearly, the maximum value of $d\phi/ds$ is $|\text{grad } \phi|$. Thus grad ϕ represents in magnitude and direction the greatest space rate of change of ϕ.

1-9. CONSERVATIVE VECTOR FIELD

By definition, a conservative vector field is a vector field for which the line integral of the vector about any closed path is zero. Thus, if the vector be denoted by $\mathbf{F}$,

$$\oint \mathbf{F} \cdot d\mathbf{s} = 0 \tag{1-35}$$

where $d\mathbf{s}$ is an element of the path and the symbol $\oint$ indicates a line integral about a closed path.

A necessary and sufficient condition for a conservative vector field is that the vector be expressible as the gradient of a scalar. This fact can be demonstrated as follows: Let $\mathbf{F} = -\operatorname{grad} \phi$. Then

$$\int_a^b \mathbf{F} \cdot d\mathbf{s} = -\int_a^b \operatorname{grad} \phi \cdot d\mathbf{s}$$
$$= -\int_a^b d\phi = \phi(a) - \phi(b) \tag{1-36}$$

From (1-36) it is evident that the line integral of the gradient of a scalar between any two points a and b is independent of the path of integration, depending solely on the value of the scalar at the initial and final points. Hence $\oint \operatorname{grad} \phi \cdot d\mathbf{s} = 0$.

According to (1-36) the value of the scalar ϕ at any point b in terms of its value at any point a is

$$\phi(b) = \phi(a) - \int_a^b \mathbf{F} \cdot d\mathbf{s} \tag{1-37}$$

where the path of integration is entirely arbitrary. Now let the coordinates of the point a be (x_1, x_2, x_3) and those of b be $(x_1 + dx_1, x_2 + dx_2, x_3 + dx_3)$. Then

$$\phi(b) - \phi(a) = d\phi = \operatorname{grad} \phi \cdot d\mathbf{s}$$

where $d\mathbf{s} = dx_1\,\mathbf{i}_1 + dx_2\,\mathbf{i}_2 + dx_3\,\mathbf{i}_3$, and (1-37) becomes

$$\operatorname{grad} \phi \cdot d\mathbf{s} = -\mathbf{F} \cdot d\mathbf{s}$$

provided that $\mathbf{F}$ is at least piece-wise continuous. Since $d\mathbf{s}$ is arbitrary, it follows that $\mathbf{F} = -\operatorname{grad} \phi$.

1-10. DIVERGENCE OF A VECTOR

It was seen in Sec. 1-8 that

$$\operatorname{grad} \phi = \frac{\partial \phi}{\partial x_1}\,\mathbf{i}_1 + \frac{\partial \phi}{\partial x_2}\,\mathbf{i}_2 + \frac{\partial \phi}{\partial x_3}\,\mathbf{i}_3 \tag{1-32}$$

It is now convenient to rewrite the expression as

$$\operatorname{grad} \phi = \left(\frac{\partial}{\partial x_1}\,\mathbf{i}_1 + \frac{\partial}{\partial x_2}\,\mathbf{i}_2 + \frac{\partial}{\partial x_3}\,\mathbf{i}_3\right) \phi$$

where the quantity in the parentheses is a vector operator known as the *del operator* and denoted by ∇. Consequently,

$$\operatorname{grad} \phi \equiv \nabla \phi$$

Application of the rule of scalar multiplication to the vectors

$$\nabla = \frac{\partial}{\partial x_1} i_1 + \frac{\partial}{\partial x_2} i_2 + \frac{\partial}{\partial x_3} i_3$$

and
$$\mathbf{F} = F_1 i_1 + F_2 i_2 + F_3 i_3$$

in the order $\nabla \cdot \mathbf{F}$ yields a scalar known as the divergence of $\mathbf{F}$ and written as

$$\nabla \cdot \mathbf{F} = \operatorname{div} \mathbf{F} = \frac{\partial}{\partial x_1} F_1 + \frac{\partial}{\partial x_2} F_2 + \frac{\partial}{\partial x_3} F_3 \qquad (1\text{-}38)$$

The above treatment has been purely formal. The physical significance of the divergence of any vector will become apparent in the consideration of Gauss' theorem (Sec. 1-15).

Note that, since the vector ∇ is an operator,

$$\nabla \cdot \mathbf{F} \neq \mathbf{F} \cdot \nabla = F_1 \frac{\partial}{\partial x_1} + F_2 \frac{\partial}{\partial x_2} + F_3 \frac{\partial}{\partial x_3} \qquad (1\text{-}39)$$

The application of the rule of scalar multiplication to the vectors ∇ and $\mathbf{F}$ in the order $\mathbf{F} \cdot \nabla$ yields a new *scalar operator*.

1-11. CURL OF A VECTOR

It was seen in the preceding section that the scalar product $\nabla \cdot \mathbf{F}$ of the del operator ∇ and any vector $\mathbf{F}$ gave rise to the scalar-point function called the divergence of the vector $\mathbf{F}$. Similarly, the vector product of ∇ and $\mathbf{F}$ in the order $\nabla \times \mathbf{F}$ gives rise to a vector-point function known as the curl of the vector $\mathbf{F}$ and written

$$\nabla \times \mathbf{F} = \operatorname{curl} \mathbf{F} = i_1 \left(\frac{\partial}{\partial x_2} F_3 - \frac{\partial}{\partial x_3} F_2 \right) + i_2 \left(\frac{\partial}{\partial x_3} F_1 - \frac{\partial}{\partial x_1} F_3 \right)$$

$$+ i_3 \left(\frac{\partial}{\partial x_1} F_2 - \frac{\partial}{\partial x_2} F_1 \right)$$

$$= \begin{vmatrix} i_1 & i_2 & i_3 \\ \dfrac{\partial}{\partial x_1} & \dfrac{\partial}{\partial x_2} & \dfrac{\partial}{\partial x_3} \\ F_1 & F_2 & F_3 \end{vmatrix} \qquad (1\text{-}40)$$

Note that, since the vector ∇ is an operator, $\nabla \times \mathbf{F} \neq -\mathbf{F} \times \nabla$, which is another vector operator.

The vanishing of the curl of a vector at all points in space is a necessary condition which any vector $\mathbf{F}$ must satisfy if it is derivable from a potential. Thus, if $\mathbf{F} = -\operatorname{grad} \phi$, then $\operatorname{curl} \mathbf{F} = 0$. The proof is as follows: Since $\mathbf{F} = -\operatorname{grad} \phi$,

$$\int \mathbf{F} \cdot d\mathbf{s} = -\int \operatorname{grad} \phi \cdot d\mathbf{s}$$

or

$$\int (F_1\, dx_1 + F_2\, dx_2 + F_3\, dx_3) = -\int \left(\frac{\partial \phi}{\partial x_1}\, dx_1 + \frac{\partial \phi}{\partial x_2}\, dx_2 + \frac{\partial \phi}{\partial x_3}\, dx_3 \right)$$

Then $\qquad F_1 = -\dfrac{\partial \phi}{\partial x_1} \qquad F_2 = -\dfrac{\partial \phi}{\partial x_2} \qquad F_3 = -\dfrac{\partial \phi}{\partial x_3}$

and $\qquad \dfrac{\partial}{\partial x_2} F_1 = -\dfrac{\partial^2 \phi}{\partial x_2\, \partial x_1} = -\dfrac{\partial^2 \phi}{\partial x_1\, \partial x_2}$

$$\frac{\partial}{\partial x_1} F_2 = -\frac{\partial^2 \phi}{\partial x_1\, \partial x_2}$$

so that $\qquad \dfrac{\partial}{\partial x_1} F_2 - \dfrac{\partial}{\partial x_2} F_1 = 0$

Similarly $\qquad \dfrac{\partial}{\partial x_2} F_3 - \dfrac{\partial}{\partial x_3} F_2 = 0 \qquad \dfrac{\partial}{\partial x_3} F_1 - \dfrac{\partial}{\partial x_1} F_3 = 0$

Hence $\qquad\qquad\qquad \text{curl } \mathbf{F} = 0 \qquad\qquad\qquad$ Q.E.D.

In Sec. 1-17 it will be shown that, if curl $\mathbf{F} = 0$, then $\oint \mathbf{F} \cdot d\mathbf{s} = 0$ and $\mathbf{F} = -\text{grad } \phi$. Hence the vanishing of the curl of a vector is both a necessary and sufficient condition for a conservative vector field.

1-12. THE LAPLACIAN OPERATOR

The scalar product of the del operator with grad ϕ yields

$$\text{div grad } \phi = \boldsymbol{\nabla} \cdot \boldsymbol{\nabla}\phi \equiv \nabla^2\phi = \left(\frac{\partial^2}{\partial x_1{}^2} + \frac{\partial^2}{\partial x_2{}^2} + \frac{\partial^2}{\partial x_3{}^2} \right) \phi \quad (1\text{-}41)$$

The quantity in the parentheses is known as the Laplacian operator or, simply, the Laplacian and is denoted by ∇^2.

One can also apply the Laplacian to a vector. For any vector $\mathbf{F}$,

$$\nabla^2 \mathbf{F} = \left(\frac{\partial^2}{\partial x_1{}^2} + \frac{\partial^2}{\partial x_2{}^2} + \frac{\partial^2}{\partial x_3{}^2} \right) \mathbf{F}$$

$$= \left(\frac{\partial^2}{\partial x_1{}^2} + \frac{\partial^2}{\partial x_2{}^2} + \frac{\partial^2}{\partial x_3{}^2} \right) F_1 \mathbf{i}_1 + \left(\frac{\partial^2}{\partial x_1{}^2} + \frac{\partial^2}{\partial x_2{}^2} + \frac{\partial^2}{\partial x_3{}^2} \right) F_2 \mathbf{i}_2$$

$$+ \left(\frac{\partial^2}{\partial x_1{}^2} + \frac{\partial^2}{\partial x_2{}^2} + \frac{\partial^2}{\partial x_3{}^2} \right) F_3 \mathbf{i}_3$$

$$= \mathbf{i}_1 \nabla^2 F_1 + \mathbf{i}_2 \nabla^2 F_2 + \mathbf{i}_3 \nabla^2 F_3 \qquad\qquad (1\text{-}42)$$

1-13. HELMHOLTZ'S THEOREM

Consider any vector field $\mathbf{F}$ such that

$$\boldsymbol{\nabla} \cdot \mathbf{F} = \rho \qquad\qquad (1\text{-}43)$$

$$\boldsymbol{\nabla} \times \mathbf{F} = \mathbf{c} \qquad\qquad (1\text{-}44)$$

where the scalar ρ and the vector $\mathbf{c}$ are given functions of x_1, x_2, x_3. Since the divergence of the curl of any vector is zero, $\nabla \cdot \mathbf{c} = 0$. Helmholtz's theorem states that $\mathbf{F}$ can be expressed as the sum of two vectors, one of which is solenoidal (i.e., its divergence is equal to zero) and the other irrotational (i.e., its curl is equal to zero); i.e.,

$$\mathbf{F} = \mathbf{X} + \mathbf{Y} \tag{1-45}$$

where $\qquad \nabla \cdot \mathbf{X} = 0 \qquad$ and $\qquad \nabla \times \mathbf{Y} = 0$

To verify the theorem, let

$$\mathbf{X} = \nabla \times \mathbf{A}$$
$$\mathbf{Y} = -\nabla \phi$$

so that $\qquad\qquad \mathbf{F} = \nabla \times \mathbf{A} - \nabla \phi \tag{1-46}$

If both $\mathbf{A}$ and ϕ can be determined, the theorem is verified. To do this, first take the divergence of (1-46). Then, using (1-43),

$$\nabla^2 \phi = -\rho \tag{1-47}$$

This equation for ϕ is known as Poisson's equation. Next take the curl of (1-46), obtaining (cf. Exercise 1-5g)

$$\nabla \times (\nabla \times \mathbf{A}) = \nabla(\nabla \cdot \mathbf{A}) - \nabla^2 \mathbf{A} = \mathbf{c} \tag{1-48}$$

Since $\mathbf{A}$ is as yet undetermined, we can assume that $\nabla \cdot \mathbf{A} = 0$, so that (1-48) reduces to

$$\nabla^2 \mathbf{A} = -\mathbf{c} \tag{1-49}$$

or
$$\nabla^2 A_1 = -c_1$$
$$\nabla^2 A_2 = -c_2$$
$$\nabla^2 A_3 = -c_3$$

These equations are of precisely the same form as Poisson's equation. Consequently, to complete the verification of Helmholtz's theorem, we need only solve Poisson's equation. This will be done in the following section.

1-14. POISSON'S EQUATION

We shall use Poisson's equation $\nabla^2 \phi = -\rho$ or, explicitly,

$$\left(\frac{\partial^2}{\partial x_1^2} + \frac{\partial^2}{\partial x_2^2} + \frac{\partial^2}{\partial x_3^2} \right) \phi(x_1, x_2, x_3) = -\rho(x_1, x_2, x_3) \tag{1-50}$$

to illustrate two methods of solving inhomogeneous equations, namely, the *Fourier transform method* and *Green's-function method*.

The problem we are to solve is: Given the function $\rho(x_1, x_2, x_3)$, find the function $\phi(x_1, x_2, x_3)$ which satisfies Eq. (1-50) and the boundary conditions that ϕ and grad ϕ approach zero as x_1, x_2, x_3 approach plus or minus infinity. The solution is easily obtained by the use of Fourier transforms.† Multiply both sides of (1-50) by $(1/2\pi)^{3/2}e^{-i(k_1x_1+k_2x_2+k_3x_3)}\,dx_1\,dx_2\,dx_3$, and integrate over x_1, x_2, x_3 from $-\infty$ to $+\infty$. Then the right-hand member becomes

$$-\bar{\rho}(k_1,k_2,k_3)$$

and the left-hand member

$$-(k_1{}^2 + k_2{}^2 + k_3{}^2)\bar{\phi}(k_1,k_2,k_3)$$

where we have integrated by parts twice and used the boundary conditions that ϕ and grad ϕ approach zero as x_1, x_2, x_3 approach plus or minus infinity. Thus

$$(k_1{}^2 + k_2{}^2 + k_3{}^2)\bar{\phi}(k_1,k_2,k_3) = \bar{\rho}(k_1,k_2,k_3)$$

so that
$$\bar{\phi}(k_1,k_2,k_3) = \frac{\bar{\rho}(k_1,k_2,k_3)}{k_1{}^2 + k_2{}^2 + k_3{}^2} \tag{1-51}$$

Now multiply both sides of (1-51) by $(1/2\pi)^{3/2}e^{i(k_1x_1+k_2x_2+k_3x_3)}\,dk_1\,dk_2\,dk_3$ and integrate over k_1, k_2, k_3 from $-\infty$ to $+\infty$. Then

$$\phi(x_1,x_2,x_3) = \left(\frac{1}{2\pi}\right)^{3/2} \int\!\!\!\int\!\!\!\int_{-\infty}^{+\infty} \frac{\bar{\rho}(k_1,k_2,k_3)}{k_1{}^2 + k_2{}^2 + k_3{}^2}\, e^{i(k_1x_1+k_2x_2+k_3x_3)}\,dk_1\,dk_2\,dk_3$$

But $$\bar{\rho}(k_1,k_2,k_3) = \left(\frac{1}{2\pi}\right)^{3/2}\int\!\!\!\int\!\!\!\int_{-\infty}^{+\infty} \rho(x_1',x_2',x_3')e^{-i(k_1x_1'+k_2x_2'+k_3x_3')}\,dx_1'\,dx_2'\,dx_3'$$

Hence

$$\phi(x_1,x_2,x_3) = \left(\frac{1}{2\pi}\right)^{3} \int\!\!\!\int\!\!\!\int_{-\infty}^{+\infty} \rho(x_1',x_2',x_3')$$

$$\left(\int\!\!\!\int\!\!\!\int_{-\infty}^{+\infty} \frac{e^{i[k_1(x_1-x_1')+k_2(x_2-x_2')+k_3(x_3-x_3')]}}{k_1{}^2 + k_2{}^2 + k_3{}^2}\, dk_1\,dk_2\,dk_3\right) dx_1'\,dx_2'\,dx_3' \tag{1-52}$$

† Two functions $f(x_1,x_2,x_3)$ and $\bar{f}(k_1,k_2,k_3)$ satisfying the relations

$$f(x_1,x_2,x_3) = \left(\frac{1}{2\pi}\right)^{3/2} \int\!\!\!\int\!\!\!\int_{-\infty}^{+\infty} \bar{f}(k_1,k_2,k_3)e^{i(k_1x_1+k_2x_2+k_3x_3)}\,dk_1\,dk_2\,dk_3$$

$$\bar{f}(k_1,k_2,k_3) = \left(\frac{1}{2\pi}\right)^{3/2} \int\!\!\!\int\!\!\!\int_{-\infty}^{+\infty} f(x_1,x_2,x_3)e^{-i(k_1x_1+k_2x_2+k_3x_3)}\,dx_1,\,dx_2,\,dx_3$$

are said to be (infinite) Fourier transforms of each other.

The integral in the parentheses in Eq. (1-52) is easily evaluated (cf. Appendix I). Its value is $2\pi^2[(x_1 - x_1')^2 + (x_2 - x_2')^2 + (x_3 - x_3')^2]^{-\frac{1}{2}}$. Consequently

$$\phi(x_1,x_2,x_3) = \frac{1}{4\pi} \iiint_{-\infty}^{+\infty} \frac{\rho(x_1',x_2',x_3')\,dx_1'\,dx_2'\,dx_3'}{[(x_1 - x_1')^2 + (x_2 - x_2')^2 + (x_3 - x_3')^2]^{\frac{1}{2}}} \quad (1\text{-}53)$$

In a notation which has become common in modern physics, Eq. (1-53) can be written

$$\phi(\mathbf{r}) = \frac{1}{4\pi} \int_{-\infty}^{+\infty} \frac{\rho(\mathbf{r})}{|\mathbf{r} - \mathbf{r}'|}\,d\mathbf{r}' \quad (1\text{-}53a)$$

In this notation a function of a vector such as $\phi(\mathbf{r})$ is to be understood as a function of the components of the vector, for example, $\phi(x_1,x_2,x_3)$. Furthermore $d\mathbf{r}'$ is not a differential vector but rather represents the volume element $d\mathbf{r}' = dx_1'\,dx_2'\,dx_3'$. This notation is clearly ambiguous. We shall, however, make use of it when it is convenient and when confusion is not likely to arise.

In electrostatics ϕ represents the potential and ρ is proportional to the distribution of charge. Thus, the potential ϕ at the *field point* (x_1,x_2,x_3) is given in terms of the charge density ρ at the *source point* (x_1',x_2',x_3') and the distance between the field and source points.

The case of a point charge q at (x_1',x_2',x_3') can be taken into account in the above method of solution by the introduction of the *Dirac delta function* $\delta(\mathbf{r} - \mathbf{r}')$. It is defined by the relations†

$$\delta(\mathbf{r} - \mathbf{r}') = 0 \qquad \mathbf{r} \neq \mathbf{r}' \quad (1\text{-}54)$$

$$\int_{-\infty}^{+\infty} f(\mathbf{r}')\delta(\mathbf{r} - \mathbf{r}')\,d\mathbf{r}' = f(\mathbf{r}) \quad (1\text{-}55)$$

for an arbitrary function f. If f is constant and equal to unity, (1-55) reduces to

$$\int_{-\infty}^{+\infty} \delta(\mathbf{r} - \mathbf{r}')\,d\mathbf{r}' = 1 \quad (1\text{-}56)$$

or, explicitly,

$$\int_{-\infty}^{+\infty} \delta(x_1 - x_1')\,dx_1' \int_{-\infty}^{+\infty} \delta(x_2 - x_2')\,dx_2' \int_{-\infty}^{+\infty} \delta(x_3 - x_3')\,dx_3' = 1$$
$$(1\text{-}56a)$$

† Written out, expressions (1-54) and (1-55) are

$$\delta(x_1 - x_1',\, x_2 - x_2',\, x_3 - x_3') \equiv \delta(x_1 - x_1')\delta(x_2 - x_2')\delta(x_3 - x_3') = 0$$
$$x_1 \neq x_1' \qquad x_2 \neq x_2' \qquad x_3 \neq x_3'$$

$$\int_{-\infty}^{+\infty} f(x_1',x_2',x_3')\delta(x_1 - x_1',\, x_2 - x_2',\, x_3 - x_3')\,dx_1'\,dx_2'\,dx_3' = f(x_1,x_2,x_3)$$

Clearly, the Dirac delta function is not a function in the conventional meaning of the term. It is therefore called a symbolic function. The integrations in (1-55) and (1-56) need not extend from $-\infty$ to $+\infty$ but may be over any domain surrounding the critical point $\mathbf{r}(x_1,x_2,x_3)$ at which the delta function does not vanish.

In the case of a point charge of magnitude q at (x_1',x_2',x_3') the source term $\rho(x_1,x_2,x_3)$ is replaced by $q\delta(x_1 - x_1')\delta(x_2 - x_2')\delta(x_3 - x_3')$, so that Poisson's equation (1-50) becomes

$$\left(\frac{\partial^2}{\partial x_1^2} + \frac{\partial^2}{\partial x_2^2} + \frac{\partial^2}{\partial x_3^2}\right)\phi(x_1,x_2,x_3) = -q\delta(x_1 - x_1')\delta(x_1 - x_1')\delta(x_1 - x_1')$$

(1-57)

Then, proceeding as above,

$$-(k_1^2 + k_2^2 + k_3^2)\bar{\phi}(k_1,k_2,k_3) = -\left(\frac{1}{2\pi}\right)^{3/2} qe^{-i(k_1x_1'+k_2x_2'+k_3x_3')}$$

so that
$$\bar{\phi}(k_1,k_2,k_3) = \left(\frac{1}{2\pi}\right)^{3/2} q\,\frac{e^{-i(k_1x_1'+k_2x_2'+k_3x_3')}}{k_1^2 + k_2^2 + k_3^2}$$

Hence

$$\phi(x_1,x_2,x_3) = \left(\frac{1}{2\pi}\right)^3 q \iiint\limits_{-\infty}^{+\infty} \frac{e^{i[k_1(x_1-x_1')+k_2(x_2-x_1')+k_3(x_3-x_3')]}}{k_1^2 + k_2^2 + k_3^2}\,dk_1\,dk_2\,dk_3$$

$$= \frac{1}{4\pi}\,\frac{q}{\sqrt{(x_1 - x_1')^2 + (x_2 - x_2')^2 + (x_3 - x_3')^2}}$$ (1-58)

The solution of Poisson's equation (1-50) by Green's-function method proceeds as follows: By definition, that solution of Eq. (1-50) corresponding to $-\rho(x_1,x_2,x_3) = \delta(x_1 - x_1')\delta(x_2 - x_2')\delta(x_3 - x_3')$ is the Green's function $G(x_1,x_2,x_3; x_1',x_2',x_3')$ for the operator ∇^2 *and* the given boundary conditions. Thus the Green's function satisfies the equation

$$\nabla^2 G(x_1,x_2,x_3; x_1',x_2',x_3') = \delta(x_1 - x_1')\delta(x_2 - x_2')\delta(x_3 - x_3') \quad (1\text{-}59)$$

with the same boundary conditions as on the function $\phi(x_1,x_2,x_3)$. The importance of the Green's function is that it enables a differential equation with suitable boundary conditions to be solved by a quadrature. Thus, the solution of (1-50) is

$$\phi(x_1,x_2,x_3) = \iiint\limits_{-\infty}^{+\infty} G(x_1,x_2,x_3; x_1',x_2',x_3')[-\rho(x_1',x_2',x_3')]\,dx_1'\,dx_2'\,dx_3' \quad (1\text{-}60)$$

where G is the solution of (1-50). But from the discussion of the point charge,

$$G(x_1,x_2,x_3; x_1',x_2',x_3') = -\frac{1}{4\pi}\,\frac{1}{\sqrt{(x_1 - x_1')^2 + (x_2 - x_2')^2 + (x_3 - x_3')^2}}$$

(1-61)

so that

$$\phi(x_1,x_2,x_3) = \frac{1}{4\pi} \int\!\!\!\int\!\!\!\int_{-\infty}^{+\infty} \frac{\rho(x_1',x_2',x_3')\, dx_1'\, dx_2'\, dx_3'}{\sqrt{(x_1 - x_1')^2 + (x_2 - x_2')^2 + (x_3 - x_3')^2}}$$

in agreement with (1-53).

An important property of the Green's function for the Laplacian operator is immediately evident from (1-61); namely,

$$G(x_1,x_2,x_3;\ x_1',x_2',x_3') = G(x_1',x_2',x_3';\ x_1,x_2,x_3) \tag{1-62}$$

i.e., the Green's function is symmetrical.

The uniqueness of the solution (1-53) to Poisson's equation will be proved in Sec. 1-16, where another method of solution will also be discussed.

1-15. GAUSS' THEOREM

Consider a volume τ in a fluid of density ρ which is flowing with a velocity **v**. The quantity of fluid which crosses an element dS of the surface S bounding τ in a time dt is $\rho\mathbf{v} \cdot d\mathbf{S}\, dt = \rho\mathbf{v} \cdot \mathbf{n}\, dS\, dt$, where **n** is a unit vector in the direction of the outward drawn normal to dS. The quantity crossing per second is termed the *flux* across dS and is given by $\rho\mathbf{v} \cdot d\mathbf{S} = \rho\mathbf{v} \cdot \mathbf{n}\, dS$. The quantity of fluid which on the whole flows out of the region τ per second is therefore given by the integral over the surface S bounding τ, $\int\!\int \rho\mathbf{v} \cdot d\mathbf{S}$.

Consider now an elementary parallelepiped (Fig. 1-1) of volume

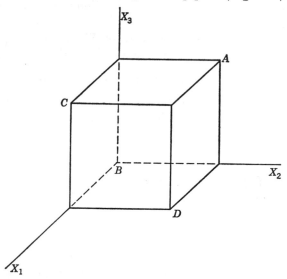

FIGURE 1-1

$d\tau = dx_1\, dx_2\, dx_3.$ The flux inward through the surface AB is

$$\rho v_1(x_1, x_2, x_3, t)\ dx_2\, dx_3$$

and that through the opposite face CD is $\rho v_1(x_1 + dx_1,\ x_2, x_3, t)\ dx_2\, dx_3$, or, on expanding by means of Taylor's theorem,

$$\left[\rho v_1(x_1, x_2, x_3, t) + \frac{\partial}{\partial x_1}(\rho v_1)\ dx_1 + \frac{1}{2!}\frac{\partial^2}{\partial x_1{}^2}(\rho v_1)(dx_1)^2 + \cdots\right] dx_2\, dx_3$$

Hence, the amount of fluid which the parallelepiped gains owing to fluxes across the faces AB and CD is

$$-\left[\frac{\partial}{\partial x_1}(\rho v_1)\ dx_1 + \frac{1}{2!}\frac{\partial^2}{\partial x_1{}^2}(\rho v_1)(dx_1)^2 + \cdots\right] dx_2\, dx_3$$

or, neglecting terms in dx_1 quadratic or higher,

$$-\frac{\partial}{\partial x_1}(\rho v_1)\ dx_1\, dx_2\, dx_3$$

When the two other pairs of faces are treated in exactly the same manner, it follows that the total gain of fluid per unit time is

$$-\left[\frac{\partial}{\partial x_1}(\rho v_1) + \frac{\partial}{\partial x_2}(\rho v_2) + \frac{\partial}{\partial x_3}(\rho v_3)\right] dx_1\, dx_2\, dx_3 \equiv -\operatorname{div} \rho\mathbf{v}\ d\tau \quad (1\text{-}63)$$

But this gain of fluid can be expressed in another manner: The amount of fluid in the volume at any time t is $\rho(x_1, x_2, x_3, t)\ dx_1\, dx_2\, dx_3$, and the amount at time $t + dt$ is

$$\left[\rho(x_1, x_2, x_3, t) + \frac{\partial\rho}{\partial t}\ dt\right] dx_1\, dx_2\, dx_3$$

where we have neglected terms in dt quadratic or higher. The gain during time dt is therefore $(\partial\rho/\partial t)\ dx_1\, dx_2\, dx_3\, dt$, and the gain in unit time is

$$\frac{\partial\rho}{\partial t}\ dx_1\, dx_2\, dx_3 \equiv \frac{\partial\rho}{\partial t}\ d\tau \qquad (1\text{-}64)$$

Equating the two expressions (1-63) and (1-64) for the amount of fluid gained by the volume in unit time, we obtain

$$\operatorname{div} \rho\mathbf{v} + \frac{\partial\rho}{\partial t} = 0 \qquad (1\text{-}65)$$

which is the well-known *equation of continuity*.

We have shown that the amount of fluid passing out of an elementary volume $d\tau$ in unit time equals div $\rho\mathbf{v}\,d\tau$.   To find the total amount of fluid passing out of a large volume per second, one need simply take the sum of the amounts flowing out of the elementary volumes.   This sum is $\iiint$ div $\rho\mathbf{v}\,d\tau$.   Since the amount of fluid leaving the volume per second is the amount passing out through the bounding surface per second, $\iint\rho\mathbf{v}\cdot d\mathbf{S}$, it follows that

$$\iiint \text{div } \rho\mathbf{v}\,d\tau = \iint\rho\mathbf{v}\cdot d\mathbf{S} \tag{1-66}$$

which is Gauss' theorem.   This relationship can be shown to hold for any vector $\mathbf{F}$ which is a function of position.   An analytical proof which does not depend on the flow of a fluid can be found in books on vector analysis.

1-16. GREEN'S THEOREM

According to Gauss' theorem

$$\iiint \text{div } \mathbf{F}\,d\tau = \iint\mathbf{F}\cdot d\mathbf{S}$$

where $\mathbf{F}$ is any vector which is a function of position and $d\mathbf{S}$ is an element of the surface S which bounds the volume τ.   If

$$\mathbf{F} = \phi \text{ grad } \psi$$

where both ϕ and ψ are scalar functions, then

$$\begin{aligned}
\iiint \text{div } \mathbf{F}\,d\tau &= \iiint \text{div } (\phi \text{ grad } \psi)\,d\tau \\
&= \iiint\boldsymbol{\nabla}\cdot(\phi\boldsymbol{\nabla}\psi)\,d\tau \\
&= \iiint(\phi\nabla^2\psi + \boldsymbol{\nabla}\phi\cdot\boldsymbol{\nabla}\psi)\,d\tau
\end{aligned}$$

which leads to the first form of Green's theorem, sometimes known as *Green's lemma*,

$$\iiint(\phi\nabla^2\psi + \boldsymbol{\nabla}\phi\cdot\boldsymbol{\nabla}\psi)\,d\tau = \iint\phi\boldsymbol{\nabla}\psi\cdot d\mathbf{S} \tag{1-67}$$

Similarly, if

$$\mathbf{F} = \psi \text{ grad } \phi$$

then

$$\iiint(\psi\nabla^2\phi + \boldsymbol{\nabla}\phi\cdot\boldsymbol{\nabla}\psi)\,d\tau = \iint\psi\boldsymbol{\nabla}\phi\cdot d\mathbf{S} \tag{1-68}$$

Subtraction of (1-68) from (1-67) yields

$$\iiint(\phi\nabla^2\psi - \psi\nabla^2\phi)\,d\tau = \iint(\phi\boldsymbol{\nabla}\psi - \psi\boldsymbol{\nabla}\phi)\cdot d\mathbf{S}$$

which is Green's theorem.

As an example of the application of Green's theorem, let us solve Poisson's equation.   We are given the source function $\rho(x_1',x_2',x_3')$ and are required to find the function ϕ at a fixed point of observation (x_1,x_2,x_3).

Poisson's equation reads

$$\nabla'^2\phi(x_1', x_2', x_3') = -\rho(x_1', x_2', x_3') \tag{1-69}$$

where ϕ and $\boldsymbol{\nabla}\phi$ both vanish as (x_1, x_2, x_3) approaches $\pm \infty$. We take the function ψ to be

$$\psi = \frac{1}{|\mathbf{r} - \mathbf{r}'|} \equiv \frac{1}{s} \tag{1-70}$$

which (cf. Sec. 1-14) satisfies the equation

$$\nabla'^2\psi = \nabla^2\psi = -4\pi\delta(x_1 - x_1')\delta(x_2 - x_2')\delta(x_3 - x_3') \tag{1-71}$$

and write Green's theorem as

$$\iiint(\phi\nabla'^2\psi - \psi\nabla'^2\phi)\,d\tau' = \iint(\phi\boldsymbol{\nabla}'\psi - \psi\boldsymbol{\nabla}'\phi)\cdot d\mathbf{S}' \tag{1-72}$$

The primes on the del operator in Eqs. (1-69) to (1-72) indicate that the differentiations are with respect to the source coordinates.

Substitution of Eqs. (1-69) to (1-71) into (1-72) yields

$$-4\pi\phi(x_1, x_2, x_3) + \iiint \frac{\rho(x_1', x_2', x_3')}{|\mathbf{r} - \mathbf{r}'|}\,d\tau' = \iint (\phi\boldsymbol{\nabla}'\psi - \psi\boldsymbol{\nabla}'\phi)\cdot d\mathbf{S}'$$

or

$$\phi(x_1, x_2, x_3) = \frac{1}{4\pi}\iiint \frac{\rho(x_1', x_2', x_3')}{|\mathbf{r} - \mathbf{r}_i|}\,d\tau'$$
$$+ \frac{1}{4\pi}\iint \left(\frac{1}{|\mathbf{r} - \mathbf{r}'|}\boldsymbol{\nabla}'\phi - \phi\boldsymbol{\nabla}'\frac{1}{|\mathbf{r} - \mathbf{r}'|}\right)\cdot d\mathbf{S}' \tag{1-73}$$

The first term of the right-hand member represents the contribution to ϕ from the source distribution in the volume τ', that is, within the surface S' which bounds τ'. The second term represents the contribution to ϕ coming from those parts of the source distribution which lie outside τ'. It is the solution of the homogeneous equation

$$\nabla'^2\phi(x_1', x_2', x_3') = 0$$

i.e., Laplace's equation. If we allow the volume τ' to become infinite and impose on ϕ the boundary condition that it vanish at least as strongly as $1/s$ at infinity, then the second term in (1-73) vanishes and

$$\phi(x_1, x_2, x_3) = \frac{1}{4\pi}\iiint \frac{\rho(x_1', x_2', x_3')}{|\mathbf{r} - \mathbf{r}'|} \tag{1-74}$$

in agreement with the result of Sec. 1-14.

The uniqueness of the solution (1-74) to Poisson's equation is easily verified. Suppose, for the time being, that there are two different solutions ϕ_1 and ϕ_2. Let $\chi = \phi_1 - \phi_2$, and substitute χ for both ϕ and ψ in Green's lemma (1-67) so that

$$\iiint (\chi \nabla^2 \chi + \nabla \chi \cdot \nabla \chi) \, d\tau = \iint \chi \nabla \chi \cdot d\mathbf{S}$$

The right-hand member vanishes because of the boundary conditions on ϕ_1 and ϕ_2 at infinity. Also, since both ϕ_1 and ϕ_2 satisfy Poisson's equation, $\nabla^2 \chi = 0$. Hence

$$\iiint |\nabla \chi|^2 \, d\tau = 0$$

which can be true only if $\nabla \chi$ vanishes everywhere. Hence ϕ_1 and ϕ_2 can differ only by a constant which, because of the boundary condition at infinity, must be zero.

1-17. STOKES' THEOREM

Consider any closed contour $\mathbf{s}$, and let S be any arbitrary surface bounded by this contour. Then, for any vector function $\mathbf{F}$, Stokes' theorem states that

$$\oint \mathbf{F} \cdot d\mathbf{s} = \iint \operatorname{curl} \mathbf{F} \cdot d\mathbf{S} = \iint \operatorname{curl} \mathbf{F} \cdot \mathbf{n} \, dS \qquad (1\text{-}75)$$

where $\mathbf{n}$ is the unit outward drawn normal to the element dS of the surface S. The directions of $\mathbf{n}$ and $\mathbf{s}$ are related by the right-hand-screw rule; i.e., the sense in which the contour $\mathbf{s}$ is described is that of rotation of a right-hand screw advancing in the direction of $\mathbf{n}$.

In proving this theorem, we shall first demonstrate its validity in the case of any element of area dS. Then we shall imagine the surface S as divided up into a multitude of elements of area dS. Finally, by summing over all these elementary areas we shall arrive at (1-75).

Consider one of the elementary areas. For convenience select the coordinate axes so that the x_3 axis is normal to the element and so that the bounding edges are parallel to the x_1 and x_2 axes as indicated in Fig. 1-2. If the coordinates of point A are x_1, x_2, those of B are $x_1 + dx_1$, x_2, those of C are $x_1 + dx_1$, $x_2 + dx_2$ and those of D are x_1, $x_2 + dx_2$. Then, at A

$$\mathbf{F} = \mathbf{F}(x_1, x_2)$$

at B

$$\mathbf{F} = \mathbf{F}(x_1 + dx_1, x_2) = \mathbf{F}(x_1, x_2) + \frac{\partial}{\partial x_1} \mathbf{F} \, dx_1 + \cdots$$

at C

$$\mathbf{F} = \mathbf{F}(x_1 + dx_1, x_2 + dx_2) = \mathbf{F}(x_1, x_2) + \frac{\partial}{\partial x_1} \mathbf{F} \, dx_1 + \frac{\partial}{\partial x_2} \mathbf{F} \, dx_2 \cdots$$

and at D

$$\mathbf{F} = \mathbf{F}(x_1, x_2 + dx_2) = \mathbf{F}(x_1, x_2) + \frac{\partial}{\partial x_2} \mathbf{F}\, dx_2 + \cdots$$

where we have neglected higher-order terms in the dx_i.

The line integral of $\mathbf{F}$ from A to B is

$$\int_A^B \mathbf{F} \cdot d\mathbf{s} = \overline{F_1}\, dx_1 = \frac{1}{2}\,[F_1(x_1 + dx_1,\, x_2) + F_1(x_1, x_2)]\, dx_1$$

$$= \left[F_1(x_1, x_2) + \frac{1}{2}\frac{\partial}{\partial x_1} F_1\, dx_1 \right] dx_1$$

where the bar over F_1 denotes the average value. Similarly, the line integral from B to C is

$$\left[F_2(x_1, x_2) + \frac{\partial}{\partial x_1} F_2\, dx_1 + \frac{1}{2}\frac{\partial}{\partial x_2} F_2\, dx_2 \right] dx_2$$

that from C to D is

$$\left[F_1(x_1, x_2) + \frac{1}{2}\frac{\partial}{\partial x_1} F_1\, dx_1 + \frac{\partial}{\partial x_2} F_1\, dx_2 \right] (-dx_1)$$

and that from D to A is

$$\left[F_2(x_1, x_2) + \frac{1}{2}\frac{\partial}{\partial x_2} F_2\, dx_2 \right] (-dx_2)$$

Therefore, the line integral $\oint \mathbf{F} \cdot d\mathbf{s}$ around the closed contour $ABCD$ is $[(\partial/\partial x_1)F_2 - (\partial/\partial x_2)F_1]\, dx_1\, dx_2$. But this quantity is simply the surface integral $(\operatorname{curl}\mathbf{F})_3\, dx_1\, dx_2$. Hence Stokes' theorem is true for an elementary area.

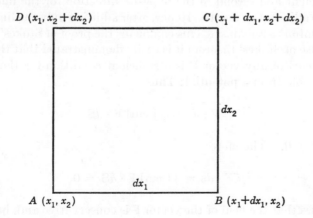

FIGURE 1-2

The next step in the proof is to show that it holds for the arbitrary surface S. Consider the elementary areas into which we have in our imagination divided up S (Fig. 1-3). The edge of each element of area not situated on the contour **s** will be shared by two elements. Consequently, if for each of the elements we form the line integral $\oint \mathbf{F} \cdot d\mathbf{s}$ and then add, the contributions from the edges of the elements of area not situated on the contour **s** will be zero, since each of these edges is

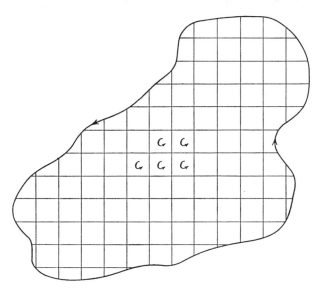

FIGURE 1-3

traversed twice, first in one direction for the line integral around a particular element and second in the opposite direction for the line integral around the adjacent element. Hence, after addition only the line integral over the contour **s** remains. This completes the proof of Stokes' theorem.

By the use of Stokes' theorem it is easily demonstrated that the vanishing of the curl of any vector **F** is a sufficient condition for the vector **F** to be derivable from a potential: Thus

$$\oint \mathbf{F} \cdot d\mathbf{s} = \int\int \operatorname{curl} \mathbf{F} \cdot d\mathbf{S}$$

But curl $\mathbf{F} = 0$. Therefore

$$\oint \mathbf{F} \cdot d\mathbf{s} = \int\int \operatorname{curl} \mathbf{F} \cdot d\mathbf{S} = 0$$

which shows that the field of the vector **F** is conservative and, hence, that **F** is derivable from a potential.

1-18. THE THEOREM OF TAIT AND McAULAY

Consider any closed contour $\mathbf{s}$, and let S be any arbitrary surface bounded by this contour. Then for any vector function $\mathbf{F}$ the theorem of Tait and McAulay states that

$$\oint \mathbf{F} \times d\mathbf{s} = \iint [(\nabla \cdot \mathbf{F})\mathbf{n} - \nabla (\mathbf{F} \cdot \mathbf{n})] \, dS \qquad (1\text{-}76)$$

where $\mathbf{n}$ is the unit outward drawn normal to the element dS of the surface S. The directions of $\mathbf{n}$ and $\mathbf{s}$ are related by the right-hand-screw rule; i.e., the sense in which the contour $\mathbf{s}$ is described is that of rotation of a right-hand screw advancing in the direction of $\mathbf{n}$.

To prove the theorem take the scalar product of any constant vector $\mathbf{c}$ with $\oint \mathbf{F} \times d\mathbf{s}$. Then

$$\mathbf{c} \cdot \oint \mathbf{F} \times d\mathbf{s} = \oint \mathbf{c} \cdot (\mathbf{F} \times d\mathbf{s}) = \oint (\mathbf{c} \times \mathbf{F}) \cdot d\mathbf{s}$$
$$= \iint [\nabla \times (\mathbf{c} \times \mathbf{F})] \cdot d\mathbf{S} = \iint [\nabla \times (\mathbf{c} \times \mathbf{F})] \cdot \mathbf{n} \, dS$$

by Stokes' theorem. Expansion of the triple vector product yields

$$\mathbf{c} \cdot \oint \mathbf{F} \times d\mathbf{s} = \iint [(\nabla \cdot \mathbf{F})\mathbf{c} - (\mathbf{c} \cdot \nabla)\mathbf{F}] \cdot \mathbf{n} \, dS$$
$$= \iint \mathbf{c} \cdot [(\nabla \cdot \mathbf{F})\mathbf{n} - \nabla (\mathbf{F} \cdot \mathbf{n})] \, dS$$
$$= \mathbf{c} \cdot \iint [(\nabla \cdot \mathbf{F})\mathbf{n} - \nabla (\mathbf{F} \cdot \mathbf{n})] \, dS$$

Since $\mathbf{c}$ is arbitrary, the theorem is proved.

1-19. ORTHOGONAL CURVILINEAR COORDINATES

Complicated problems are best approached by making use of curvilinear coordinates which are adapted to the symmetry conditions of the problem. Let the coordinates be denoted by u_1, u_2, u_3, and let them be orthogonal coordinates so that the three sets of coordinate surfaces, $u_1 = $ constant, $u_2 = $ constant, and $u_3 = $ constant, intersect at right angles. In Fig. 1-4

$$u_1 = \text{constant on } ABCD = u_1{}^0$$
and
$$u_1 = \text{constant on } EFGH = u_1{}^0 + du_1$$

The distance from B to E is, in general, not du_1 but rather $h_1 \, du_1$, where h_1 is a function of the other coordinates u_2 and u_3. For example, in polar coordinates, if the displacement is along the radius, it is given by $ds = dr$, while if it is along a tangent to a circle of radius r, it is given by $ds = r \, d\theta$. Thus, in polar coordinates, the h connected with the coordinate r is unity while that connected with θ is r.

Since we have confined ourselves to a discussion of orthogonal coordinates, the expression for any arbitrary element of length ds is

$$ds^2 = h_1{}^2 du_1{}^2 + h_2{}^2 du_2{}^2 + h_3{}^2 du_3{}^2 \qquad (1\text{-}77)$$

But
$$ds^2 = dx_1{}^2 + dx_2{}^2 + dx_3{}^2 \qquad (1\text{-}78)$$

Hence we have a simple method for deriving the h_i: Express x_1, x_2, and x_3 as functions of u_1, u_2, and u_3, and form ds^2. The factors multiplying $du_1{}^2$, $du_2{}^2$, and $du_3{}^2$ are, respectively, $h_1{}^2$, $h_2{}^2$, and $h_3{}^2$.

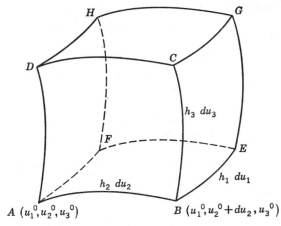

FIGURE 1-4

Since the component of grad ϕ in any direction is the directional derivative of ϕ (cf. Sec. 1-8) in that direction, the u_1 component of grad ϕ is

$$(\text{grad }\phi)_{u_i} = \lim_{du_i \to 0} \frac{\phi(u_i{}^0 + du_i) - \phi(u_i{}^0)}{h_i\,du_i}$$

$$= \frac{1}{h_i}\frac{\partial \phi}{\partial u_i} \qquad (1\text{-}79)$$

To calculate the divergence of a vector $\mathbf{F}$ in curvilinear coordinates, apply Gauss' theorem to the volume element $d\tau = h_1 h_2 h_3\,du_1\,du_2\,du_3$ in Fig. 1-4. If the vector $\mathbf{F}$ has components F_1, F_2, F_3 along the three curvilinear axes, it is clear from Fig. 1-4 that the inward flux through the face $ABCD$ is $F_1 h_2\,du_2\,h_3\,du_3$ and the flux outward through the opposite face $EFGH$ is $F_1 h_2\,du_2\,h_3\,du_3 + (\partial/\partial u_1)(F_1 h_2\,du_2\,h_3\,du_3)\,du_1$. Subtracting, we obtain as the net flux outward through these two faces $(\partial/\partial u_1)(F_1 h_2\,du_2\,h_3\,du_3)\,du_1$. Similar expressions are obtained on consideration of the other two sets of faces. Addition then yields

div $\mathbf{F}h_1 h_2 h_3\,du_1\,du_2\,du_3$

$$= \left[\frac{\partial}{\partial u_1}(F_1 h_2 h_3) + \frac{\partial}{\partial u_2}(F_2 h_3 h_1) + \frac{\partial}{\partial u_3}(F_3 h_1 h_2)\right] du_1\,du_2\,du_3$$

Hence

$$\text{div } \mathbf{F} = \frac{1}{h_1 h_2 h_3} \left[\frac{\partial}{\partial u_1} (F_1 h_2 h_3) + \frac{\partial}{\partial u_2} (F_2 h_3 h_1) + \frac{\partial}{\partial u_3} (F_3 h_1 h_2) \right] \quad (1\text{-}80)$$

To obtain the Laplacian in curvilinear coordinates, simply set

$$\mathbf{F} = \text{grad } \phi$$

and substitute in (1-80). Then

$$\text{div } \mathbf{F} = \text{div grad } \phi = \nabla^2 \phi$$

giving

$$\nabla^2 \phi = \frac{1}{h_1 h_2 h_3} \left[\frac{\partial}{\partial u_1} \left(\frac{\partial \phi}{\partial u_1} \frac{h_2 h_3}{h_1} \right) + \frac{\partial}{\partial u_2} \left(\frac{\partial \phi}{\partial u_2} \frac{h_3 h_1}{h_2} \right) + \frac{\partial}{\partial u_3} \left(\frac{\partial \phi}{\partial u_3} \frac{h_1 h_2}{h_3} \right) \right]$$

$$(1\text{-}81)$$

To obtain the curl in curvilinear coordinates, consider Fig. 1-4 again. The line integral about $ABCD$ of an arbitrary vector $\mathbf{F}$ is

$$F_2 h_2 \, du_2 + \left[F_3 h_3 \, du_3 + \frac{\partial}{\partial u_2} (F_3 h_3) \, du_2 \, du_3 \right]$$

$$- \left[F_2 h_2 \, du_2 + \frac{\partial}{\partial u_3} (F_2 h_2) \, du_3 \, du_2 \right] - F_3 h_3 \, du_3$$

or

$$\left[\frac{\partial}{\partial u_2} (F_3 h_3) - \frac{\partial}{\partial u_3} (F_2 h_2) \right] du_2 \, du_3$$

Application of Stokes' theorem then yields

$$(\text{curl } \mathbf{F})_1 h_2 \, du_2 \, h_3 \, du_3 = \left[\frac{\partial}{\partial u_2} (F_3 h_3) - \frac{\partial}{\partial u_3} (F_2 h_2) \right] du_2 \, du_3$$

or

$$(\text{curl } \mathbf{F})_1 = \frac{1}{h_2 h_3} \left[\frac{\partial}{\partial u_2} (F_3 h_3) - \frac{\partial}{\partial u_3} (F_2 h_2) \right] \quad (1\text{-}82)$$

The components of curl $\mathbf{F}$ in the directions of u_2 and u_3 are obtained from (1-82) by cyclic change of the indices.

It readily follows from (1-82) that

$$(\nabla \times \nabla \times \mathbf{F})_1 = (\text{curl curl } \mathbf{F})_1$$

$$= \frac{1}{h_2 h_3} \left\{ \frac{\partial}{\partial u_2} [(\text{curl } \mathbf{F})_3 h_3] - \frac{\partial}{\partial u_3} [(\text{curl } \mathbf{F})_2 h_2] \right\}$$

The other two components are obtained by cyclic change of the indices 1, 2, 3.

In order to compute $\nabla^2 \mathbf{F}$ in orthogonal curvilinear coordinates, use is made of the relation (cf. Exercise 1-5g)

$$\nabla^2 \mathbf{F} = \nabla (\nabla \cdot \mathbf{F}) - \nabla \times \nabla \times \mathbf{F}$$

Thus

$$(\nabla^2 \mathbf{F})_1 = \frac{1}{h_1} \frac{\partial}{\partial u_1} (\nabla \cdot \mathbf{F}) - (\nabla \times \nabla \times \mathbf{F})_1$$

where $\mathbf{\nabla} \cdot \mathbf{F}$ is given by (1-80). The other two components of $\nabla^2\mathbf{F}$ are obtained by cyclic change of the indices 1, 2, 3.

1-20. TENSORS OF ZEROTH AND FIRST RANK

A tensor of zeroth rank is another name for the physical quantity we have thus far called a scalar. Thus, a tensor of zeroth rank is completely specified by the assignment of a single number in a given coordinate system, and this number is the same for all coordinate systems.

A tensor of the first rank is what we have thus far called a vector quantity. Consequently, it is completely specified by the assignment of three numbers (its components) in a given coordinate system. In general, it will be specified by a different set of components in a different coordinate system.

Tensors of the first rank are of two types. Consider a vector $d\mathbf{r}$ with components dx_1, dx_2, dx_3 in the $OX_1X_2X_3$ coordinate system. The components in the $O'X_1'X_2'X_3'$ coordinate system are given by

$$dx_1' = \frac{\partial x_1'}{\partial x_1}\,dx_1 + \frac{\partial x_1'}{\partial x_2}\,dx_2 + \frac{\partial x_1'}{\partial x_3}\,dx_3 \qquad \text{etc.}$$

or, in the compact notation,

$$dx_i' = \frac{\partial x_i'}{\partial x_j}\,dx_j \tag{1-83}$$

Any set of quantities which transform according to this relation is called a *contravariant vector*. Thus if A^1, A^2, A^3 become A'^1, A'^2, A'^3 in the primed coordinate system, where

$$A'^i = \frac{\partial x_i'}{\partial x_j}\,A^j \tag{1-84}$$

then A^1, A^2, A^3 are the components of a contravariant vector. The upper position of the index will be reserved to designate contravariant vectors. Thus, for consistency, Eq. (1-83) should be written

$$dx'^i = \frac{\partial x'^i}{\partial x^j}\,dx^j$$

and Eq. (1-84)

$$A'^i = \frac{\partial x'^i}{\partial x^j}\,A^j$$

If ϕ is a scalar quantity, the components of grad ϕ transform according to the relations

$$\frac{\partial \phi}{\partial x'^1} = \frac{\partial x^1}{\partial x'^1}\frac{\partial \phi}{\partial x^1} + \frac{\partial x^2}{\partial x'^1}\frac{\partial \phi}{\partial x^2} + \frac{\partial x^3}{\partial x'^1}\frac{\partial \phi}{\partial x^3} \qquad \text{etc.}$$

or
$$\frac{\partial \phi}{\partial x'^i} = \frac{\partial x^j}{\partial x'^i}\frac{\partial \phi}{\partial x^j} \qquad (1\text{-}85)$$

Any set of quantities which transform according to this relation is called a *covariant vector*. Thus, if A is a covariant vector, its components transform according to the relation

$$A'_i = \frac{\partial x^j}{\partial x'^i} A_j \qquad (1\text{-}86)$$

If only orthogonal coordinate systems are considered, the transformation laws (1-84) and (1-86) are equivalent and the distinction between covariant and contravariant vectors vanishes.

1-21. TENSORS OF THE SECOND RANK

Let us consider a physical quantity $\mathfrak{A}$ which is completely defined in the $OX_1X_2X_3$ coordinate system by the set of nine numbers

$$A = \begin{pmatrix} A_{11} & A_{12} & A_{13} \\ A_{21} & A_{22} & A_{23} \\ A_{31} & A_{32} & A_{33} \end{pmatrix} \qquad (1\text{-}87)$$

For convenience, we have written the nine numbers A_{ij} as elements of a 3×3 matrix.

Suppose that in the $O'X'_1X'_2X'_3$ coordinate system the physical quantity $\mathfrak{A}$ is described by the matrix

$$A' = \begin{pmatrix} A'_{11} & A'_{12} & A'_{13} \\ A'_{21} & A'_{22} & A'_{23} \\ A'_{31} & A'_{32} & A'_{33} \end{pmatrix} \qquad (1\text{-}88)$$

If the elements A_{ij} and A'_{ij} are related by

$$A'_{kl} = \frac{\partial x^i}{\partial x'^k}\frac{\partial x^j}{\partial x'^l} A_{ij} \qquad (1\text{-}89)$$

the physical quantity $\mathfrak{A}$ is said to be a *covariant tensor of the second rank*. The matrix A is the representative of this tensor in the $OX_1X_2X_3$ coordinate system; the matrix A' its representative in the $O'X'_1X'_2X'_3$ coordinate system.

There are two other types of second-rank tensors. These satisfy the relations

$$A'^{kl} = \frac{\partial x'^k}{\partial x^i} \frac{\partial x'^l}{\partial x^j} A^{ij} \tag{1-90}$$

$$A_k'^l = \frac{\partial x'^l}{\partial x^i} \frac{\partial x^j}{\partial x'^k} A_j{}^i \tag{1-91}$$

and are known as *contravariant* and *mixed tensors*, respectively.

In most of what follows we shall consider the representation of a tensor $\mathfrak{A}$ in only a single coordinate system. In such a case, we shall not distinguish between the tensor $\mathfrak{A}$ and its matrix representative and use the notation $\mathfrak{A}$ for both.

1-22. INNER PRODUCT OF A TENSOR AND A VECTOR

The inner product of a tensor $\mathfrak{T}$ and a vector **A** is, by definition, a vector **B** such that

$$\mathbf{B} = \mathfrak{T}\mathbf{A} \tag{1-92}$$

In the $OX_1X_2X_3$ coordinate system in which the tensor $\mathfrak{T}$ and the vector **A** are represented by

$$\begin{pmatrix} T_{11} & T_{12} & T_{13} \\ T_{21} & T_{22} & T_{23} \\ T_{31} & T_{32} & T_{33} \end{pmatrix} \quad \text{and} \quad \begin{pmatrix} A_1 \\ A_2 \\ A_3 \end{pmatrix}$$

respectively, the vector **B** is represented by

$$\begin{pmatrix} B_1 \\ B_2 \\ B_3 \end{pmatrix} = \begin{pmatrix} T_{11} & T_{12} & T_{13} \\ T_{21} & T_{22} & T_{23} \\ T_{31} & T_{32} & T_{33} \end{pmatrix} \begin{pmatrix} A_1 \\ A_2 \\ A_3 \end{pmatrix} \tag{1-93}$$

or, more concisely,

$$B_i = T_{ij}A_j \tag{1-93a}$$

Equations (1-93) and (1-93a) define the multiplication of a 3-column by a 3×3 matrix.

1-23. SYMMETRY PROPERTIES OF TENSORS

Consider a tensor $\mathfrak{T}$ whose representative in a given coordinate system is the matrix

$$\underline{T} = \begin{pmatrix} T_{11} & T_{12} & T_{13} \\ T_{21} & T_{22} & T_{23} \\ T_{31} & T_{32} & T_{33} \end{pmatrix} \tag{1-94}$$

If the elements T_{ij} are zero for all i and j, the matrix $\underline{\underline{T}}$ is called a *null* or *zero* matrix. If only the off-diagonal elements T_{ij}, $i \neq j$, are zero, the matrix is said to be *diagonal*.

A matrix in which $T_{ij} = T_{ji}$ for $i \neq j$ is called a *symmetric* matrix. If $T_{ij} = -T_{ji}$ and $T_{ii} = 0$, the matrix is said to be *antisymmetric* or *skew-symmetric*. Symmetry properties of a tensor are independent of the coordinate system. Thus, if a tensor is represented by a (anti-) symmetric matrix in one coordinate system, its representatives in all coordinate systems will be (anti-) symmetric matrices.

1-24. ANTISYMMETRIC TENSORS AND VECTORS

Consider the inner product **B** of an antisymmetric tensor $\mathfrak{I}$ and a vector **A**, $\mathbf{B} = \mathfrak{I}\mathbf{A}$. If the representatives of $\mathfrak{I}$ and **A** in the $OX_1X_2X_3$ coordinate system are

$$\begin{pmatrix} 0 & -T_{12} & T_{31} \\ T_{12} & 0 & -T_{23} \\ -T_{31} & T_{23} & 0 \end{pmatrix} \quad \text{and} \quad \begin{pmatrix} A_1 \\ A_2 \\ A_3 \end{pmatrix}$$

respectively, then the vector **B** is represented by

$$\begin{pmatrix} B_1 \\ B_2 \\ B_3 \end{pmatrix} = \begin{pmatrix} 0 & -T_{12} & T_{31} \\ T_{12} & 0 & -T_{23} \\ -T_{31} & T_{23} & 0 \end{pmatrix} \begin{pmatrix} A_1 \\ A_2 \\ A_3 \end{pmatrix} \qquad (1\text{-}95)$$

We note that the antisymmetric tensor $\mathfrak{I}$ is completely defined in the given coordinate system by the set of three numbers T_{12}, T_{31}, and T_{23}. We further note that the matrix equation (1-95) represents the set of three equations

$$\begin{aligned} B_1 &= T_{31}A_3 - T_{12}A_2 \\ B_2 &= T_{12}A_1 - T_{23}A_3 \\ B_3 &= T_{23}A_2 - T_{31}A_1 \end{aligned} \qquad (1\text{-}96)$$

and that this set of equations can be expressed as the vector product

$$\mathbf{B} = \mathbf{C} \times \mathbf{A} \qquad (1\text{-}97)$$

where
$$\mathbf{C} = T_{23}\mathbf{i}_1 + T_{31}\mathbf{i}_2 + T_{12}\mathbf{i}_3 \qquad (1\text{-}98)$$

Consequently, given a physical quantity described by the three numbers T_{23}, T_{31}, and T_{12} in a given coordinate system, it is sometimes convenient to represent the quantity by means of an antisymmetric tensor and sometimes by means of a line segment with components T_{23}, T_{31}, and T_{12}.

1-25. SYMMETRIC TENSORS AND PRINCIPAL AXES

Consider the inner product $\mathbf{B}$ of a symmetric tensor $\mathfrak{J}$ and a vector $\mathbf{A}$. In the $OX_1X_2X_3$ coordinate system this product is represented by

$$\begin{pmatrix} B_1 \\ B_2 \\ B_3 \end{pmatrix} = \begin{pmatrix} T_{11} & T_{12} & T_{31} \\ T_{12} & T_{22} & T_{23} \\ T_{31} & T_{23} & T_{33} \end{pmatrix} \begin{pmatrix} A_1 \\ A_2 \\ A_3 \end{pmatrix} \tag{1-99}$$

It is possible to select another coordinate system, say $O'X_1'X_2'X_3'$, in which the matrix representing the tensor $\mathfrak{J}$ is diagonal. In this coordinate system the representative of the inner product $\mathfrak{J}\mathbf{A}$ is

$$\begin{pmatrix} B_1' \\ B_2' \\ B_3' \end{pmatrix} = \begin{pmatrix} T_1' & 0 & 0 \\ 0 & T_2' & 0 \\ 0 & 0 & T_3' \end{pmatrix} \begin{pmatrix} A_1' \\ A_2' \\ A_3' \end{pmatrix} \tag{1-100}$$

To find the diagonal matrix and the coordinate system $O'X_1'X_2'X_3'$ in which it is the representative of the tensor $\mathfrak{J}$, we proceed as follows: Consider the matrix equation

$$\begin{pmatrix} T_{11} & T_{12} & T_{31} \\ T_{12} & T_{22} & T_{23} \\ T_{31} & T_{23} & T_{33} \end{pmatrix} \begin{pmatrix} a_1 \\ a_2 \\ a_3 \end{pmatrix} = \lambda \begin{pmatrix} a_1 \\ a_2 \\ a_3 \end{pmatrix} \tag{1-101}$$

where the *eigenvalues* λ and the *eigencolumns* $\underline{a}$ are to be determined. The necessary and sufficient condition that (1-101) have a nontrivial solution $\underline{a}$ is that the determinant of the coefficients of the a_i vanish,

$$\begin{vmatrix} T_{11} - \lambda & T_{12} & T_{31} \\ T_{12} & T_{22} - \lambda & T_{23} \\ T_{31} & T_{23} & T_{33} - \lambda \end{vmatrix} = 0 \tag{1-102}$$

Thus, before a solution to (1-101) can be found, it is necessary to find the λ's satisfying the cubic equation (1-102). Let T_1', T_2', and T_3' denote the three values of λ satisfying (1-102). Then solve the three matrix equations

$$\begin{pmatrix} T_{11} & T_{12} & T_{31} \\ T_{12} & T_{22} & T_{23} \\ T_{31} & T_{23} & T_{33} \end{pmatrix} \begin{pmatrix} a_{i1} \\ a_{i2} \\ a_{i3} \end{pmatrix} = T_i' \begin{pmatrix} a_{i1} \\ a_{i2} \\ a_{i3} \end{pmatrix} \qquad i = 1, 2, 3 \tag{1-103}$$

for the eigencolumns $\underline{a_i}$. The eigencolumns are determined to within a multiplicative scalar constant. Consequently, we normalize the solutions such that

$$a_{i1}{}^2 + a_{i2}{}^2 + a_{i3}{}^2 = 1 \qquad i = 1, 2, 3 \tag{1-104}$$

The nine quantities a_{ij} so determined are the direction cosines of the axes of the $O'X_1'X_2'X_3'$ coordinate system in which the matrix representing the tensor $\mathfrak{I}$ is diagonal relative to the axes of the $OX_1X_2X_3$ coordinate system. That this is so is easily verified. Write

$$\begin{pmatrix} T_{11} & T_{12} & T_{31} \\ T_{12} & T_{22} & T_{23} \\ T_{31} & T_{23} & T_{33} \end{pmatrix} \begin{pmatrix} a_{j1} \\ a_{j2} \\ a_{j3} \end{pmatrix} = T_j' \begin{pmatrix} a_{j1} \\ a_{j2} \\ a_{j3} \end{pmatrix} \qquad j = 1, 2, 3 \qquad (1\text{-}105)$$

Then multiply (1-103) from the left by $(a_{j1}\, a_{j2}\, a_{j3})$ and (1-105) from the left by $(a_{i1}\, a_{i2}\, a_{i3})$. Because $\underline{\underline{T}}$ is a symmetrical matrix, the left-hand members of the resulting equations are equal. Hence, subtraction of one equation from the other yields

$$0 = (T_i' - T_j')(a_{i1}a_{j1} + a_{i2}a_{j2} + a_{i3}a_{j3})$$

and, if $T_i' \neq T_j'$,

$$0 = a_{i1}a_{j1} + a_{i2}a_{j2} + a_{i3}a_{j3}$$

Combination of this result with (1-104) gives

$$a_{ij}a_{kj} = \delta_{ik} \qquad (1\text{-}3)$$

Thus the nine quantities a_{ij} which we have determined are, indeed, the direction cosines of the axes of the $O'X_1'X_2'X_3'$ coordinate system in which the matrix representing the tensor $\mathfrak{I}$ is diagonal relative to the axes of the $OX_1X_2X_3$ coordinate system. Then

$$\begin{pmatrix} B_1 \\ B_2 \\ B_3 \end{pmatrix} = \begin{pmatrix} u_{11} & a_{21} & a_{31} \\ a_{12} & a_{22} & a_{32} \\ a_{13} & a_{23} & a_{33} \end{pmatrix} \begin{pmatrix} B_1' \\ B_2' \\ B_3' \end{pmatrix}$$

and

$$\begin{pmatrix} A_1 \\ A_2 \\ A_3 \end{pmatrix} = \begin{pmatrix} a_{11} & a_{21} & a_{31} \\ a_{12} & a_{22} & a_{32} \\ a_{13} & a_{23} & a_{33} \end{pmatrix} \begin{pmatrix} A_1' \\ A_2' \\ A_3' \end{pmatrix}$$

Substitution of these relations into (1-99) gives

$$\begin{pmatrix} a_{11} & a_{21} & a_{31} \\ a_{12} & a_{22} & a_{32} \\ a_{13} & a_{23} & a_{33} \end{pmatrix} \begin{pmatrix} B_1' \\ B_2' \\ B_3' \end{pmatrix} = \begin{pmatrix} T_{11} & T_{12} & T_{31} \\ T_{12} & T_{22} & T_{23} \\ T_{31} & T_{23} & T_{33} \end{pmatrix} \begin{pmatrix} a_{11} & a_{21} & a_{31} \\ a_{12} & a_{22} & a_{32} \\ a_{13} & a_{23} & a_{33} \end{pmatrix} \begin{pmatrix} A_1' \\ A_2' \\ A_3' \end{pmatrix}$$

or, using (1-3b),

$$\begin{pmatrix} B_1' \\ B_2' \\ B_3' \end{pmatrix} = \begin{pmatrix} a_{11} & a_{12} & a_{13} \\ a_{21} & a_{22} & a_{23} \\ a_{31} & a_{32} & a_{33} \end{pmatrix} \begin{pmatrix} T_{11} & T_{12} & T_{31} \\ T_{12} & T_{22} & T_{32} \\ T_{31} & T_{23} & T_{33} \end{pmatrix} \begin{pmatrix} a_{11} & a_{21} & a_{31} \\ a_{12} & a_{22} & a_{32} \\ a_{13} & a_{23} & a_{33} \end{pmatrix} \begin{pmatrix} A_1' \\ A_2' \\ A_3' \end{pmatrix} \qquad (1\text{-}106)$$

But from (1-103)

$$\begin{pmatrix} T_{11} & T_{12} & T_{31} \\ T_{12} & T_{22} & T_{23} \\ T_{31} & T_{23} & T_{33} \end{pmatrix} \begin{pmatrix} a_{11} & a_{21} & a_{31} \\ a_{12} & a_{22} & a_{32} \\ a_{13} & a_{23} & a_{33} \end{pmatrix} = \begin{pmatrix} T'_1 a_{11} & T'_2 a_{21} & T'_3 a_{31} \\ T'_1 a_{12} & T'_2 a_{22} & T'_3 a_{32} \\ T'_1 a_{13} & T'_2 a_{23} & T'_3 a_{33} \end{pmatrix}$$

Hence (1-106) reduces to

$$\begin{pmatrix} B'_1 \\ B'_2 \\ B'_3 \end{pmatrix} = \begin{pmatrix} T'_1 & 0 & 0 \\ 0 & T'_2 & 0 \\ 0 & 0 & T'_3 \end{pmatrix} \begin{pmatrix} A'_1 \\ A'_2 \\ A'_3 \end{pmatrix}$$

which is (1-100). Thus we have found the coordinate system in which the matrix representing the tensor $\mathfrak{T}$ is diagonal and found the elements of the matrix in that coordinate system. The axes of the coordinate system are known as the *principal axes* of the tensor.

EXERCISES

1-1. Verify that

$$\begin{pmatrix} 4.5 \\ -\tfrac{1}{2}\sqrt{3} \\ 4 \end{pmatrix} = \begin{pmatrix} \tfrac{1}{2} & \tfrac{1}{2}\sqrt{3} & 0 \\ -\tfrac{1}{2}\sqrt{3} & \tfrac{1}{2} & 0 \\ 0 & 0 & 1 \end{pmatrix} \begin{pmatrix} 3 \\ 2\sqrt{3} \\ 4 \end{pmatrix}$$

1-2. Verify that

$$\begin{pmatrix} \tfrac{1}{2} & \tfrac{1}{2}\sqrt{3} & 0 \\ -\tfrac{1}{2}\sqrt{3} & \tfrac{1}{2} & 0 \\ 0 & 0 & 1 \end{pmatrix} \begin{pmatrix} \tfrac{1}{2} & -\tfrac{1}{2}\sqrt{3} & 0 \\ \tfrac{1}{2}\sqrt{3} & \tfrac{1}{2} & 0 \\ 0 & 0 & 1 \end{pmatrix} = \begin{pmatrix} 1 & 0 & 0 \\ 0 & 1 & 0 \\ 0 & 0 & 1 \end{pmatrix}$$

1-3. Vectors are drawn from the origin to two points, $(-4,2,+4)$ and $(-8,4,-1)$. Form the scalar product of these two vectors, and find the cosine of the angle between them.

1-4. Write out the vector product of the two vectors

$$\mathbf{A} = \mathbf{i}_1 - 2\mathbf{i}_2 + 2\mathbf{i}_3 \qquad \mathbf{B} = 3\mathbf{i}_1 + \mathbf{i}_2 + \mathbf{i}_3$$

and show by calculation that the resulting vector is perpendicular to both $\mathbf{A}$ and $\mathbf{B}$.

1-5. Let a and b be scalar point functions and $\mathbf{A}$ and $\mathbf{B}$ be vector point functions. Then verify that

(a) grad $(ab) \equiv \nabla(ab) = a\nabla b + b\nabla a$

(b) div $(a\mathbf{A}) \equiv \nabla \cdot (a\mathbf{A}) = a\nabla \cdot \mathbf{A} + \nabla a \cdot \mathbf{A}$

(c) curl $(a\mathbf{A}) \equiv \nabla \times (a\mathbf{A}) = a\nabla \times \mathbf{A} + \nabla a \times \mathbf{A}$

(d) grad $(\mathbf{A} \cdot \mathbf{B}) \equiv \nabla(\mathbf{A} \cdot \mathbf{B})$
$= (\mathbf{A} \cdot \nabla)\mathbf{B} + (\mathbf{B} \cdot \nabla)\mathbf{A} + \mathbf{A} \times (\nabla \times \mathbf{B}) + \mathbf{B} \times (\nabla \times \mathbf{A})$

(e) div $(\mathbf{A} \times \mathbf{B}) = \nabla \cdot (\mathbf{A} \times \mathbf{B}) = \mathbf{B} \cdot \nabla \times \mathbf{A} - \mathbf{A} \cdot \nabla \times \mathbf{B}$

(f) curl $(\mathbf{A} \times \mathbf{B}) \equiv \nabla \times (\mathbf{A} \times \mathbf{B})$
$= \mathbf{A}(\nabla \cdot \mathbf{B}) - \mathbf{B}(\nabla \cdot \mathbf{A}) + (\mathbf{B} \cdot \nabla)\mathbf{A} - (\mathbf{A} \cdot \nabla)\mathbf{B}$

(g) curl curl $\mathbf{A} \equiv \nabla \times (\nabla \times \mathbf{A}) = \nabla(\nabla \cdot \mathbf{A}) - \nabla^2\mathbf{A}$

1-6. Let a be a scalar-point function and $\mathbf{A}$ a vector-point function. Then show by actual expansion that curl grad $a = 0$ and div curl $\mathbf{A} = 0$.

1-7. Given $F_1 = x_2/r^n$, $F_2 = -x_1/r^n$, $F_3 = 0$, where $r = \sqrt{x_1{}^2 + x_2{}^2}$ and n is a constant, show that F represents a vector tangent to the circle about the origin in the x_1x_2 plane.

1-8. Find which of the following vector fields are derivable from potentials and set up the potentials where possible. a and b are constants, and $r = \sqrt{x_1{}^2 + x_2{}^2}$.

(a) $F_1 = -ax_1$, $F_2 = -bx_2$, $F_3 = 0$

(b) $F_1 = x_2/r^3$, $F_2 = -x_1/r^3$, $F_3 = 0$

(c) $F_1 = x_2/r^2$, $F_2 = -x_1/r^2$, $F_3 = 0$

(d) $F_1 = x_2/r$, $F_2 = -x_1/r$, $F_3 = 0$

1-9. Take $\mathbf{F}$ as given in Exercise 1-8c. Then calculate the line integral $\oint \mathbf{F} \cdot d\mathbf{s}$ around (a) a circle of arbitrary radius in the x_1x_2 plane with center at the origin and (b) a square of side $2a$ with its center at $x_1 = 2a$, $x_2 = 0$ and its sides parallel to the x_1 and x_2 axes.

1-10. By direct substitution of $x_1 = r \cos \theta$ and $x_2 = r \sin \theta$ into $\nabla^2 \equiv \partial^2/\partial x_1{}^2 + \partial^2/\partial x_2{}^2$, derive the expression for the Laplacian operator ∇^2 in plane polar coordinates.

1-11. Obtain the expression for the Laplacian operator in (a) plane polar and (b) space polar coordinates by using the transformation (1-81) for orthogonal coordinate systems.

1-12. Obtain the expression for the Laplacian operator in parabolic coordinates u, v, w defined by

$$x_1 = uv \cos w \qquad x_2 = uv \sin w \qquad x_3 = \tfrac{1}{2}(u^2 - v^2)$$

1-13. Show that $1/r$ satisfies Laplace's equation when $r = \sqrt{x_1{}^2 + x_2{}^2 + x_3{}^2} \neq 0$

1-14. Verify that

$$\begin{pmatrix} 3.45 \\ 3.15 \\ 2.15 \end{pmatrix} = \begin{pmatrix} 5.0 & 0.4 & 0.2 \\ 0.4 & 2.0 & 0.2 \\ 0.2 & 0.2 & 0.8 \end{pmatrix} \begin{pmatrix} 0.50 \\ 1.25 \\ 2.25 \end{pmatrix}$$

Then determine the direction cosines a_{ij} such that

$$\begin{pmatrix} T'_1 & 0 & 0 \\ 0 & T'_2 & 0 \\ 0 & 0 & T'_3 \end{pmatrix} = \begin{pmatrix} a_{11} & a_{12} & a_{13} \\ a_{21} & a_{22} & a_{23} \\ a_{31} & a_{32} & a_{33} \end{pmatrix} \begin{pmatrix} 5.0 & 0.4 & 0.2 \\ 0.4 & 2.0 & 0.2 \\ 0.2 & 0.2 & 0.8 \end{pmatrix} \begin{pmatrix} a_{11} & a_{21} & a_{31} \\ a_{12} & a_{22} & a_{32} \\ a_{13} & a_{23} & a_{33} \end{pmatrix}$$

REFERENCES

Abraham, M., and R. Becker: "The Classical Theory of Electricity and Magnetism," chaps. I and II, Hafner Publishing Company, Inc., New York, 1950.

Coffin, J. G.: "Vector Analysis," 2d ed., John Wiley & Sons, Inc., New York, 1938.

Goertzel, G., and N. Tralli: "Some Mathematical Methods of Physics," chaps. 1, 4, and 12 and Appendix 2B, McGraw-Hill Book Company, Inc., New York, 1960.

Jeffreys, H., and B. S. Jeffreys: "Methods of Mathematical Physics," 3d ed., chaps. 2, 3, and 4, Cambridge University Press, London, 1956.

Margenau, H., and G. M. Murphy: "The Mathematics of Physics and Chemistry," 2d ed., chaps. 4 and 5, D. Van Nostrand Company, Inc., Princeton, N.J., 1956.

Morse, P. M., and H. Feshbach: "Methods of Theoretical Physics," chaps. 1, 2, and 7, McGraw-Hill Book Company, Inc., New York, 1953.

Wills, A. P.: "Vector Analysis," Dover Publications, Inc., New York, 1959.

CHAPTER 2

The Electrostatic Field

2-1. INTRODUCTION

In this chapter we begin our study of electrostatics. We commence with a discussion of Coulomb's law. In so doing we define such quantities as permittivity and dielectric constant and introduce a system of units. In Sec. 2-3 we define electric intensity and potential. Sections 2-4 to 2-6 deal with Gauss' law and its implications and applications. Green's reciprocity theorem is treated in Sec. 2-7. Coefficients of potential, capacitance, and induction are discussed in Secs. 2-8 and 2-9. The capacitance of several simple capacitors is treated in Sec. 2-10. The final section of the chapter deals with the derivation of some equivalent expressions for the energy in the electrostatic field.

2-2. COULOMB'S LAW

As a result of his experiments with the torsion balance, Coulomb, in 1785, discovered that the force $\mathbf{F}$ between any two charges q and q' in a homogeneous isotropic medium is directly proportional to their product and inversely proportional to the square of the distance r between them and directed along the line joining them. Thus

$$\mathbf{F} \propto \frac{qq'}{r^2} \mathbf{i}_r \tag{2-1}$$

where $\mathbf{i}_r$ is a unit vector in the direction of the force. In order to replace the expression (2-1) by an equation, it is necessary to introduce a constant of proportionality. It is now customary to write this constant as $1/4\pi\epsilon$, where ϵ is known as the *permittivity* of the medium. Then

$$\mathbf{F} = \frac{qq'}{4\pi\epsilon r^2} \mathbf{i}_r \tag{2-2}$$

In the case of a vacuum, Eq. (2-2) reduces to

$$\mathbf{F}_0 = \frac{qq'}{4\pi\epsilon_0 r^2} \mathbf{i}_r \tag{2-3}$$

where ϵ_0 is known as the *permittivity of free space*.

36

Division of Eq. (2-3) by Eq. (2-2) yields

$$\frac{F_0}{F} = \frac{\epsilon}{\epsilon_0} = K \qquad (2\text{-}4)$$

where K, the ratio of the force between the charges in vacuum to that between them in the given medium, is known as the *dielectric constant* of the medium. Note that it is a dimensionless constant. Since the force between the charges in a homogeneous isotropic medium is less than that between them in vacuum, the dielectric constant in such a medium is of magnitude greater than unity, its value in the case of vacuum.

From Eq. (2-4) it follows that

$$\epsilon = K\epsilon_0 \qquad (2\text{-}5)$$

which defines ϵ in terms of K and ϵ_0.

The reader should note that in discussing the force between two charges we have considered only a special case, namely, the force in a homogeneous isotropic medium. This was done because homogeneous isotropic media are common and relatively simple to treat. However, the reader is warned not to generalize from this special case. Although the force between two charges a given distance apart in a homogeneous isotropic medium is independent of the orientation of the charges, this is not so in anisotropic media. Because the force between the charges depends on the orientation of the charges in these media, the dielectric constants K and the permittivities ϵ are not scalar quantities. Anisotropic media are discussed in Sec. 4-7.

Thus far no mention has been made of units. In the cgs system of units one takes $\epsilon_0 = 1/4\pi$, so that Eq. (2-3) becomes

$$\mathbf{F}_0 = \frac{qq'}{r^2}\, \mathbf{i}_r \qquad (2\text{-}6)$$

The definition of the cgs unit of charge then follows directly. If $q = q'$ and F_0 and r are set equal to unity, the charges become unit. Consequently, the cgs unit of charge is that charge which will repel an equal charge of the same sign placed at a distance of one centimeter in vacuum with a force of one dyne. The unit of charge and all other cgs units based on Eq. (2-6) are known as electrostatic units and designated by the abbreviation esu.

It turns out that in many cases it is much more practical to use the mks system of units, in which force is measured in newtons, distance in meters, and charge in coulombs, where

$$1 \text{ newton} = 10^5 \text{ dynes}$$
$$1 \text{ meter} = 10^2 \text{ centimeters}$$
$$1 \text{ coulomb} = c/10 \text{ esu of charge}$$

in which the constant c is equal to 2.998×10^{10}, the numerical value of the velocity of light in centimeters per second. The use of the mks units requires that ϵ_0 be taken numerically equal to $10^7/4\pi c^2 = 8.85 \times 10^{-12}$ and that it have the dimensions farads per meter, where

$$1 \text{ farad} = 1 \frac{\text{coulomb}}{\text{volt}} \tag{2-7}$$

$$1 \text{ volt} = 1 \frac{\text{newton meter}}{\text{coulomb}} \tag{2-8}$$

Thus while ϵ_0 is dimensionless in the cgs system of units it has dimensions (farads per meter) in the mks system.

The mks system of units will be used in all that follows.

2-3. ELECTRIC INTENSITY AND POTENTIAL

An electric field is said to exist in a region if a stationary electric charge in that region experiences a force. If a test body with charge q' is placed at some point P in the presence of a number of given charges which are held rigidly in position, it will experience a force **F** which will be a measure of the intensity and direction of the electrostatic field at that point. Since this force is proportional to the charge q' on the test body, one defines the *electrostatic field intensity* or simply the *electric intensity* **E** at the point P as the force which a unit positive charge at the point will experience when all other charges are held rigidly in position. Thus

$$\mathbf{E} = \frac{\mathbf{F}}{q'} \tag{2-9}$$

and has the dimensions newton/coulomb = volt/meter.

In using Eq. (2-9) as the definition of the electric field intensity **E**, it must be remembered that all the charges producing the field must be rigidly held in position. Another definition which obviates the necessity of holding the charges producing the field fixed is

$$\mathbf{E} = \lim_{q' \to 0} \frac{\mathbf{F}}{q'} \tag{2-9a}$$

The $\lim_{q' \to 0}$ guarantees that the charge on the test body will not alter the charge distribution which existed prior to the introduction of the test body.

From Eqs. (2-2) and (2-9) it follows that

$$\mathbf{E} = \frac{q}{4\pi \epsilon r^2}\, \mathbf{i}_r \qquad (2\text{-}10)$$

is the electric intensity at a point r distant from a point charge q. By taking the curl of (2-10), it is readily verified that

$$\text{curl } \mathbf{E} = 0 \qquad (2\text{-}11)$$

i.e., the electrostatic field is a conservative field. Hence a potential function ϕ exists such that

$$\mathbf{E} = -\text{ grad } \phi \qquad (2\text{-}12)$$

The potential difference between two points P and P' in an electrostatic field is then given by

$$\phi(P) - \phi(P') = \int_{r'}^{r} \text{grad } \phi \cdot ds = -\int_{r'}^{r} \mathbf{E} \cdot ds \qquad (2\text{-}13)$$

where ds is an element of the path followed in going from the point P' at r' to the point P at r. Since $\mathbf{E}$ represents the force on a unit positive charge, $\phi(P) - \phi(P')$ represents the work done against the field in bringing a unit positive charge from the point P' to the point P. The unit of potential difference is the volt.

Substitution for $\mathbf{E}$ by means of (2-10) yields

$$\phi(P) - \phi(P') = -\int_{r'}^{r} \frac{q}{4\pi \epsilon r^2}\, \mathbf{i}_r \cdot ds$$

If each element of path ds is divided into two components, one along $\mathbf{i}_r$, which is denoted by dr, and the other perpendicular to $\mathbf{i}_r$,

$$\phi(P) - \phi(P') = -\int_{r'}^{r} \frac{q}{4\pi \epsilon r^2}\, dr = \frac{q}{4\pi \epsilon}\left(\frac{1}{r} - \frac{1}{r'} \right)$$

If the point P' is taken at infinity, then

$$\phi(P) = -\int_{\infty}^{r} \frac{q}{4\pi \epsilon r^2}\, dr = \frac{q}{4\pi \epsilon r} \qquad (2\text{-}14)$$

i.e., the potential at any point P in an electrostatic field is the work done against the field in bringing a unit positive charge to the point from infinity (i.e., from outside the field), the charges producing the field being held rigidly in place.

2-4. GAUSS' LAW

Consider a volume τ containing a total charge Q. Let dS be an element of the surface S which bounds the volume τ. Then

$$\iint \mathbf{E} \cdot d\mathbf{S} = \frac{Q}{\epsilon} \tag{2-15}$$

where ϵ is the permittivity of the medium. Equation (2-15) is the mathematical expression of Gauss' law. In words, the integral of the electric intensity over the bounding surface of a body is equal to the total charge contained by the body divided by the permittivity of the medium.

Gauss' law can be obtained as a direct consequence of Coulomb's law: Consider first a point charge q. The flux through an element dS of a sphere of radius r with the charge q at its center is $\mathbf{E} \cdot d\mathbf{S} = (q/4\pi\epsilon r^2)r^2\,d\Omega$, where $d\Omega$ is the element of solid angle subtended at the center of the sphere by the area dS. Integration over the entire surface yields

$$\iint \mathbf{E} \cdot d\mathbf{S} = \frac{q}{\epsilon} \tag{2-16}$$

For a surface S surrounding n point charges $q_1, q_2, \ldots, q_n$, Gauss' law states that

$$\iint \mathbf{E} \cdot d\mathbf{S} = \frac{1}{\epsilon}(q_1 + q_2 + \cdots + q_n) \tag{2-17}$$

To verify this, suppose each point charge q_i to be surrounded by a small sphere S_i. The surface S bounds all these small spheres. For each small sphere

$$\iint \mathbf{E}_i \cdot d\mathbf{S}_i = \frac{q_i}{\epsilon}$$

so that (2-17) follows directly on summation.

Thus far the verification of Gauss' law has been limited to the case of discrete charge distributions. Consider now a continuous distribution of charge ρ per unit volume. Such a volume distribution can be considered as a series of discrete charges $\rho\,d\tau$, and hence Gauss' law holds equally well in this case. Since the total contained charge is $\iiint\rho\,d\tau$, Gauss' law takes the form

$$\iint \mathbf{E} \cdot d\mathbf{S} = \frac{1}{\epsilon}\iiint \rho\,d\tau \tag{2-18}$$

in any region where there is a continuous charge distribution ρ per unit volume and no point charges.

According to Gauss' theorem (cf. Sec. 1-16)

$$\iint \mathbf{E} \cdot d\mathbf{S} = \iiint \text{div } \mathbf{E} \, d\tau \qquad (2\text{-}19)$$

Hence

$$\iiint \text{div } \mathbf{E} \, d\tau = \frac{1}{\epsilon} \iiint \rho \, d\tau$$

or

$$\iiint \left(\text{div } \mathbf{E} - \frac{\rho}{\epsilon} \right) d\tau = 0$$

Since the volume elements are arbitrary, the result implies that

$$\text{div } \mathbf{E} = \frac{\rho}{\epsilon} \qquad (2\text{-}20)$$

which is known as the differential statement of Gauss' law, in contrast to the integral statement (2-18).

Substitution for $\mathbf{E}$ in Eq. (2-20) by means of (2-12) yields

$$\text{div grad } \phi = \nabla^2 \phi = -\frac{\rho}{c} \qquad (2\text{-}21)$$

which is *Poisson's equation*. In the particular case of zero charge density ($\rho = 0$) it reduces to *Laplace's equation*,

$$\nabla^2 \phi = 0 \qquad (2\text{-}22)$$

2-5. IMPLICATIONS OF GAUSS' LAW

From Eq. (2-21) it immediately follows that the electrostatic potential cannot have a maximum (minimum) value except at points where there is positive (negative) charge. At a point where the potential is an extremum, the directional derivative in an arbitrary direction must be zero; i.e.,

$$\frac{d\phi}{ds} = \nabla\phi \cdot \mathbf{i}_s = 0$$

where $\mathbf{i}_s$ is an arbitrarily directed unit vector. Hence $\nabla\phi = 0$ and $\partial\phi/\partial x_i = 0$ for all i. For a maximum, $\partial^2\phi/\partial x_i^2$ must be less than zero for all i, and consequently, $\nabla^2\phi < 0$. But this result is consistent with (2-21) only if ρ is positive. Similarly, for a minimum, $\nabla^2\phi > 0$, and this result is consistent with (2-21) only if ρ is negative.

It also follows that no charge can be in stable equilibrium in an electrostatic field under the influence of electrical forces alone. This theorem, known as *Earnshaw's theorem*, can be verified as follows: The potential energy of a movable charge q is $q\phi$. Stable equilibrium of q at some point P implies that $q\phi$ is a minimum at P. But we have just demonstrated that this is impossible unless there is a negative charge at P. Therefore, there can be no point of stable equilibrium in an electrostatic field.

2-6. APPLICATIONS OF GAUSS' LAW

1. *Conducting spherical shell.* Let the shell be of radius a, and let the total charge on the shell be q. Describe a sphere of radius r concentric with the shell of radius a. Then, from symmetry, it is clear that the electric field is directed along the radius $\mathbf{r}$ and, furthermore, that it is the same at all points on the surface of the sphere. Hence

$$\iint \mathbf{E} \cdot d\mathbf{S} = \iint E\, dS = E \iint dS = 4\pi r^2 E$$

and from Gauss' law,

$$4\pi r^2 E = \frac{q}{\epsilon} \qquad \text{for } r > a$$
$$= 0 \qquad \text{for } r < a$$

Thus (a) the electric field outside a sphere with total charge q is $q/4\pi\epsilon r^2$, the same as the field which would be produced by a point charge q at the center of the sphere, and (b) the electric field inside a charged conductor is zero.

2. *Infinitely long cylindrical conductor.* Let the radius of the cylinder be a and the charge per unit length be λ. Describe a cylinder of radius r coaxial with the conducting cylinder. From symmetry the electric field is directed radially and is the same at all points on the cylinder of radius r. Therefore

$$\iint \mathbf{E} \cdot d\mathbf{S} = \iint E\, dS = 2\pi r h E$$

where $h \to \infty$ is the length of the cylinder. From Gauss' law

$$2\pi r h E = \frac{\lambda h}{\epsilon} \qquad \text{for } r > a$$
$$= 0 \qquad \text{for } r < a$$

Hence, for $r > a$,

$$E = -\frac{\partial \phi}{\partial r} = \frac{\lambda}{2\pi r \epsilon} \tag{2-23}$$

and

$$\phi = -\frac{\lambda}{2\pi\epsilon} \ln r + \text{constant} \tag{2-24}$$

Note that the potential (2-24) has a singularity at $r = \infty$. This singularity is a consequence of the fact that the charge density is unbounded. Because of this the potential cannot be referred to infinity as was the potential of the point charge.

The case of an infinite line source is obtained by letting the radius a of the infinite cylinder approach zero.

3. *Charged plate of infinite extension.* Let the charge per unit area of the plate be σ. Describe a pillbox with top and bottom of area S parallel to and on opposite sides of the charged plate. From symmetry, the electric field is normal to the plate. Hence

$$\iint \mathbf{E} \cdot d\mathbf{S} = \iint E \, dS = 2SE$$

and, from Gauss' law,

$$2SE = \frac{\sigma S}{\epsilon}$$

or

$$E = -\frac{\partial \phi}{\partial x_1} = \frac{\sigma}{2\epsilon} \tag{2-25}$$

where x_1 is perpendicular to the plate. Then

$$\phi = -\frac{\sigma}{2\epsilon} x_1 + \text{constant} \tag{2-26}$$

Note that $\phi \to -\infty$ as $x_1 \to \infty$. Thus the potential due to a charged plate of infinite extension also cannot be referred to infinity.

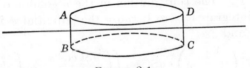

FIGURE 2-1

4. *Arbitrary conductor.* Since the electric field inside a charged conductor is zero, the surface of the conductor is an equipotential and it follows that the field just outside the surface is normal to the surface. Consider the boundary surface between a conductor and a medium of permittivity ϵ. Describe (Fig. 2-1) a pillbox-shaped surface $ABCD$ about an element of area dS of the conductor, the height DC being very small compared with the diameter of the base. The total charge inside the pillbox is $\sigma \, dS$. Since the electric field is zero inside the conductor and normal to the surface outside the conductor, application of Gauss' law to the pillbox yields

$$E_n \, dS = \frac{\sigma}{\epsilon} \, dS$$

or

$$E_n = \frac{\sigma}{\epsilon} \tag{2-27}$$

2-7. GREEN'S RECIPROCITY THEOREM

Consider a volume τ' of a medium of permittivity ϵ which is bounded by a surface S'. Let ρ denote the charge per unit volume of the medium. Then, according to (1-73), the potential ϕ at a field point $\mathbf{r}$ within the volume τ' is

$$\phi(\mathbf{r}) = \frac{1}{4\pi\epsilon} \iiint \frac{\rho(\mathbf{r}')\, d\tau'}{|\mathbf{r} - \mathbf{r}'|} + \frac{1}{4\pi} \iint \frac{\nabla'\phi \cdot d\mathbf{S}'}{|\mathbf{r} - \mathbf{r}'|} - \frac{1}{4\pi} \iint \phi \nabla' \frac{1}{|\mathbf{r} - \mathbf{r}'|} \cdot d\mathbf{S}'$$

where the prime on the del operator indicates that the differentiations are with respect to the source coordinates.

Let us now consider the case in which the bounding surface S' consists of a surface at infinity plus the surfaces of n conductors which are embedded in the medium. The contribution to the surface integrals from the surface at infinity is zero. The contribution of the surfaces of the n conductors to the first of the surface integrals is

$$\frac{1}{4\pi\epsilon} \iint \frac{\sigma(\mathbf{r}')\, dS'}{|\mathbf{r} - \mathbf{r}'|}$$

because

$$\nabla'\phi \cdot d\mathbf{S}' = E_n(\mathbf{r}')\, dS = \frac{\sigma(r')}{\epsilon}\, dS'$$

where $E_n(\mathbf{r}')$ is the component of the electric field intensity which is normal to the surface element dS' at $\mathbf{r}'$ and $\sigma(\mathbf{r}')$ is the charge per unit surface area at $\mathbf{r}'$. The contribution of the n conductors to the second of the surface integrals is zero because the potential ϕ is a constant on each conductor and

$$\iint \nabla' \left(\frac{1}{|\mathbf{r} - \mathbf{r}'|} \right) \cdot d\mathbf{S}' = \iint \frac{dS' \cos\theta}{|\mathbf{r} - \mathbf{r}'|^2} = \int d\omega = 0$$

for each conductor, where θ is the angle between $\mathbf{r} - \mathbf{r}'$ and $d\mathbf{S}'$ and $d\omega = (dS' \cos\theta)/|\mathbf{r} - \mathbf{r}'|^2$ is the solid angle subtended at $\mathbf{r}$ by dS'.

Thus, the potential at any point $\mathbf{r}$ in a volume τ' with a charge distribution ρ per unit volume and σ per unit surface area is given by

$$\phi(\mathbf{r}) = \frac{1}{4\pi\epsilon} \iiint \frac{\rho(\mathbf{r}')\, d\tau'}{|\mathbf{r} - \mathbf{r}'|} + \frac{1}{4\pi\epsilon} \iint \frac{\sigma(\mathbf{r}')\, dS'}{|\mathbf{r} - \mathbf{r}'|} \qquad \mathbf{r} \neq \mathbf{r}' \qquad (2\text{-}28)$$

where in the first integral $d\tau'$ is the volume element located at position $\mathbf{r}'$ and in the second integral dS' is the surface element at $\mathbf{r}'$.

Likewise, the potential at $\mathbf{r}$ due to a different charge distribution ρ_1 per unit volume and σ_1 per unit surface area is

$$\phi_1(\mathbf{r}) = \frac{1}{4\pi\epsilon} \iiint \frac{\rho_1(\mathbf{r}')\, d\tau'}{|\mathbf{r} - \mathbf{r}'|} + \frac{1}{4\pi\epsilon} \iint \frac{\sigma_1(\mathbf{r}')\, dS'}{|\mathbf{r} - \mathbf{r}'|} \qquad \mathbf{r} \neq \mathbf{r}' \qquad (2\text{-}29)$$

Green's reciprocity theorem states that

$$\iiint \phi_1(\mathbf{r})\rho(\mathbf{r})\, d\tau + \iint \phi_1(\mathbf{r})\sigma(\mathbf{r})\, dS = \iiint \phi(\mathbf{r})\rho_1(\mathbf{r})\, d\tau + \iint \phi(\mathbf{r})\sigma_1(\mathbf{r})\, dS$$

$$(2\text{-}30)$$

To verify the theorem proceed as follows: First, multiply (2-28) by $\rho_1(\mathbf{r})\, d\tau$ and integrate. Then

$$\iiint \phi(\mathbf{r})\rho_1(\mathbf{r})\, d\tau = \frac{1}{4\pi\epsilon} \iiint \rho_1(\mathbf{r})\, d\tau \iiint \frac{\rho(\mathbf{r}')\, d\tau'}{|\mathbf{r} - \mathbf{r}'|}$$

$$+ \frac{1}{4\pi\epsilon} \iiint \rho_1(\mathbf{r})\, d\tau \iint \frac{\sigma(\mathbf{r}')\, dS'}{|\mathbf{r} - \mathbf{r}'|}$$

$$= \frac{1}{4\pi\epsilon} \iiint \rho(\mathbf{r}')\, d\tau' \iiint \frac{\rho_1(\mathbf{r})\, d\tau}{|\mathbf{r} - \mathbf{r}'|}$$

$$+ \frac{1}{4\pi\epsilon} \iint \sigma(\mathbf{r}')\, dS' \iiint \frac{\rho_1(\mathbf{r})\, d\tau}{|\mathbf{r} - \mathbf{r}'|} \quad (2\text{-}31)$$

on interchanging the order of integration. Similarly, multiplication of (2-28) by $\sigma_1(\mathbf{r})\, dS$ and integration yields

$$\iint \phi(\mathbf{r})\sigma_1(\mathbf{r})\, dS = \frac{1}{4\pi\epsilon} \iiint \rho(\mathbf{r}')\, d\tau' \iint \frac{\sigma_1(\mathbf{r})\, dS}{|\mathbf{r} - \mathbf{r}'|}$$

$$+ \frac{1}{4\pi\epsilon} \iint \sigma(\mathbf{r}')\, dS' \iint \frac{\sigma_1(\mathbf{r})\, dS}{|\mathbf{r} - \mathbf{r}'|} \quad (2\text{-}32)$$

Addition of (2-31) and (2-32) gives

$$\iiint \phi(\mathbf{r})\rho_1(\mathbf{r})\, d\tau + \iint \phi(\mathbf{r})\sigma_1(\mathbf{r})\, dS$$

$$= \frac{1}{4\pi\epsilon} \iiint \rho(\mathbf{r}')\, d\tau' \left[\iiint \frac{\rho_1(\mathbf{r})\, d\tau}{|\mathbf{r} - \mathbf{r}'|} + \iint \frac{\sigma_1(\mathbf{r})\, dS}{|\mathbf{r} - \mathbf{r}'|} \right]$$

$$+ \frac{1}{4\pi\epsilon} \iint \sigma(\mathbf{r}')\, dS' \left[\iiint \frac{\rho_1(\mathbf{r})\, d\tau}{|\mathbf{r} - \mathbf{r}'|} + \iint \frac{\sigma_1(\mathbf{r})\, dS}{|\mathbf{r} - \mathbf{r}'|} \right]$$

$$= \iiint \phi_1(\mathbf{r}')\rho(\mathbf{r}')\, d\tau' + \iint \phi_1(\mathbf{r}')\sigma(\mathbf{r}')\, dS'$$

verifying (2-30).

If the electric field is due solely to the n charged conductors, (2-30) reduces to

$$\sum_{i=1}^{n} \iint_{i} \phi_1(\mathbf{r})\sigma(\mathbf{r})\, dS = \sum_{i=1}^{n} \iint_{i} \phi(\mathbf{r})\sigma_1(\mathbf{r})\, dS \quad (2\text{-}33)$$

where the subscript i on the integral sign indicates that the integration is over the ith conductor only. Since a conductor is an equipotential,

Eq. (2-33) can be written

$$\sum_{i=1}^{n} \phi_{1_i} \iint_i \sigma(\mathbf{r}) \, dS = \sum_{i=1}^{n} \phi_i \iint_i \sigma_1(\mathbf{r}) \, dS$$

or
$$\sum_{i=1}^{n} \phi_{1_i} q_i = \sum_{i=1}^{n} \phi_i q_{1_i} \qquad (2\text{-}34)$$

where q_i is the total charge on the ith conductor.

One important application of Green's reciprocity theorem for conductors is obtained by setting $q_r = q_{1_s} = q$ and all the remaining q_{1_i} and q_i equal to zero in (2-34). This yields $\phi_{1_r} = \phi_s$. Hence, the potential to which an uncharged conductor s is raised by putting a charge q on conductor r is the same as that to which r, when uncharged, will be raised by putting the charge q on s.

2-8. COEFFICIENTS OF POTENTIAL

According to the discussion in the preceding section, placing a charge on any conductor of a group of initially uncharged conductors will affect the potential of all the other conductors in a definite manner which depends only on the geometrical configuration of the system of conductors and the dielectric constant of the medium in which they are embedded. The ratio of the rise in potential of the ith conductor to the charge q_j placed on the jth conductor to produce this rise is called the *coefficient of potential* and is denoted by p_{ji}. According to the application of Green's reciprocity theorem discussed in the preceding section, $p_{ji} = p_{ij}$. By superimposing solutions, the potential of the ith conductor due to charges q_j ($j = 1, 2, \ldots , n$) placed on the n conductors in the group is given by

$$\phi_i = \sum_{j=1}^{n} p_{ji} q_j \qquad i = 1, 2, \ldots , n \qquad (2\text{-}35)$$

Consequently, p_{ji} is the potential to which the ith conductor is raised when a unit charge is placed on the jth conductor, all the other conductors being present but uncharged. Since placing a positive charge on a conductor always raises the potential of neighboring insulated conductors, the coefficient p_{ji} is always positive.

2-9. COEFFICIENTS OF CAPACITANCE AND INDUCTION

The set of equations (2-35) can be solved to yield the charge on a conductor in terms of the potentials of all the conductors. Thus

$$q_i = \sum_{j=1}^{n} c_{ji} \phi_j \qquad i = 1, 2, \ldots , n \qquad (2\text{-}36)$$

where c_{ji} is the minor of p_{ji} in the determinant

$$\Delta \equiv \begin{vmatrix} p_{11} & p_{21} & \cdots & p_{n1} \\ p_{12} & p_{22} & \cdots & p_{n2} \\ \cdot & \cdot & \cdots & \cdot \\ \cdot & \cdot & \cdots & \cdot \\ p_{1n} & p_{2n} & \cdots & p_{nn} \end{vmatrix}$$ (2-37)

divided by Δ. The matrix of the c_{ji} is the reciprocal of the matrix of the p_{ji}.

The quantity c_{ji}, $j \neq i$, is called the *coefficient of induction*. It may be defined as the ratio of the charge induced in the ith conductor to the potential of the jth conductor when all conductors except the jth are grounded. Since the induced charge is always opposite in sign to the inducing charge (potential), these coefficients are either negative or zero.

The quantity c_{jj} is called the *coefficient of capacitance*. It is defined as the ratio of the charge on the jth conductor to its potential when all the other conductors are present but grounded. Since the potential has the same sign as the charge, these coefficients are always positive.

2-10. CAPACITANCE AND CAPACITORS

By definition, the capacitance of a conductor is the quantity of charge placed on the conductor which is required to produce unit potential. Thus

$$C = \frac{q}{\phi}$$ (2-38)

Isolated sphere. Let the charge on a sphere of radius a be q. Then the electric intensity E at any point $r > a$ is

$$E = -\frac{d\phi}{dr} = \frac{q}{4\pi\epsilon r^2}$$

so that

$$\phi(r) = \frac{q}{4\pi\epsilon r} + \text{constant}$$

Since $\phi \to 0$ as $r \to \infty$, the constant must be zero. Hence

$$\phi(a) = \frac{q}{4\pi\epsilon a}$$

and

$$C = 4\pi\epsilon a$$ (2-39)

According to the results of the preceding section, when several conductors are present, no definite capacitance can be associated with each one, since the potential of each depends not only on its charge but also on the charges on the other conductors. In the special case of two conductors with charges that are equal in magnitude and opposite in sign, however, one has

$$C_a = \frac{q}{\phi_a} \qquad C_b = -\frac{q}{\phi_b}$$

so that

$$q = C(\phi_a - \phi_b)$$

where

$$\frac{1}{C} = \frac{1}{C_a} + \frac{1}{C_b}$$

Such a combination of conductors is known as a capacitor. Several examples of capacitors are considered below.

Concentric spheres. Consider two concentric spherical conductors. Let the first be of radius r_a and have a charge $+q$. Let the second be of radius $r_b > r_a$ and be grounded on its outer surface. The charge on its inner surface is therefore $-q$. Then in the region between the two spherical shells

$$E = -\frac{d\phi}{dr} = \frac{q}{4\pi\epsilon r^2}$$

Hence

$$\int_{\phi_b}^{\phi_a} d\phi = -\frac{q}{4\pi\epsilon} \int_{r_b}^{r_a} \frac{dr}{r^2}$$

and

$$\phi_a - \phi_b = \frac{q}{4\pi\epsilon}\left(\frac{1}{r_a} - \frac{1}{r_b}\right)$$

so that

$$C = \frac{q}{\phi_a - \phi_b} = 4\pi\epsilon \frac{r_a r_b}{r_b - r_a} \tag{2-40}$$

It is sometimes convenient to rewrite (2-40) in terms of the areas of the spheres and of their separation. Let the areas be $A_a = 4\pi r_a^2$ and $A_b = 4\pi r_b^2$, and let the separation be $d = r_b - r_a$. Then

$$C = \frac{\epsilon \sqrt{A_a A_b}}{d} \tag{2-41}$$

Coaxial cylinders. Let the first cylinder be of radius r_a and have a charge $+\lambda$ per unit length. Let the second be of radius $r_b > r_a$ and have a charge $-\lambda$ per unit length. Then in the region between the cylinders

$$E = -\frac{d\phi}{dr} = \frac{\lambda}{2\pi\epsilon r}$$

$$\int_{\phi_b}^{\phi_a} d\phi = -\frac{\lambda}{2\pi\epsilon} \int_{r_b}^{r_a} \frac{dr}{r}$$

and

$$\phi_a - \phi_b = \frac{\lambda}{2\pi\epsilon} \ln\frac{r_b}{r_a}$$

Therefore

$$C = \frac{\lambda}{\phi_a - \phi_b} = \frac{2\pi\epsilon}{\ln(r_b/r_a)} \tag{2-42}$$

is the capacitance per unit length of the cylinders.

Parallel plates.   The capacitance of a parallel-plate capacitor is easily obtained from that for two concentric spheres given above.   Let the radii r_a and r_b of the spheres become very large, keeping $d = r_b - r_a$ fixed.   Then both A_a and A_b approach the value A and (2-41) reduces to

$$C = \frac{\epsilon A}{d} \tag{2-43}$$

which is the capacitance of two parallel plates of area A separated by a distance d.

2-11. ENERGY IN THE ELECTROSTATIC FIELD

Consider again an electric field produced by a charge distribution ρ per unit volume and σ per unit surface area.   The potential at any point $\mathbf{r}$ is given by

$$\phi(\mathbf{r}) = \frac{1}{4\pi\epsilon} \iiint \frac{\rho(\mathbf{r}') \, d\tau'}{|\mathbf{r} - \mathbf{r}'|} + \frac{1}{4\pi\epsilon} \iint \frac{\sigma(\mathbf{r}') \, dS'}{|\mathbf{r} - \mathbf{r}'|} \qquad \mathbf{r} \neq \mathbf{r}'$$

We desire to find the energy associated with the electric field.   To do this we suppose that the final charge densities ρ and σ were built up step by step, their ratios always being kept constant.   Thus suppose that at one step the charges present are $\lambda\rho$ and $\lambda\sigma$, where $0 \leq \lambda \leq 1$. The corresponding potential at the point $\mathbf{r}$ is

$$\lambda\phi(\mathbf{r}) = \frac{1}{4\pi\epsilon} \iiint \frac{\lambda\rho(\mathbf{r}') \, d\tau'}{|\mathbf{r} - \mathbf{r}'|} + \frac{1}{4\pi\epsilon} \iint \frac{\lambda\sigma(\mathbf{r}') \, dS'}{|\mathbf{r} - \mathbf{r}'|} \qquad \mathbf{r}' \neq \mathbf{r}'$$

Now let us bring up charges $\rho \, \delta\lambda$ and $\sigma \, \delta\lambda$.   The work that we do is

$$\delta W = \iiint [\rho(\mathbf{r}) \, \delta\lambda] \lambda\phi(\mathbf{r}) \, d\tau + \iint [\sigma(\mathbf{r}) \, \delta\lambda] \lambda\phi(\mathbf{r}) \, dS$$

Hence the total work done in bringing up the complete charge distribution ρ per unit volume and σ per unit surface area is

$$\begin{aligned} W &= \int_0^1 \lambda \, d\lambda \left[\iiint \rho(\mathbf{r})\phi(\mathbf{r}) \, d\tau + \iint \sigma(\mathbf{r})\phi(\mathbf{r}) \, dS \right] \\ &= \tfrac{1}{2} \left[\iiint \rho(\mathbf{r})\phi(\mathbf{r}) \, d\tau + \iint \sigma(\mathbf{r})\phi(\mathbf{r}) \, dS \right] \end{aligned} \tag{2-44}$$

and this is the energy associated with the electric field.

It is interesting to express the energy in the electric field in terms of the field intensity $\mathbf{E}$.   Since

$$\text{div } \mathbf{E} = \frac{\rho}{\epsilon}$$

the first term in (2-44) can be written

$$\frac{1}{2}\iiint\rho(\mathbf{r})\phi(\mathbf{r})\,d\tau = \frac{1}{2}\iiint\epsilon\phi(\mathbf{r})\ \text{div } \mathbf{E}(\mathbf{r})\,d\tau$$
$$= \frac{1}{2}\iiint\epsilon[\text{div }(\phi\mathbf{E}) - \mathbf{E}\cdot\text{grad }\phi]\,d\tau$$
$$= \frac{1}{2}\iint\epsilon\phi(\mathbf{r})E_n(\mathbf{r})\,dS + \frac{1}{2}\iiint\epsilon\mathbf{E}(\mathbf{r})\cdot\mathbf{E}(\mathbf{r})\,d\tau$$

where E_n is the component of $\mathbf{E}$ in the direction of the outward drawn normal to the element dS of the surface S bounding the volume τ. The surface integral is taken over a sphere at infinity and over the surface of each conductor in the field where

$$E_n(\mathbf{r}) = -\frac{\sigma(\mathbf{r})}{\epsilon}$$

The integral over the sphere at infinity vanishes. Therefore

$$\frac{1}{2}\iiint\rho(\mathbf{r})\phi(\mathbf{r})\,d\tau = -\frac{1}{2}\iint\sigma(\mathbf{r})\phi(\mathbf{r})\,dS + \frac{1}{2}\iiint\epsilon\mathbf{E}(\mathbf{r})\cdot\mathbf{E}(\mathbf{r})\,d\tau$$

and (2-44) reduces to

$$W = \frac{1}{2}\iiint\epsilon\mathbf{E}(\mathbf{r})\cdot\mathbf{E}(\mathbf{r})\,d\tau \tag{2-45}$$

The quantity $(\epsilon/2)\mathbf{E}\cdot\mathbf{E}$ is known as the energy density in the electrostatic field.

If the electric field is due to n charged conductors only, (2-44) reduces to

$$W = \frac{1}{2}\sum_{i=1}^{n}\iint_i \sigma(\mathbf{r})\phi(\mathbf{r})\,dS \tag{2-46}$$

where the subscript i on the integration sign indicates that the integration is over the ith conductor alone. Since a conductor is an equipotential, (2-46) can be written

$$W = \frac{1}{2}\sum_{i=1}^{n}\phi_i\iint_i \sigma(\mathbf{r})\,dS$$

or

$$W = \frac{1}{2}\sum_{i=1}^{n}\phi_i q_i \tag{2-47}$$

where q_i is the total charge on the ith conductor. By the use of Eq. (2-35), the energy W can be expressed in terms of the charges q_i only. Thus

$$W = \frac{1}{2}\sum_{i=1}^{n}q_i\sum_{j=1}^{n}p_{ji}q_j = \frac{1}{2}\sum_{i,j=1}^{n}p_{ji}q_jq_i \tag{2-48}$$

In a like manner, using (2-36), W can be expressed in terms of the potentials ϕ_i alone. Thus

$$W = \tfrac{1}{2} \sum_{i=1}^{n} \phi_i \sum_{j=1}^{n} c_{ji}\phi_j = \tfrac{1}{2} \sum_{i,j=1}^{n} c_{ji}\phi_j\phi_i \tag{2-49}$$

EXERCISES

2-1. Consider a conducting spherical shell of radius a and charge σ per unit area. Find by integration the potential at a point r distant from its center. Then show that

$$E = \frac{\sigma}{\epsilon} \frac{a^2}{r^2} \quad \text{for } r > a$$
$$= 0 \quad \text{for } r < a$$

2-2. Consider an infinite line source of strength λ per unit length. Show by integration that the potential at a point r distant from the line is given by

$$\phi = -\frac{\lambda}{2\pi\epsilon} \ln r + \text{constant}$$

Then find the electric field intensity at r.

2-3. Find by integration the potential at a point x distant from an infinite plane conductor with charge σ per unit area. Then find the electric field intensity at x.

2-4. Two infinite plane conductors are separated by a distance d. The first has a charge σ per unit area; the second a charge $-\sigma$ per unit area. Find the electric field intensity at any point between the conductors. Find the electric field intensity at any other point.

2-5. Consider a sphere of radius a and charge $\rho(r)$ per unit volume, where r is the distance from its center. Show that the potential at r is given by

$$\phi(r) = \frac{1}{4\pi\epsilon} \int_r^{\infty} \frac{Q(r')}{r'^2} \, dr'$$

where $Q(r')$ is the total charge inside a sphere of radius r'. Verify that this can be written in the form

$$\phi(r) = \frac{1}{4\pi\epsilon} \left[\frac{Q(r)}{r} + \int_r^{\infty} 4\pi r'\rho(r') \, dr' \right]$$

2-6. A point P lies between two conductors, 1 and 2. Conductor 2 completely encloses conductor 1. If the potential at point P is ϕ_P when the conductors are at potentials ϕ_1 and ϕ_2, show that, when the conductors 1 and 2 are grounded and a charge q is placed at the point P, the charges q_1 and q_2 induced on the conductors satisfy

$$\frac{q_1}{\phi_P - \phi_2} = \frac{q_2}{\phi_1 - \phi_P} = \frac{q}{\phi_2 - \phi_1}$$

2-7. Apply the result of Exercise 2-6 to a charge q at a point P in the region between (a) two concentric spherical shells, (b) two concentric cylindrical shells, and (c) two parallel plates.

2-8. Consider a system of n conductors. Let conductor 1 be completely surrounded by conductor 2. Show that
  (a) If the charge on conductor 1 is $q_1 = 0$, then $p_{1i} = p_{2i}$, $i = 2, 3, \ldots, n$.
  (b) If $q_1 = 1$ and $q_i = 0$ for $i = 2, 3, \ldots, n$, then $p_{11} > p_{22}$.

(c) If $\phi_2 = 0$ and $q_1 = 0$, then $c_{31} = c_{41} = \cdots = c_{n1} = 0$.

(d) If $\phi_1 = 1$ and $\phi_i = 0$ for $i = 2, 3, \ldots, n$, then $c_{11} = -c_{12}$.

2-9. Apply Eqs. (2-35) to the spherical condenser described in Sec. 2-10. Let the inner sphere of radius r_a be conductor 1 and the outer sphere of radius r_b be conductor 2. Show that

$$c_{11} = -c_{12} = -c_{21} = \frac{4\pi\epsilon ab}{b - a} \qquad c_{22} = \frac{4\pi\epsilon b^2}{b - a}$$

REFERENCES

Abraham, M., and R. Becker: "The Classical Theory of Electricity and Magnetism," chaps. 3 and 5, Hafner Publishing Company, Inc., New York, 1950.

Panofsky, W. K. H., and M. Phillips: "Classical Electricity and Magnetism," chap. 1, Addison-Wesley Publishing Company, Inc., Cambridge, Mass., 1955.

Smythe, W. R.: "Static and Dynamic Electricity," 2d ed., chaps. 1, 2, and 3, McGraw-Hill Book Company, Inc., New York, 1950.

Sommerfeld, A.: "Electrodynamics," paragraphs 7 and 10, Academic Press, Inc., New York, 1952.

Stratton, J. A.: "Electromagnetic Theory," chaps. 2 and 3, McGraw-Hill Book Company, Inc., New York, 1941.

CHAPTER 3

Special Methods for Solving Electrostatic Problems

3-1. INTRODUCTION

This chapter is devoted to an exposition of two special methods for solving electrostatic problems. The first method, known as the *method of images*, is introduced in Sec. 3-2. Its utility is demonstrated by the treatment of the problems of the point charge and the conducting plane, the point charge and the conducting sphere, and the line charge and the conducting cylinder in Secs. 3-2 to 3-4. The second method, known as the *method of conformal representation*, is used to solve electrostatic problems in which the potential is a function of but two variables. Such problems are discussed in Sec. 3-5. The method of conformal representation is described in Sec. 3-6.

The methods of images and conformal representation are of value not only because they can be used to solve simple electrostatic problems but also because they provide Green's functions for the solution of complex problems. Green's functions will be discussed in Sec. 6-8.

3-2. POINT CHARGE AND CONDUCTING PLANE

Consider two point charges $+q$ and $-q$ a distance $2h$ apart in a medium of permittivity ϵ (Fig. 3-1). The potential at any point P is

$$\phi(P) = \frac{1}{4\pi\epsilon}\left(\frac{q}{r} - \frac{q}{r'}\right) \tag{3-1}$$

where r and r' are, respectively, the distances of P from $+q$ and $-q$. It is quite clear that, along the midplane AB where $r = r'$, $\phi = 0$. Thus ϕ of Eq. (3-1) is a potential function which

1. Gives zero potential all over the infinite plane AB
2. Tends to infinity like $(1/4\pi\epsilon)(q/r)$ at the location of the charge $+q$
3. Tends to zero at large distances

53

Now consider a grounded conducting plane AB and a point charge $+q$ at a distance h from it (Fig. 3-2). The potential in this problem satisfies precisely the same conditions (1, 2, 3) as that in the previous problem of the two equal and opposite charges $\pm q$ separated by a distance $2h$. Hence we can say that, if a charge $+q$ is at a distance h from an infinite conducting plane AB which has been grounded (that is, $\phi = 0$ on it), the potential in the region to the right of AB is precisely the

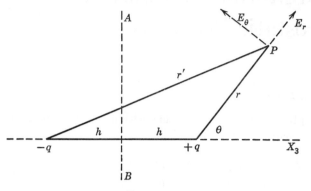

FIGURE 3-1

same as if the plane were removed and replaced by a charge $-q$ a distance h to the left of AB and on the same perpendicular to AB as the charge $+q$. We refer to $-q$ as the *image charge* of $+q$ in the plane AB.

The electric intensity at the field point P is easily obtained from (3-1):

$$\phi(P) = \frac{q}{4\pi\epsilon}\left(\frac{1}{r} - \frac{1}{\sqrt{r^2 + 4h^2 + 4hr\cos\theta}}\right)$$

$$E_r = -\frac{\partial\phi}{\partial r} = \frac{q}{4\pi\epsilon}\left[\frac{1}{r^2} - \frac{r + 2h\cos\theta}{(r^2 + 4h^2 + 4hr\cos\theta)^{3/2}}\right]$$

$$E_\theta = -\frac{1}{r}\frac{\partial\phi}{\partial\theta} = \frac{q}{4\pi\epsilon}\frac{2h\sin\theta}{(r^2 + 4h^2 + 4hr\cos\theta)^{3/2}}$$

$$E_{x_3} = E_r\cos\theta - E_\theta\sin\theta$$

$$= \frac{q}{4\pi\epsilon}\left[\frac{\cos\theta}{r^2} - \frac{r\cos\theta + 2h}{(r^2 + 4h^2 + 4hr\cos\theta)^{3/2}}\right]$$

where $r' = (r^2 + 4h^2 + 4hr\cos\theta)^{1/2}$.

For a point at the conducting plane $r' = r \equiv a$, so that

$$E_{x_3} = \frac{q}{4\pi\epsilon}\left(\frac{\cos\theta}{a^2} - \frac{a\cos\theta + 2h}{a^3}\right)$$

$$= -\frac{q}{4\pi\epsilon}\frac{2h}{a^3}$$

at the conducting plane. Since $E_{x_3} = \sigma/\epsilon$, where σ is the charge induced per unit area of the conducting plane,

$$\sigma = -\frac{h}{2\pi a^3} q \qquad (3\text{-}2)$$

The total induced charge on the plane is then

$$\int_0^\infty \sigma 2\pi x \, dx = -hq \int_0^\infty \frac{x}{a^3} \, dx = -hq \int_h^\infty \frac{a \, da}{a^3} = -q$$

the image charge.

The force on the plane is

$$\int_0^\infty \sigma \frac{q \cos \alpha}{4\pi \epsilon a^2} 2\pi x \, dx = -\frac{h^2 q^2}{4\pi \epsilon} \int_h^\infty \frac{da}{a^5} = -\frac{1}{4\pi \epsilon} \frac{q^2}{4h^2}$$

the force between $+q$ and its image $-q$.

As an example of problems to which the method of images can be readily extended, consider two semi-infinite perpendicular planes OX_1

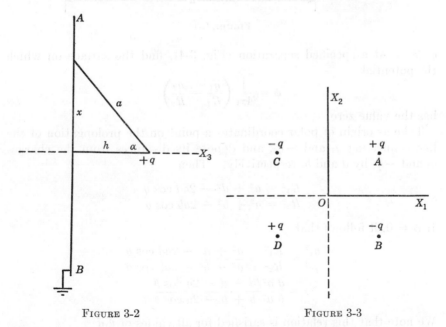

FIGURE 3-2   FIGURE 3-3

and OX_2 at zero potential (Fig. 3-3) and a charge $+q$ placed at the point A. The image system consists of the charge $+q$ at A, together with the image charges $-q$, $-q$, and $+q$ at B, C, and D, respectively. The potential at any point P in the quadrant $X_1 O X_2$ is then

$$\phi(P) = \frac{q}{4\pi\epsilon}\left(\frac{1}{AP} - \frac{1}{BP} - \frac{1}{CP} + \frac{1}{DP}\right)$$

3-3. POINT CHARGE AND CONDUCTING SPHERE

Before proceeding to investigate the charge induced on a conducting sphere, consider the following problem. Given two charges q_1 and $-q_2$,

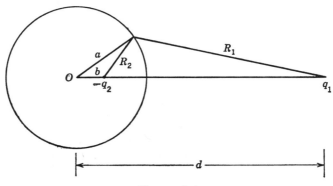

FIGURE 3-4

$q_1 > q_2$, at a specified separation (Fig. 3-4), find the surface on which the potential

$$\phi = \frac{1}{4\pi\epsilon}\left(\frac{q_1}{R_1} - \frac{q_2}{R_2}\right)$$

has the value zero.

Take as origin of polar coordinates a point on the prolongation of the line connecting q_1 and $-q_2$, and denote its distances from the charges q_1 and $-q_2$ by d and b, respectively. Then

$$R_1{}^2 = a^2 + d^2 - 2ad\cos\theta$$
$$R_2{}^2 = a^2 + b^2 - 2ab\cos\theta$$

If $\phi = 0$, it follows that

$$\frac{q_1{}^2}{q_2{}^2} = \frac{R_1{}^2}{R_2{}^2} = \frac{a^2 + d^2 - 2ad\cos\theta}{a^2 + b^2 - 2ab\cos\theta}$$
$$= \frac{d}{b}\frac{a^2/d + d - 2a\cos\theta}{a^2/b + b - 2a\cos\theta}$$

We note that this relation is satisfied for all values of θ if

1. $a^2 = db$
2. $\dfrac{q_1{}^2}{q_2{}^2} = \dfrac{d}{b}$

The potential is therefore zero on a sphere whose center divides the line joining the two point charges externally in the ratio of the square of the charges and whose radius is such that the points where the charges are placed are "inverse" to each other with respect to the sphere.

Now consider a grounded conducting sphere of radius a with a point charge q_1 at a distance d from its center. It is clear from the above that the field outside the sphere is the same as that obtained if the sphere were removed and a charge

$$-q_2 = -\sqrt{\frac{b}{d}}\, q_1 = -\frac{a}{d}\, q_1$$

were placed at a distance $b = a^2/d$ from its center on the line connecting the center to q_1.

The potential at any exterior point P at a distance r from the center of the sphere is

$$\begin{aligned}
\phi(P) &= \frac{1}{4\pi\epsilon}\left(\frac{q_1}{r_1} - \frac{q_2}{r_2}\right) = \frac{q_1}{4\pi\epsilon}\left(\frac{1}{r_1} - \frac{a/d}{r_2}\right) \\
&= \frac{q_1}{4\pi\epsilon}\left[\frac{1}{(r^2 + d^2 - 2rd\cos\theta)^{\frac{1}{2}}} - \frac{a/d}{(r^2 + b^2 - 2rb\cos\theta)^{\frac{1}{2}}}\right] \\
&= \frac{q_1}{4\pi\epsilon}\left\{\frac{1}{(r^2 + d^2 - 2rd\cos\theta)^{\frac{1}{2}}} - \frac{a/d}{[r^2 + a^4/d^2 - 2r(a^2/d)\cos\theta]^{\frac{1}{2}}}\right\}
\end{aligned}$$

The components of the electric field intensity are therefore

$$\begin{aligned}
E_r &= -\frac{\partial\phi}{\partial r} = -\frac{q_1}{4\pi\epsilon}\left\{\frac{d\cos\theta - r}{(r^2 + d^2 - 2rd\cos\theta)^{\frac{3}{2}}}\right. \\
&\qquad\qquad\qquad\left. -\frac{a/d[(a^2/d)\cos\theta - r]}{[r^2 + a^4/d^2 - 2r(a^2/d)\cos\theta]^{\frac{3}{2}}}\right\} \\
E_\theta &= -\frac{1}{r}\frac{\partial\phi}{\partial\theta} = -\frac{q_1}{4\pi\epsilon r}\left\{\frac{-rd\sin\theta}{(r^2 + d^2 - 2rd\cos\theta)^{\frac{3}{2}}}\right. \\
&\qquad\qquad\qquad\left. +\frac{r(a^3/d^2)\sin\theta}{[r^2 + a^4/d^2 - 2r(a^2/d)\cos\theta]^{\frac{3}{2}}}\right\}
\end{aligned}$$

On the surface of the sphere of radius $r = a$, the expressions for E_r and E_θ reduce to

$$\begin{aligned}
E_r &= -\frac{q_1}{4\pi\epsilon}\left[\frac{d^2 - a^2}{a(a^2 + d^2 - 2ad\cos\theta)^{\frac{3}{2}}}\right] \\
E_\theta &= 0
\end{aligned}$$

But $E_r = \sigma/\epsilon$, where σ is the charge induced per unit area of the conducting sphere. Hence

$$\sigma = -\frac{q_1}{4\pi a}\frac{d^2 - a^2}{(a^2 + d^2 - 2ad\cos\theta)^{\frac{3}{2}}}$$

The force between the sphere and the charge q_1 is

$$-\frac{1}{4\pi\epsilon}\frac{q_1q_2}{(d-b)^2} = -\frac{1}{4\pi\epsilon}\frac{aq_1{}^2}{d(d-b)^2}$$

3-4. LINE CHARGE AND CONDUCTING CYLINDER

Consider two parallel line charges separated by the distance d (Fig. 3-5). Let the charge per unit length be $+\lambda$ on one line and $-\lambda$ on the other.

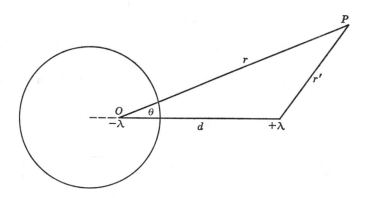

FIGURE 3-5

Let the field point P be r distant from the line with charge $-\lambda$ per unit length and r' distant from the other.   Then (cf. Sec. 2-6)

$$\phi(P) = +\frac{\lambda}{2\pi\epsilon}\ln r' - \frac{\lambda}{2\pi\epsilon}\ln r + C$$

$$= +\frac{\lambda}{4\pi\epsilon}\ln\frac{r'^2}{r^2} + C \qquad (3\text{-}3)$$

where C is a constant.

Clearly, $\phi = 0$ on all surfaces such that

$$C = -\frac{\lambda}{4\pi\epsilon}\ln\frac{r'^2}{r^2}$$

i.e., all surfaces such that

$$\frac{r'^2}{r^2} = \frac{r^2 + d^2 - 2rd\cos\theta}{r^2} = \text{constant} \equiv m^2 \qquad 0 < m < \infty$$

To see what these surfaces are let

$$x = r\cos\theta$$
$$y = r\sin\theta$$
Then $\qquad\qquad r^2 + d^2 - 2rd\cos\theta = m^2r^2$

reduces to

$$\left(x + \frac{d}{m^2 - 1}\right)^2 + y^2 = \frac{m^2 d^2}{(m^2 - 1)^2}$$

which shows that the equipotential surfaces are cylinders of radii

$$a = \frac{md}{m^2 - 1}$$

with central axis at

$$x = \frac{-d}{m^2 - 1} \qquad y = 0$$

For $m > 1$, the axis is at a distance $d/(m^2 - 1)$ to the left of the origin O. Since $d/(m^2 - 1)$ is less than a, the cylinders encircle the line charge at the origin.

The distance p between the center of a cylinder and the line with charge $+\lambda$ per unit length is

$$p = d + \frac{d}{m^2 - 1} = \frac{m^2 d}{m^2 - 1} = am$$

Hence
$$|x| = \frac{d}{m^2 - 1} = \frac{a}{m} = \frac{a^2}{p}$$

Now consider a grounded conducting cylinder of radius a with a line carrying charge $+\lambda$ per unit length at a distance p from its axis. It is clear from the above discussion that the field outside the cylinder is the same as that obtained if the cylinder were removed and a line with charge $-\lambda$ per unit length were placed at a distance a^2/p from its center on the line connecting the center to the $+\lambda$ per unit length charged line. It is left as an exercise for the reader to obtain the expressions for the potential and field intensity at an exterior point P.

3-5. TWO-DIMENSIONAL POTENTIAL PROBLEMS. CONJUGATE FUNCTIONS

In those cases where the potential ϕ is a function of but two of the rectangular coordinates, say $\phi(x_1, x_2)$, Laplace's equation (2-22) reduces to

$$\nabla^2 \phi \equiv \frac{\partial^2 \phi}{\partial x_1{}^2} + \frac{\partial^2 \phi}{\partial x_2{}^2} = 0 \tag{3-4}$$

The determination of the potential in such cases consists of solving (3-4) subject to the relevant boundary conditions.

In order to obtain the solutions of (3-4), let us consider an arbitrary analytic function† $f(z)$ of the complex variable $z = x_1 + ix_2$, where $i = \sqrt{-1}$. We write

$$f(z) = f(x_1 + ix_2) = \phi(x_1,x_2) + i\psi(x_1,x_2) \tag{3-5}$$

Then

$$\frac{\partial f}{\partial x_1} = \frac{df}{dz}\frac{\partial z}{\partial x_1} = \frac{df}{dz}$$

$$\frac{\partial f}{\partial x_2} = \frac{df}{dz}\frac{\partial z}{\partial x_2} = i\frac{df}{dz} \tag{3-6}$$

and

$$\frac{\partial^2 f}{\partial x_1{}^2} = \frac{d^2 f}{dz^2}$$

$$\frac{\partial^2 f}{\partial x_2{}^2} = -\frac{d^2 f}{dz^2}$$

Hence

$$\frac{\partial^2 f}{\partial x_1{}^2} + \frac{\partial^2 f}{\partial x_2{}^2} = 0 \tag{3-7}$$

i.e., any analytic function of the complex variable $z = x_1 + ix_2$ satisfies Laplace's equation (3-4) for two dimensions. Separation of the real and imaginary parts of (3-7) yields

$$\nabla^2\phi(x_1,x_2) = 0$$
$$\nabla^2\psi(x_1,x_2) = 0 \tag{3-8}$$

Hence ϕ and ψ as defined by (3-5) both satisfy Laplace's equation. They are called conjugate functions of x_1, x_2.

From Eqs. (3-6) we obtain

$$\frac{\partial f}{\partial x_2} = i\frac{\partial f}{\partial x_1}$$

so that

$$\frac{\partial \phi}{\partial x_2} + i\frac{\partial \psi}{\partial x_2} = i\left(\frac{\partial \phi}{\partial x_1} + i\frac{\partial \psi}{\partial x_1}\right)$$

or

$$\frac{\partial \phi}{\partial x_2} = -\frac{\partial \psi}{\partial x_1} \quad\text{and}\quad \frac{\partial \psi}{\partial x_2} = \frac{\partial \phi}{\partial x_1} \tag{3-9}$$

† A function $f(z)$ of the complex variable $z = x_1 + ix_2$ is said to be analytic in a region R of the complex plane if and only if any of the following four conditions hold:
1. $f(z)$ has a derivative at each point z_0 in R, that is,

$$\frac{df}{dz}\bigg|_{z=z_0} = \lim_{\Delta z \to 0} \frac{f(z_0 + \Delta z) - f(z_0)}{\Delta z}$$

where Δz approaches zero through any complex values.
2. $f(z)$ has a Taylor's-series expansion in powers of $(z - z_0)$ about each point z_0 in R.
3. The line integral $\oint f(z)\,dz$ about any closed path in R is zero.
4. $f(z)$ can be expressed as $f(z) = u(x_1,x_2) + iv(x_1,x_2)$ where $u(x_1,x_2)$ and $v(x_1,x_2)$ have continuous partial derivatives that satisfy the Cauchy-Riemann differential equations

$$\frac{\partial u}{\partial x_1} = \frac{\partial v}{\partial x_2} \qquad \frac{\partial u}{\partial x_2} = -\frac{\partial v}{\partial x_1}$$

Hence

$$\nabla\phi \cdot \nabla\psi = 0$$

and the two families of curves

$$\phi(x_1,x_2) = \text{constant} \qquad \psi(x_1,x_2) = \text{constant}$$

intersect orthogonally.

We can therefore interpret ϕ as the potential function and call ψ the stream function. Since the contours $\phi = $ constant are equipotentials, $\psi = $ constant must be the equation for the lines of force.

From (3-5) and (3-6), the components of the electric field **E** are given by

$$E_1 = -\frac{\partial\phi}{\partial x_1} = -\text{ real part of } \frac{df}{dz}$$

$$E_2 = -\frac{\partial\phi}{\partial x_2} = \text{ imaginary part of } \frac{df}{dz}$$

Consequently,

$$|\mathbf{E}| = |\nabla\phi| = \left|\frac{df}{dz}\right| \tag{3-10}$$

and the angle which **E** makes with the x_1 axis is $-\arg(df/dz)$. Thus, the electric field can be determined directly from the function f.

In the following two sections we shall consider some methods for finding the required $f(z)$ in a given problem. We consider here two special cases where the form of the function is evident by inspection:

Uniform electric field. Let

$$E_1 = -\frac{\partial\phi}{\partial x_1} = -\frac{\partial\psi}{\partial x_2} = \text{constant}$$

$$E_2 = -\frac{\partial\phi}{\partial x_2} = \frac{\partial\psi}{\partial x_1} = \text{constant}$$

Then

$$\phi = -E_1 x_1 - E_2 x_2 + a$$
$$\psi = E_2 x_1 - E_1 x_2 + b$$

where a and b are constants of integration, and

$$f(z) = -\mathcal{E}z + (a + ib) \tag{3-11}$$

in which $\mathcal{E} = E_1 + iE_2$ and $z = x_1 + ix_2$. If the field makes an angle α with the x_1 axis, (3-11) can be written

$$f(z) = -Ee^{i\alpha}(z - z_0) \tag{3-12}$$

where $E = \sqrt{E_1{}^2 + E_2{}^2}$ and we have set $a + ib = Ee^{i\alpha}z_0$.

Line with charge λ per unit length. We have (cf. Sec. 2-6)

$$E_r = -\frac{\partial \phi}{\partial r} = -\frac{1}{r}\frac{\partial \psi}{\partial \theta} = \frac{\lambda}{2\pi\epsilon r}$$

$$E_\theta = -\frac{1}{r}\frac{\partial \phi}{\partial \theta} = \frac{\partial \psi}{\partial r} = 0$$

Hence

$$\phi = -\frac{\lambda}{2\pi\epsilon}\ln r + a = -\frac{\lambda}{2\pi\epsilon}(\ln r - \ln r_0)$$

$$\psi = -\frac{\lambda}{2\pi\epsilon}\theta + b = -\frac{\lambda}{2\pi\epsilon}(\theta - \theta_0)$$

where $a = (\lambda/2\pi\epsilon)\ln r_0$ and $b = (\lambda/2\pi\epsilon)\theta_0$ are constants of integration, and

$$f(z) = -\frac{\lambda}{2\pi\epsilon}\ln\frac{z}{z_0} \tag{3-13}$$

in which $z = x_1 + ix_2 = re^{i\theta}$ and $z_0 = r_0 e^{i\theta_0}$.

The function $f(z)$ here gives the complex potential at a point z due to a line with charge λ per unit length located perpendicular to the complex plane at the point z_0. The function for n lines with charges $\lambda_1, \lambda_2, \ldots, \lambda_n$ per unit length located at the points $z_0{}^{(1)}, z_0{}^{(2)}, \ldots, z_0{}^{(n)}$, respectively, is

$$f(z) = -\frac{1}{2\pi\epsilon}\sum_{i=1}^{n}\lambda_i \ln\frac{z}{z_0{}^{(i)}} \tag{3-14}$$

3-6. CONFORMAL REPRESENTATION

The results of the preceding section show that two-dimensional electrostatic problems can be easily solved by the use of conjugate functions ϕ and ψ provided that the proper function $f(z) = \phi + i\psi$ can be found. The method of conformal representation is sometimes very effective in determining this function.

Let $z = x_1 + ix_2$ and $\zeta = \xi_1 + i\xi_2$ be two complex variables such that

$$\zeta = g(z) \tag{3-15}$$

where $g(z)$ is an analytic function. The functional relationship (3-15) sets up a correspondence between the points $z = x_1 + ix_2$ of the complex z plane and $\zeta = \xi_1 + i\xi_2$ of the complex ζ plane. Let R be a region in the complex z plane in which $g(z)$ is analytic. Then if C is a curve in the region R and the point z is allowed to move along C, the corresponding point ζ will trace a curve C' in the ζ plane. C' is called the *map* of the curve C, and the process is called *mapping*.

Since $d\zeta = g'(z)\,dz$, where $g'(z) = dg/dz$, it follows that

$$|d\zeta| = |g'(z)|\,|dz| \tag{3-16}$$

$$\arg d\zeta = \arg g'(z) + \arg dz \tag{3-17}$$

In the region R in the complex plane in which $g(z)$ is analytic, $g'(z)$ exists and the transformation from z to ζ is continuous. If $dz/d\zeta = 1/g'(z)$ exists, the inverse transformation from ζ to z is continuous. Equation (3-16) states that the magnitude of the line element $d\zeta$ at the point ζ in the complex ζ plane is $|g'(z)|$ times the magnitude of the line element dz at the point z in the complex z plane. Equation (3-17) states that the line element dz is rotated through the angle $\arg g'(z)$ in the transformation from the z plane to the ζ plane. Thus, any element of area in the z plane is mapped into an element of the same shape in the ζ plane. For this reason the transformation (mapping) is said to be *conformal*.

Several illustrations of the use of the method of conformal mapping in determining the function $f(z) = \phi + i\psi$ for solving two-dimensional electrostatic problems are given below:

1. It is desired to find the potential at a point P r distant from the axis of an infinite cylinder of radius $r_0 < r$ with charge λ per unit length. Let

$$\zeta \equiv re^{i\theta} = g(z) = e^z = e^{x_1}e^{ix_2} \tag{3-18}$$

so that

$$r = e^{x_1} \qquad \theta = x_2 \tag{3-19}$$

Clearly, this transformation maps vertical lines, $x_1 = $ constant, in the z plane into circles, $r = $ constant, in the ζ plane and maps horizontal lines, $x_2 = $ constant, in the z plane into radial lines, $\theta = $ constant, in the ζ plane. Hence the problem is transformed into that of finding the potential at a point $x_1 - x_{01}$ ($r_0 = e^{x_{01}}$) distant from an infinite plane with charge $\lambda/2\pi$ per unit area. But the solution to this problem is

$$\phi(x_1,x_2) = -\frac{\lambda}{2\pi\epsilon}(x_1 - x_{01}) \tag{3-20}$$

Hence, by transforming back, using (3-19), the solution to the original problem is found to be

$$\phi(r,\theta) = -\frac{\lambda}{2\pi\epsilon}\ln\frac{r}{r_0} \tag{3-21}$$

From (3-20) it follows that the function $f(z)$ is

$$f(z) = -\frac{\lambda}{2\pi\epsilon}(z - z_0) \tag{3-22}$$

where $z = x_1 + ix_2 = \ln r + i\theta$.

2. A line with charge $+\lambda$ per unit length is placed at a distance R from the axis of a grounded conducting cylinder of radius r_0. It is desired to find the potential at a field point (r,θ). Begin by taking the polar axis as the line connecting the axis of the cylinder with the line charge. Then the transformations (3-18) and (3-19) transform the problem into that of finding the potential at a field point (x_1,x_2) due to a grounded plane at $x_{01} = \ln r_0$ and a line charge $+\lambda$ per unit length at $X_1 = \ln R$. But the solution to this problem has already been found by the method of images (cf. Sec. 3-4 and Exercise 3-8). The potential at a field point (x_1,x_2) is that due to a line charge $+\lambda$ per unit length at $(\ln R, 0)$ plus an image charge $-\lambda$ per unit length at $(\ln r_0^2/R, 0)$:

$$\phi(x_1,x_2) = \frac{-\lambda}{4\pi\epsilon} \ln \frac{(x_1 - \ln R)^2 + x_2^2}{(x_1 - \ln r_0^2/R)^2 + x_2^2} \tag{3-23}$$

Hence, using (3-19), the solution to the original problem is the potential due to a line charge $+\lambda$ per unit length at $(R,0)$ plus an image charge $-\lambda$ per unit length at $(r_0^2/R, 0)$:

$$\phi(r,\theta) = \frac{-\lambda}{2\pi\epsilon} \ln \left[\frac{r^2 + R^2 - 2rR\cos\theta}{r^2 + r_0^4/R^2 - (2rr_0^2/R)\cos\theta} \right]^{\frac{1}{2}} \tag{3-24}$$

From (3-23) it follows that the function $f(z)$ is

$$\begin{aligned} f(z) &= \frac{-\lambda}{4\pi\epsilon} \ln \frac{(z - Z)(z^* - Z^*)}{(z - 2z_0 + Z)(z^* - 2z_0^* + Z^*)} \\ &= \frac{-\lambda}{2\pi\epsilon} \ln \frac{|z - Z|}{|z - 2z_0 + Z|} \end{aligned} \tag{3-25}$$

where the asterisk denotes the complex conjugate and $z = x_1 + ix_2$, $z_0 = x_{01} = \ln r_0$, and $Z = X_1 = \ln R$.

3. As a final example consider the problem of a line with charge $+\lambda$ per unit length at a point (r_0,θ_0) placed parallel to two infinite planes at zero potential located at $\theta = 0$ and $\theta = \pi/n$, where n need not be an integer. The transformation

$$\zeta = re^{i\theta} = z^{1/n} = (x_1 + ix_2)^{1/n}$$

or
$$x_1 = r^n \cos n\theta \qquad x_2 = r^n \sin n\theta \tag{3-26}$$

maps the space between the planes $\theta = 0$ and $\theta = \pi/n$ in the ζ plane into the whole space above the x_1 axis in the z plane. Hence the problem is transformed into that of a line charge $+\lambda$ per unit length situated a distance x_{02} from an infinite plane at zero potential. The solution to this problem is

$$\phi(x_1,x_2) = \frac{-\lambda}{4\pi\epsilon} \ln \left[\frac{(x_1)^2 + (x_2 - x_{02})^2}{(x_1)^2 + (x_2 + x_{02})^2} \right] \tag{3-27}$$

Hence, using (3-26), the solution to the original problem is

$$\phi(r,\theta) = \frac{-\lambda}{4\pi\epsilon} \ln \left[\frac{(r^n \cos n\theta)^2 + (r^n \sin n\theta - r_0{}^n \sin n\theta_0)^2}{(r^n \cos n\theta)^2 + (r^n \sin n\theta + r_0{}^n \sin n\theta_0)^2} \right] \quad (3\text{-}28)$$

From (3-27) it follows that the function $f(z)$ is

$$\begin{aligned} f(z) &= \frac{-\lambda}{4\pi\epsilon} \ln \left[\frac{(z - z_0)(z^* - z_0^*)}{(z + z_0)(z^* + z_0^*)} \right] \\ &= \frac{-\lambda}{2\pi\epsilon} \ln \frac{|z - z_0|}{|z + z_0|} \end{aligned} \quad (3\text{-}29)$$

where $z = x_1 + ix_2$, $z_0 = ix_{02}$.

3-7. THE SCHWARZ TRANSFORMATION

In the examples of the preceding section use was made of two specific conformal mappings. The first is

$$\zeta \equiv re^{i\theta} = g(z) \equiv e^z = e^{x_1}e^{ix_2}$$

which maps vertical lines, $x_1 =$ constant, in the z plane into circles, $r =$ constant, in the ζ plane and maps horizontal lines, $x_2 =$ constant, in the z plane into radial lines, $\theta =$ constant, in the ζ plane. The second is

$$\zeta \equiv re^{i\theta} = g(z) \equiv z^{1/n} = (x_1 + ix_2)^{1/n}$$

which maps the space between the lines $\theta = 0$ and $\theta = \pi/n$ in the ζ plane into the whole space above the x_1 axis in the z plane.

These transformations are simple examples which are very special in character. A much more general transformation is due to Schwarz. Consider a rectilinear polygon† in the z plane whose sides change direction by an angle $\alpha_i\pi$ when one passes the ith vertex in a counterclockwise direction. The transformation

$$z = A \int \frac{d\zeta}{(\zeta - \beta_1)^{\alpha_1}(\zeta - \beta_2)^{\alpha_2} \cdots (\zeta - \beta_n)^{\alpha_n}} + B \quad (3\text{-}30)$$

maps the interior of the polygon into the upper half of the ζ plane. The β_i are the (real) points on the ξ_1 axis of the ζ plane onto which the n vertices of the polygon are mapped. The constants A and B are determined by the scale and orientation of the polygon. The size of the polygon determines the modulus of A. Its orientation determines the argument of A. The value of B is determined by the location of the polygon. Three of the β_i in (3-30) can be chosen at will, and the remainder calcu-

† The polygon need not be closed.

lated.   It is usually convenient to take the three chosen at will equal to some of the values 0, ± 1, and ∞.

Two illustrations of the use of the Schwarz transformation in solving two-dimensional electrostatic problems are given below.

1. *Single-angle transformation.*   Two grounded conducting planes of infinite extent intersect at right angles.   Let the positions of the planes be given by the lines $x_1 = 0$ and $x_2 = 0$ in the z plane.   It is desired to find the potential at a field point (x_1,x_2) in the first quadrant.   In this case the Schwarz transformation (3-30) reduces to

$$z = A \int \frac{d\zeta}{(\zeta - \beta_1)^{\frac{1}{2}}} + B$$
$$= 2A(\zeta - \beta_1)^{\frac{1}{2}} + B \qquad (3\text{-}31)$$

For convenience we take $\beta_1 = 0$, i.e., at the origin of coordinates in the ζ plane.   If B is chosen equal to zero, (3-31) reduces to

$$z = 2A\zeta^{\frac{1}{2}} \qquad (3\text{-}32)$$

and maps the first quadrant of the z plane into the upper half of the ζ plane.   Consequently, the original problem is reduced to that of finding the potential at a distance ξ_2 from the plane represented by the $\xi_2 = 0$ in the ζ plane.   But the solution to this new problem is

$$\phi(\zeta_1,\zeta_2) = -\frac{\sigma'}{2\epsilon} \zeta_2 \qquad (3\text{-}33)$$

where σ' is the constant charge per unit area of the plane.   According to (3-32)

$$(x_1 + ix_2)^2 = 2A(\xi_1 + i\xi_2)$$

or $\qquad x_1{}^2 - x_2{}^2 = 4A^2\xi_1 \qquad$ and $\qquad x_1 x_2 = 2A^2\xi_2 \qquad (3\text{-}34)$

Hence, the solution to the original problem is

$$\phi(x_1,x_2) = -\frac{\sigma'}{4A^2\epsilon} x_1 x_2 \qquad (3\text{-}35)$$

This shows that the equipotential surfaces are equilateral hyperbolic cylinders.   From (3-34) it follows that the equations for the lines of force are the hyperbolas $x_1{}^2 - x_2{}^2 = $ constant.

The components of the electric field intensity are

$$E_1 = -\frac{\partial \phi}{\partial x_1} = \frac{\sigma'}{4A^2\epsilon} x_2$$
$$E_2 = -\frac{\partial \phi}{\partial x_2} = \frac{\sigma'}{4A^2\epsilon} x_1$$

Since $E_2 = \sigma/\epsilon$, where σ is the charge per unit area of the conducting plane represented by the line $x_2 = 0$,

$$\sigma = \frac{\sigma'}{4A^2}\, x_1$$

that is, the charge density is zero on the line of intersection of the two conducting planes and increases linearly with the distance from this line. The charge density on the conducting plane represented by $x_2 = 0$ behaves in the same way.

2. *Three conducting planes intersect orthogonally to form a rectangular trough of width 2a.* Let the planes be grounded and be represented by the lines $x_1 = \pm a$ and $x_2 = 0$ in the z plane. It is desired to find the potential at a field point (x_1,x_2), where $-a < x_1 < +a$ and $0 < x_2 < +\infty$. The Schwarz transformation for this problem is

$$z = A \int \frac{d\zeta}{(\zeta - \beta_1)^{\frac{1}{2}}(\zeta - \beta_2)^{\frac{1}{2}}} + B \tag{3-36}$$

We take $\beta_1 = b$ and $\beta_2 = -b$, so that (3-36) reduces to

$$z = A \int \frac{d\zeta}{(\zeta^2 - b^2)^{\frac{1}{2}}} + B$$

$$= iA\,\sin^{-1}\frac{\zeta}{b} + B \tag{3-37}$$

If B is taken equal to zero, $\zeta = 0$ when $z = 0$. Then, in order for z to equal $\pm a$ when $\zeta = \pm b$, iA must equal $2a/\pi$. Hence (3-37) becomes

$$z = \frac{2a}{\pi}\,\sin^{-1}\frac{\zeta}{b} \tag{3-38}$$

and maps the line $\xi_2 = 0$ in the ζ plane into the rectangular trough in the z plane. Hence the original problem is reduced to that of finding the potential at a distance ξ_2 from the plane $\xi_2 = 0$. The solution to this new problem is

$$\phi(\xi_1,\xi_2) = -\frac{\sigma'}{2\epsilon}\,\xi_2$$

But from (3-38)

$$(x_1 + ix_2) = \frac{2a}{\pi}\,\sin^{-1}\frac{\xi_1 + i\xi_2}{b}$$

or $\qquad \xi_1 = b \sin\dfrac{\pi x_1}{2a} \cosh\dfrac{\pi x_2}{2a} \qquad \xi_2 = b \cos\dfrac{\pi x_1}{2a} \sinh\dfrac{\pi x_2}{2a} \tag{3-39}$

Hence the solution to the original problem is

$$\phi(x_1, x_2) = -\frac{\sigma' b}{2\epsilon} \cos\frac{\pi x_1}{2a} \sinh\frac{\pi x_2}{2a} \tag{3-40}$$

The components for the electric field intensity are

$$
\begin{aligned}
E_1 &= -\frac{\partial\phi}{\partial x_1} = -\frac{\sigma' b\pi}{4\epsilon a} \sin\frac{\pi x_1}{2a} \sinh\frac{\pi x_2}{2a} \\
E_2 &= -\frac{\partial\phi}{\partial x_2} = \frac{\sigma' b\pi}{4\epsilon a} \cos\frac{\pi x_1}{2a} \cosh\frac{\pi x_2}{2a}
\end{aligned}
\tag{3-41}
$$

EXERCISES

3-1. Two equal point charges q are placed a distance p apart. The line joining the charges is a distance h from a grounded infinite conducting plane. Find the force between the charges.

3-2. Two semi-infinite planes at zero potential intersect at an angle $\pi/4$. A point charge q is placed at a point in the region between the planes. Find the potential at a field point P also in the region between the planes. (Note that, if the angle between the planes is π/n, where n is an integer, the number of image charges is $2n$. If n is not an integer, the method of images breaks down.)

3-3. A point charge is placed at a distance d from the center of a uniformly charged spherical shell with total charge Q. Find the potential and field intensity at a field point P outside the sphere. What is the charge distribution on the sphere?

3-4. Find the capacitance of a charged spherical conductor of radius a at a distance $d/2$ from a grounded infinite conducting plane, where $a \ll d$.

3-5. Find the capacitance of two equal and oppositely charged conducting spheres of radius a placed at a center-to-center distance d, where $a \ll d$.

3-6. An infinite conducting plane with a hemispherical boss of radius a is grounded, and a point charge q is placed on the axis of symmetry a distance h from the plane. Show that the image consists of three charges, and find the force between the plane and the charge q.

3-7. A line with charge $+\lambda$ per unit length is placed at a distance p from the axis of a grounded conducting cylinder of radius a. Find the potential and field intensity at a field point P. Find the charge per unit length of the cylinder.

3-8. A line with charge $+\lambda$ per unit length is placed at a distance h from a grounded infinite conducting plane. Find the potential at a field point P and the charge per unit area of the plane.

3-9. Two infinitely long conducting cylinders of radius a are placed at an axis-to-axis distance d. Let the charge on one be $+\lambda$ per unit length and that on the other $-\lambda$ per unit length. Find the potential at a field point P. Find the capacitance per unit length.

3-10. A line with charge $+\lambda$ per unit length is placed parallel to, in the plane of, and at a distance d from the edge of a semi-infinite conducting plane. Find the potential and intensity at a field point (x_1, x_2).

3-11. Two parallel earthed conducting planes are a distance d apart. An infinite line with charge $+\lambda$ per unit length is placed parallel to and in between the planes at a distance a from one of them. Find the potential and electric intensity at a point (x_1, x_2) in the region between the planes.

3-12. Find the potential and electric intensity at a point in the neighborhood of a plane conducting sheet with a slit of width $2a$ in it. Also find the surface charge density on the sheet.

REFERENCES

Abraham, M., and R. Becker: "The Classical Theory of Electricity and Magnetism," chap. 3, Hafner Publishing Company, Inc., New York, 1950.

Morse, P. M., and H. Feshbach: "Methods of Theoretical Physics," chaps. 4 and 10, McGraw-Hill Book Company, Inc., New York, 1953.

Panofsky, W. K. H., and M. Phillips: "Classical Electricity and Magnetism," chaps. 3 and 4, Addison-Wesley Publishing Company, Inc., Cambridge, Mass., 1955.

Smythe, W. R.: "Static and Dynamic Electricity," 2d ed., Chaps. 4 and 5, McGraw-Hill Book Company, Inc., New York, 1950.

Sommerfeld, A.: "Electrodynamics," paragraph 9, Academic Press, Inc., New York, 1952.

Stratton, J. A.: "Electromagnetic Theory," chap. 3, McGraw-Hill Book Company, Inc., New York, 1941.

CHAPTER 4

Dielectrics

4-1. INTRODUCTION

It was pointed out in Sec. 2-2 that the force between two point charges in a nonconducting medium was found to be less than that between them in vacuum. The ratio of the force between the charges in vacuum to that between them in the medium is known as the *dielectric constant* of the medium, and the medium is called a *dielectric*. In order to understand this phenomenon it is necessary to consider in detail what happens when a dielectric is placed in an electric field **E**. This is the purpose of the present chapter.

4-2. CLUSTER OF POINT CHARGES

Consider a cluster of n point charges. Let q_i denote the ith charge and (x_{1i}, x_{2i}, x_{3i}) its coordinates. The potential at a point (x_1, x_2, x_3) due to this charge is then

$$\phi_i(x_1, x_2, x_3) = \frac{q_i}{4\pi\epsilon \sqrt{(x_1 - x_{1i})^2 + (x_2 - x_{2i})^2 + (x_3 - x_{3i})^2}}$$

$$= \frac{q_i}{4\pi\epsilon |\mathbf{r} - \mathbf{r}_i|} \tag{4-1}$$

where $\mathbf{r} = x_1\mathbf{i}_1 + x_2\mathbf{i}_2 + x_3\mathbf{i}_3$ and $\mathbf{r}_i = x_{1i}\mathbf{i}_1 + x_{2i}\mathbf{i}_2 + x_{3i}\mathbf{i}_3$.

The potential at the point (x_1, x_2, x_3) due to the entire cluster of charges is then

$$\phi(x_1, x_2, x_3) = \sum_{i=1}^{n} \phi_i(x_1, x_2, x_3)$$

$$= \sum_{i=1}^{n} \frac{q_i}{4\pi\epsilon |\mathbf{r} - \mathbf{r}_i|} \tag{4-2}$$

It is sometimes convenient to rewrite (4-2) as an expansion known as a moments or multipole expansion of the potential. Thus for $|\mathbf{r}| > |\mathbf{r}_i|$,

$$\phi(x_1,x_2,x_3) = \frac{1}{4\pi\epsilon} \sum_i \frac{q_i}{r \sqrt{1 + (\mathbf{r}_i - 2\mathbf{r}) \cdot \mathbf{r}_i/r^2}}$$

$$= \frac{1}{4\pi\epsilon} \sum_i \frac{q_i}{r} \left\{ 1 - \frac{(\mathbf{r}_i - 2\mathbf{r}) \cdot \mathbf{r}_i}{2r^2} + 3 \frac{[(\mathbf{r}_i - 2\mathbf{r}) \cdot \mathbf{r}_i]^2}{8r^4} + \cdots \right\}$$

$$= \frac{1}{4\pi\epsilon} \sum_i \left\{ \frac{q_i}{r} + q_i \frac{(\mathbf{r} \cdot \mathbf{r}_i)}{r^3} + q_i \frac{[3(\mathbf{r} \cdot \mathbf{r}_i)^2 - r^2 r_i^2]}{2r^5} + \cdots \right\}$$

$$\tag{4-3}$$

Note that near $r = 0$, the first term in this expansion goes to infinity as $1/r$, the second as $1/r^2$, the third as $1/r^3$, etc. The first term is known as a monopole potential, the second as a dipole potential, the third as a quadrupole potential, etc.

The first term in (4-3) can be written $Q/4\pi\epsilon r$, where $Q \equiv \sum_i q_i$. Thus in the first approximation to ϕ in which only the first term in the expansion (4-3) is kept, the cluster of point charges behaves as a point charge of strength $Q = \sum_i q_i$ located at the origin of coordinates.

The second term in the expansion (4-3) can be written

$$\frac{1}{4\pi\epsilon} \frac{\mathbf{p} \cdot \mathbf{r}}{r^3} = - \frac{1}{4\pi\epsilon} \mathbf{p} \cdot \nabla \left(\frac{1}{r} \right) \tag{4-4}$$

where $\mathbf{p} \equiv \sum_i q_i \mathbf{r}_i$. Thus in the second approximation to ϕ the cluster of charges behaves as a point charge of strength Q *plus* a dipole (see next section) of moment $\mathbf{p} \equiv \sum_i q_i \mathbf{r}_i$, both located at the origin of coordinates.

The third term in the expansion (4-3) can be written as

$$\cdot \quad \frac{1}{8\pi\epsilon} \sum_i q_i \mathbf{r}_i \cdot \nabla \left[\mathbf{r}_i \cdot \nabla \left(\frac{1}{r} \right) \right]$$

Consequently, the expansion (4-3) can be rewritten

$$\phi(x_1,x_2,x_3) = \frac{1}{4\pi\epsilon} \sum_i q_i \left\{ \frac{1}{r} - \mathbf{r}_i \cdot \nabla \left(\frac{1}{r} \right) + \frac{1}{2} \mathbf{r}_i \cdot \nabla \left[\mathbf{r}_i \cdot \nabla \left(\frac{1}{r} \right) \right] + \cdots \right\}$$

$$\tag{4-5}$$

4-3. THE ELECTRIC DIPOLE

We now consider the physical nature of the second term in the multipole expansion (4-3) for the potential due to a cluster of point charges.

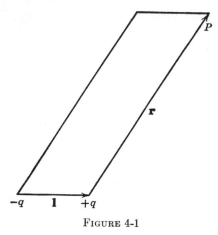

FIGURE 4-1

Let 1 denote the vector from a charge $-q$ to an equal positive charge $+q$. If $|1|$ is allowed to approach zero while q tends to infinity in such a way that

$$|\mathbf{p}| = q|1|$$

retains the constant value ql, then the combination of charges is called an electric dipole or doublet. The vector $\mathbf{p} = q\mathbf{l}$ is called the moment of the dipole.

The potential ϕ at any point P r distant from the dipole can be obtained as follows. From Fig. 4-1 it is seen that the potential at P due to the charge $+q$ is

$$\phi_+(P) = \frac{q}{4\pi\epsilon r}$$

while that due to the charge $-q$ is

$$\phi_-(P) = -\frac{q}{4\pi\epsilon r} + \mathbf{\nabla}\left(-\frac{q}{4\pi\epsilon r}\right)\cdot 1$$

Hence, the total potential at P is

$$\phi(P) = \phi_+(P) + \phi_-(P)$$

$$= \mathbf{\nabla}\left(-\frac{q}{4\pi\epsilon r}\right)\cdot 1$$

$$= -\frac{1}{4\pi\epsilon}\,\mathbf{p}\cdot\mathbf{\nabla}\left(\frac{1}{r}\right) \tag{4-6}$$

Note that, when the operation gradient is applied to $1/r$ in (4-6), the differentiation is with respect to the coordinates of the field point P.

If the dipole is located at the origin of coordinates, the potential at P can be written

$$\phi(P) = \frac{1}{4\pi\epsilon}\frac{\mathbf{p}\cdot\mathbf{r}}{r^3} = \frac{1}{4\pi\epsilon}\frac{p\cos\theta}{r^2} \tag{4-7}$$

where θ is the angle between $\mathbf{p}$ and $\mathbf{r}$.

The electric field at P due to the dipole is

$$\mathbf{E}(P) = -\operatorname{grad}\phi = \frac{1}{4\pi\epsilon}\,\mathbf{\nabla}\left[\mathbf{p}\cdot\mathbf{\nabla}\left(\frac{1}{r}\right)\right] \tag{4-8}$$

It is most conveniently expressed in terms of its radial and transverse components E_r and E_θ:

$$E_r = -\frac{\partial \phi}{\partial r} = \frac{2p \cos \theta}{4\pi \epsilon r^3}$$

$$E_\theta = -\frac{1}{r}\frac{\partial \phi}{\partial \theta} = \frac{p \sin \theta}{4\pi \epsilon r^3}$$

(4-9)

Consider a dipole of moment $\mathbf{p} = q\mathbf{l}$ in the presence of a constant electric field $\mathbf{E}$. The field exerts a force $+q\mathbf{E}$ on the charge $+q$ and a force $-q\mathbf{E}$ on the charge $-q$. These forces constitute a couple of magnitude $qEl \sin \alpha = pE \sin \alpha$, where α is the angle between $\mathbf{p}$ and $\mathbf{E}$. The couple tending to reduce α is

$$\mathbf{L} = -\mathbf{l} \times q\mathbf{E} = -\mathbf{p} \times \mathbf{E} \tag{4-10}$$

If W is the potential energy of the dipole in the field, then

$$L = -pE \sin \alpha = -\frac{\partial W}{\partial \alpha}$$

so that
$$W = -pE \cos \alpha = -\mathbf{p} \cdot \mathbf{E} \tag{4-11}$$

where we have chosen the zero of potential energy at $\alpha = \pi/2$.

The force $\mathbf{F}$ on a dipole of moment $\mathbf{p}$ which is fixed in an inhomogeneous electric field $\mathbf{E}$ is

$$\mathbf{F} = -\nabla W = \nabla(\mathbf{p} \cdot \mathbf{E}) = (\mathbf{p} \cdot \nabla)\mathbf{E} \tag{4-12}$$

where use has been made of the results of Exercise 1-3d and the fact that the electric field is conservative.

Consider a dipole of moment $\mathbf{p}_1$ located at the origin of coordinates and a dipole of moment $\mathbf{p}_2$ located at a point P $\mathbf{r}$ distant from the origin. The mutual potential energy of these two dipoles is

$$W = -\mathbf{p}_2 \cdot \frac{1}{4\pi \epsilon} \nabla \left[\mathbf{p}_1 \cdot \nabla \left(\frac{1}{r} \right) \right]$$

$$= \frac{1}{4\pi \epsilon} \left[\frac{\mathbf{p}_1 \cdot \mathbf{p}_2}{r^3} - \frac{3}{r^5} (\mathbf{p}_1 \cdot \mathbf{r})(\mathbf{p}_2 \cdot \mathbf{r}) \right] \tag{4-13}$$

4-4. THE DIPOLE SHEET

Consider two surfaces separated by a distance $|\mathbf{l}|$. Let the charge on one surface be $+\sigma$ per unit area and the charge on the other be $-\sigma$ per unit area. If $|\mathbf{l}|$ is allowed to approach zero while σ tends to infinity in such a way that

$$|\tau| = \sigma|\mathbf{l}|$$

retains the constant value σl, then the combination of the two charged surfaces is called an electric double layer or dipole sheet. The vector $\tau = \sigma l$ is called the dipole moment per unit area of the sheet.

Let dS be an element of area of the sheet. Then the potential at a point P $\mathbf{r}$ distant from dS is

$$d\phi(P) = \frac{1}{4\pi\epsilon} \frac{(\tau\, dS) \cdot \mathbf{r}}{r^3} \tag{4-14}$$

according to (4-7). The potential at P due to the entire sheet is then obtained by integrating (4-14) over the surface of the sheet. Thus

$$\phi(P) = \frac{1}{4\pi\epsilon} \iint \frac{\tau \cdot \mathbf{r}}{r^3}\, dS$$

$$= \frac{1}{4\pi\epsilon} \iint \frac{\tau \cos\theta}{r^2}\, dS \tag{4-15}$$

$$\phi(P) = \frac{1}{4\pi\epsilon} \int \tau\, d\omega \tag{4-16}$$

where θ is the angle between τ and $\mathbf{r}$ and $d\omega = (dS\cos\theta)/r^2$ is the solid angle subtended at P by dS.

If the dipole sheet is of uniform strength, i.e., if $\tau = $ constant, (4-16) reduces to

$$\phi(P) = \frac{1}{4\pi\epsilon} \tau\omega \tag{4-17}$$

where ω is the solid angle subtended at P by the sheet. Note that the difference of potential between points 1 and 2 just on either side of the uniform dipole sheet is

$$\phi(1) - \phi(2) = \frac{1}{4\pi\epsilon} \tau[2\pi - (-2\pi)] = \frac{\tau}{\epsilon} \tag{4-18}$$

The electric field produced by a dipole sheet of uniform strength is, from (4-15),

$$\mathbf{E}(P) = -\nabla\phi = -\frac{1}{4\pi\epsilon} \iint \nabla\left(\frac{\tau \cdot \mathbf{r}}{r^3}\right) dS \tag{4-19}$$

where in applying the operation ∇ the differentiation is with respect to the field point P. In the following it will be convenient to differentiate with respect to the source point. Then

$$\mathbf{E}(P) = \frac{1}{4\pi\epsilon} \iint \nabla_s\left(\frac{\tau \cdot \mathbf{r}}{r^3}\right) dS$$

$$= -\frac{1}{4\pi\epsilon} \iint \nabla_s\left[\tau \cdot \nabla_s\left(\frac{1}{r}\right)\right] dS$$

$$= \frac{1}{4\pi\epsilon} \iint \left\{\left[\nabla_s \cdot \nabla_s\left(\frac{1}{r}\right)\right]\tau - \nabla_s\left[\tau \cdot \nabla_s\left(\frac{1}{r}\right)\right]\right\} dS$$

since $\nabla_s \cdot \nabla_s(1/r) = \nabla_s^2(1/r) = 0$ for $r \neq 0$. Writing $\tau = \tau\mathbf{n}$, where $\mathbf{n}$ is a unit vector in the direction of the normal to dS,

$$\mathbf{E}(P) = \frac{\tau}{4\pi\epsilon} \iint \left\{ \left[\nabla_s \cdot \nabla_s \left(\frac{1}{r}\right) \right] \mathbf{n} - \nabla_s \left[\mathbf{n} \cdot \nabla_s \left(\frac{1}{r}\right) \right] \right\} dS$$

Application of the theorem of Tait and McAulay (cf. Sec. 1-18) then yields

$$\mathbf{E}(P) = \frac{\tau}{4\pi\epsilon} \oint \nabla_s \left(\frac{1}{r}\right) \times d\mathbf{s}$$

or

$$\mathbf{E}(P) = \frac{\tau}{4\pi\epsilon} \oint \frac{d\mathbf{s} \times \mathbf{r}}{r^3} \tag{4-20}$$

where $d\mathbf{s}$ is an element of the closed contour $\mathbf{s}$ which bounds the dipole sheet and $\mathbf{r}$ is the vector from $d\mathbf{s}$ to P.

4-5. HOMOGENEOUS ISOTROPIC DIELECTRICS

Consider two parallel plates of area S which are separated by a distance d. Let one plate have a positive charge σ_F per unit area and the other an equal negative charge. (The significance of the subscript F on σ will be discussed below.) Then let the plates be connected to a quadrant electrometer which indicates the potential difference between them.

If the two plates are in vacuum, the electric field in the region between them is

$$|\mathbf{E}_0| = \frac{\sigma_F}{\epsilon_0} = \frac{\phi_1 - \phi_2}{d} \tag{4-21}$$

where $\phi_1 - \phi_2$ is the potential difference between the plates.

If a homogeneous isotropic block of dielectric of thickness d and cross section S, having a dielectric constant K, is introduced into the space between the plates, the potential difference will be observed to decrease. The electric field in the dielectric is therefore

$$|\mathbf{E}| = \frac{|\mathbf{E}_0|}{K} = \frac{\sigma_F}{K\epsilon_0} = \frac{\sigma_F}{\epsilon} = \frac{(\phi_1 - \phi_2)/K}{d} \tag{4-22}$$

If the slab of dielectric is removed from between the plates, the potential difference returns to its original value.

Subtraction of (4-22) from (4-21) yields

$$\sigma_F - \frac{\sigma_F}{K} \equiv \sigma_P = \epsilon_0(|\mathbf{E}_0| - |\mathbf{E}|) = \epsilon_0(K - 1)|\mathbf{E}| \tag{4-23}$$

Since there are no means of conduction, the charge density on the plates must always be the same. Hence, we are led to believe that, when the dielectric block is placed between the plates, it develops on its surfaces of area S a charge of magnitude $|\sigma_P|$ per unit area and of sign opposite to that of the charge on the facing plate. Consequently, when the dielectric block is between the plates, it has an electric moment $\mathbf{p} = \sigma_P S d = \sigma_P S (\mathbf{E}/|\mathbf{E}|) d$. The electric moment per unit volume, called the *polarization* and denoted by $\mathbf{P}$, is then

$$\mathbf{P} = \frac{1}{Sd} \mathbf{p} = \sigma_P \frac{\mathbf{E}}{|\mathbf{E}|} = \epsilon_0(K - 1)\mathbf{E} \tag{4-24}$$

or
$$\mathbf{P} = \epsilon_0 \chi \mathbf{E} \tag{4-25}$$

where
$$\chi = K - 1 \tag{4-26}$$

and is called the *electric susceptibility*.

Note that, according to Eqs. (4-22) and (4-23), the electric field in the dielectric can be expressed by

$$|\mathbf{E}| = \frac{\sigma_F}{\epsilon} = \frac{\sigma_F}{K\epsilon_0} = \frac{\sigma_F - \sigma_P}{\epsilon_0} \equiv \frac{\sigma}{\epsilon_0} \tag{4-27}$$

where σ is the effective total charge per unit area of the plates and is the sum of the true, free, movable net charge per unit area σ_F and the bound *polarization charge* $-\sigma_P$.

It follows from (4-24) that P_n, the component of $\mathbf{P}$ normal to the surface of the dielectric, is equal to the polarization charge σ_P. From the above discussion one is led to believe that the polarization charge is produced from the originally uncharged dielectric by the motion of positive charge in the direction of $\mathbf{E}$ and of negative charge in the opposite direction. Thus, suppose that in equilibrium two equal charges of opposite sign lie so closely together that they exert no appreciable external effect. By means of an external field, such as occurred when the dielectric was placed between the plates, these charges can be displaced relative to each other by a distance $\mathbf{l}$. The charges then form a dipole of moment $\mathbf{p} = q\mathbf{l}$. In producing such a dipole there is clearly a current

$$q \frac{d\mathbf{l}}{dt} = q\mathbf{v} = \frac{d\mathbf{p}}{dt}$$

The result of adding the dipole moments of all the polarization charges in a unit volume is the polarization vector, or dipole moment per unit volume,

$$\mathbf{P} = \sum_{\text{unit volume}} \mathbf{p}$$

The current density due to the polarization charges is

$$\mathbf{j}_P = \sum_{\text{unit volume}} q\mathbf{v} \equiv \rho_P \mathbf{v} = \frac{d\mathbf{P}}{dt} \tag{4-28}$$

where

$$\rho_P = \sum_{\text{unit volume}} q$$

If one considers any arbitrary surface in the dielectric, it is clear that, while polarization is being produced, charges must cross this surface. Moreover, the charges which cross the surface are exactly those contained in a cylinder of base equal to the surface and length $|l|$. The charge which passes through an element dS of the surface is

$$ql_n \, dS = P_n \, dS \tag{4-29}$$

where l_n is the component of 1 normal to the surface. If dS is an element of the outer surface of the dielectric, Eq. (4-29) gives the charges appearing on dS. Thus we have two equivalent definitions of the polarization P,

1. The electric moment per unit volume
2. The quantity of charge passing through unit area perpendicular to P

According to Gauss' theorem, any arbitrary volume on being polarized loses the charge

$$\iint P_n \, dS = \iiint \operatorname{div} \mathbf{P} \, d\tau$$

Since the charge passing out through the surface of the volume is equal and opposite in sign to that remaining in the volume, it follows that the charge arising in the volume because of the polarization is given by

$$\iiint \rho_P \, d\tau = -\iiint \operatorname{div} \mathbf{P} \, d\tau$$

Since the volume τ is arbitrary,

$$\rho_P = -\operatorname{div} \mathbf{P} \tag{4-30}$$

4-6. THE ELECTRIC DISPLACEMENT

According to Eq. (4-24)

$$\epsilon_0 \mathbf{E} + \mathbf{P} = \epsilon_0 K \mathbf{E} = \epsilon \mathbf{E} \equiv \mathbf{D} \tag{4-31}$$

The vector **D** defined by (4-31) is known as the electric displacement vector.

Since

$$\operatorname{div} \mathbf{E} = \frac{\rho_F}{\epsilon} \tag{2-20}$$

where ρ_F is the true, free, movable net charge per unit volume,

$$\operatorname{div} \mathbf{D} = \operatorname{div} (\epsilon \mathbf{E}) = \rho_F \tag{4-32}$$

provided that ϵ is constant.

From

$$\operatorname{div} \mathbf{D} = \operatorname{div} (\epsilon_0 \mathbf{E} + \mathbf{P})$$

and Eqs. (4-30) and (4-32) it follows that

$$\operatorname{div} (\epsilon_0 \mathbf{E}) = \rho_F + \rho_P \equiv \rho \tag{4-33}$$

Thus, $\mathbf{D}$ represents the field due to the free charges alone, $\mathbf{P}$ the field due to the polarization charges alone, and $\epsilon_0 \mathbf{E}$ the field due to all the charges.

According to Gauss' theorem and Eq. (4-32),

$$\iint \mathbf{D} \cdot d\mathbf{S} = \iiint \operatorname{div} \mathbf{D} \, d\tau = \iiint \rho_F \, d\tau = q_F \tag{4-34}$$

where q_F is the total free charge in the volume τ.

4-7. BOUNDARY CONDITIONS ON D AND E

Consider the boundary surface between two media, one of permittivity ϵ_1, the other of permittivity ϵ_2. Describe a pillbox-shaped surface $ABCD$ (Fig. 4-2) about an area S of the surface of separation. Then, from (4-34),

$$\iint \mathbf{D} \cdot \mathbf{n} \, dS = \iiint \rho_F \, d\tau \tag{4-34a}$$

where $d\tau$ is an element of the volume τ of the pillbox, $\mathbf{n}$ is the unit outward drawn normal to the element dS of the pillbox surface, and ρ_F is the density of free charge enclosed by the box. In the limit as the height of the pillbox goes to zero, (4-34a) becomes

$$\mathbf{n} \cdot (\mathbf{D}_2 - \mathbf{D}_1)S = \sigma_F S$$

where σ_F is the density of free charge on the interface. When $\sigma_F = 0$, it follows that

$$D_{2n} = D_{1n} \tag{4-35}$$

i.e., the normal component of the electric displacement is continuous across an uncharged interface.

Consider now the rectangle $EFGH$ (Fig. 4-2) which lies with its longest sides parallel to the surface of separation, one in each medium. Since the electrostatic field is a conservative one, $\oint \mathbf{E} \cdot ds = 0$, where ds is an

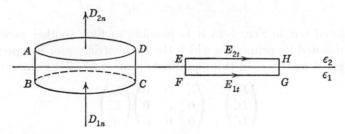

FIGURE 4-2

element of the rectangle. In the limit as the lengths of the sides EF and GH go to zero, the line integral reduces to

$$(\mathbf{E}_2 - \mathbf{E}_1) \cdot \mathbf{s} = (E_{2t} - E_{1t})s = 0$$

where s is the length of the sides EH and FG. Hence

$$E_{2t} = E_{1t} \tag{4-36}$$

i.e., the tangential component of the electric field intensity is continuous across the surface of separation.

4-8. CRYSTALLINE DIELECTRICS

In a homogeneous crystalline dielectric the directions of the electric intensity and the electric displacement are not the same except for certain orientations of the electric field with respect to the crystal. However, any change in the magnitude of $\mathbf{E}$ changes that of $\mathbf{D}$ proportionately without changing the angle α between them. This fact can be expressed by the equation

$$\mathbf{D} = (\boldsymbol{\beta} \cdot \boldsymbol{\beta})\mathbf{E} - \boldsymbol{\beta}(\boldsymbol{\beta} \cdot E) \tag{4-37}$$

or, in matrix notation,

$$\begin{pmatrix} D_1 \\ D_2 \\ D_3 \end{pmatrix} = \begin{pmatrix} \beta_2{}^2 + \beta_3{}^2 & -\beta_1\beta_2 & -\beta_1\beta_3 \\ -\beta_1\beta_2 & \beta_3{}^2 + \beta_1{}^2 & -\beta_2\beta_3 \\ -\beta_1\beta_3 & -\beta_2\beta_3 & \beta_1{}^2 + \beta_2{}^2 \end{pmatrix} \begin{pmatrix} E_1 \\ E_2 \\ E_3 \end{pmatrix} \tag{4-37a}$$

where the vector $\boldsymbol{\beta}$ with components β_1, β_2, and β_3 is as yet undetermined. Thus, the vector $\mathbf{D}$ is given by the inner product of a symmetric tensor and the vector $\mathbf{E}$. In the given coordinate system the tensor is represented by the symmetric matrix

$$\begin{pmatrix} \beta_2{}^2 + \beta_3{}^2 & -\beta_1\beta_2 & -\beta_1\beta_3 \\ -\beta_1\beta_2 & \beta_3{}^2 + \beta_1{}^2 & -\beta_2\beta_3 \\ -\beta_1\beta_3 & -\beta_2\beta_3 & \beta_1{}^2 + \beta_2{}^2 \end{pmatrix}$$

As pointed out in Sec. 1-25 it is possible to find another coordinate system (denoted by primes) in which the symmetric tensor is represented by a diagonal matrix. In this coordinate system (4-37a) becomes

$$\begin{pmatrix} D_1' \\ D_2' \\ D_3' \end{pmatrix} = \begin{pmatrix} \epsilon_1' & 0 & 0 \\ 0 & \epsilon_2' & 0 \\ 0 & 0 & \epsilon_3' \end{pmatrix} \begin{pmatrix} E_1' \\ E_2' \\ E_3' \end{pmatrix} \tag{4-38}$$

The procedure to be used to find the desired primed coordinate system and the ϵ_i' was described in Sec. 1-25. The directions of the coordinate axes in this coordinate system are called the electrical axes of the crystal. If $\epsilon_1' = \epsilon_2' = \epsilon_3'$, the medium is isotropic. If only two of the ϵ_i' are the same, the crystal is said to be uniaxial. If all three of the ϵ_i' are different, the crystal is biaxial.

We now proceed to the determination of β. It is easily demonstrated that, if E and D are known, then β is known: Take the scalar product of each side of (4-37) with itself. Then

$$\begin{aligned} D^2 &= \beta^4 E^2 - 2\beta^2(\beta \cdot E)^2 + \beta^2(\beta \cdot E)^2 \\ &= \beta^4 E^2(1 + \cos^2 \theta) \\ &= \beta^4 E^2 \sin^2 \theta \end{aligned}$$

or
$$D = \beta^2 E \sin \theta \tag{4-39}$$

where θ is the angle between β and E. But

$$\cos \alpha = \frac{E \cdot D}{ED} = \frac{\beta^2 E^2 - \beta^2 E^2 \cos^2 \theta}{ED}$$

$$= \beta^2 \frac{E}{D} \sin^2 \theta \tag{4-40}$$

Hence, dividing (4-39) by (4-40),

$$\cos \alpha = \sin \theta$$

which determines the direction of β. The magnitude of β is then obtained from (4-39):

$$\beta = \left(\frac{D}{E \sin \theta} \right)^{1/2} = \left(\frac{D}{E \cos \alpha} \right)^{1/2}$$

EXERCISES

4-1. Given a dipole of moment p_1 located at the origin of coordinates and a dipole of moment p_2 located at a point P distant r from the origin, show that the mutual potential energy can be written

$$W = \frac{p_1 p_2}{4\pi\epsilon r^3} (\cos \alpha - 3 \cos \theta_1 \cos \theta_2)$$

where α is the angle between the dipoles and θ_1 and θ_2 are the two angles between the dipoles and $\mathbf{r}$. Then calculate the force along $\mathbf{r}$ and the couple exerted on p_2 and p_1.

4-2. Consider a surface separating two dielectric media of permittivity ϵ_1 and ϵ_2. If the electric field intensity in medium 1 makes an angle θ_1 with the normal to the surface, show that the angle θ_2 which the field intensity in medium 2 makes with the normal to the surface is given by

$$\epsilon_1 \cot \theta_1 = \epsilon_2 \cot \theta_2$$

4-3. Let $\mathbf{E}$ be the electric field intensity in a dielectric of permittivity ϵ. Find the electric field intensity in each of the following two small cavities which are excavated in the dielectric: (a) a thin disk whose plane is perpendicular to the direction of $\mathbf{E}$, (b) a needle-shaped cavity pointing in the direction of $\mathbf{E}$.

4-4. The whole of space for which $x_3 < 0$ is filled with a dielectric of permittivity ϵ_2, while that for which $x_3 > 0$ is filled with a dielectric of permittivity ϵ_1. A charge q is placed at the point $(0,0,h)$, $h > 0$. Using the method of images, show that the electric field in the dielectric ϵ_1 is the same as if the whole of space were occupied by the dielectric ϵ_1 and an additional charge

$$q' = \frac{\epsilon_1 - \epsilon_2}{\epsilon_1 + \epsilon_2} q$$

were located at the image point $(0,0,-h)$. Show also that the field in ϵ_2 is that which would exist if the whole of space were occupied by a dielectric ϵ and there were only a charge

$$q'' = \frac{2\epsilon_2}{\epsilon_1 + \epsilon_2}$$

at $(0,0,h)$.

4-5. Find the force which the charge q in Exercise 4-4 exerts on the dielectric ϵ_2.

4-6. A line with charge $+\lambda$ per unit length is placed in a dielectric of permittivity ϵ_1 parallel to and at a distance h from the plane boundary with another dielectric of permittivity ϵ_2. Find the potential in both dielectrics and the force per unit length acting on the line charge.

4-7. Let $\mathbf{E}$ denote the electric field intensity in a homogeneous isotropic dielectric. Consider one of the molecules constituting this dielectric, and show that the actual field acting on the molecule is given by

$$\mathbf{E}_{\text{eff}} = \mathbf{E} + \frac{P}{3\epsilon_0} \tag{4-41}$$

where $\mathbf{P}$ is the polarization.

4-8. The dipole moment p acquired by the molecule in Exercise 4-7 in the presence of the field is $p = \alpha\epsilon_0 \mathbf{E}_{\text{eff}}$, where α is a proportionality constant called the *polarizability*. If N is the number of molecules per unit volume of the dielectric, the polarization is

$$\mathbf{P} = Np = \alpha N \epsilon_0 \mathbf{E}_{\text{eff}} \tag{4-42}$$

Show that by combining (4-42) with (4-41) and (4-31) there results the *Clausius-Mosotti relation*

$$\frac{K - 1}{K + 2} = \frac{\alpha N}{3} \tag{4-43}$$

where K is the dielectric constant. If d is the density and M the molecular weight of the dielectric material, (4-43) can be written

$$\frac{K - 1}{K + 2} = \frac{\alpha d N_0}{3M} \tag{4-43a}$$

where N_0 is Avogadro's number.

REFERENCES

Abraham, M., and R. Becker: "The Classical Theory of Electricity and Magnetism," chaps. 2 and 4, Hafner Publishing Company, Inc., New York, 1950.

Panofsky, W. K. H., and M. Phillips: "Classical Electricity and Magnetism," chap. 2, Addison-Wesley Publishing Company, Inc., Cambridge, Mass., 1955.

Smythe, W. R.: "Static and Dynamic Electricity," 2d ed., chaps. 1 and 2, McGraw-Hill Book Company, Inc., New York, 1950.

Sommerfeld, A.: "Electrodynamics," paragraph 11, Academic Press, Inc., New York, 1952.

Stratton, J. A.: "Electromagnetic Theory," chap. 3, McGraw-Hill Book Company, Inc., New York, 1941.

CHAPTER 5

Energy and Mechanical Forces in the Electrostatic Field

5-1. INTRODUCTION

A number of different expressions for the energy W in an electrostatic field were derived in Sec. 2-11. In this chapter we shall use these expressions to determine the mechanical forces and torques in certain electrostatic fields and to verify some energy theorems. Thus, in Sec. 5-2 the expression (2-46) is used to determine the mechanical force on a charged conducting surface and in Sec. 5-3 the expressions (2-47), (2-48), and (2-49) are used in the study of forces and torques on charged conductors. In Sec. 5-4 we verify Thomson's theorem, which states that charges will distribute themselves on the surfaces of conductors in such a way that the energy of the resultant electrostatic field is a minimum. In Sec. 5-5 it is demonstrated that the energy of a system of charged conductors decreases with an increase in the permittivity of the medium in which they are embedded. The expression for the force per unit volume on a dielectric in an electrostatic field is derived in Sec. 5-6. The electric stress tensor is derived in Sec. 5-7.

5-2. MECHANICAL FORCE ON A CHARGED CONDUCTING SURFACE

It was shown in Sec. 2-11 that the energy in an electrostatic field due to n charged conductors is given by

$$W = \frac{1}{2} \sum_{i=1}^{n} \iint_i \sigma(\mathbf{r})\phi(\mathbf{r}) \, dS \qquad (2\text{-}46)$$

In the case of but a single conductor this expression reduces to

$$W = \frac{1}{2}\iint \sigma(\mathbf{r})\phi(\mathbf{r}) \, dS$$

so that the energy associated with unit area of the surface of the conductor is

$$w = \frac{1}{2}\sigma(\mathbf{r})\phi(\mathbf{r}) \qquad (5\text{-}1)$$

83

where $\sigma(\mathbf{r})$ is the charge per unit area of the surface of the conductor and ϕ is the (constant) potential of this surface.

The component of the force on unit area of the surface in any arbitrary direction s is given by the negative of the directional derivative of w in this direction:

$$f_s = -\frac{dw}{ds} = -\frac{1}{2}\sigma \frac{d}{ds}\phi = -\frac{1}{2}\sigma \,\mathrm{grad}\,\phi \cdot \mathbf{i}_s$$
$$= \frac{1}{2}\sigma \mathbf{E} \cdot \mathbf{i}_s \tag{5-2}$$

where $\mathbf{E}$ is the field intensity at the surface and $\mathbf{i}_s$ is a unit vector in the direction of s.

Since the electric field intensity at the surface of a charged conductor is normal to the surface and of magnitude (cf. Sec. 2-6)

$$E_n = \frac{\sigma}{\epsilon} \tag{2-27}$$

where ϵ is the permittivity of the medium in which the conductor is embedded, it follows from (5-2) that the normal component of the force on unit area of the surface is

$$f_n = \frac{1}{2}\frac{\sigma^2}{\epsilon} \tag{5-3}$$

and that the component tangential to the surface is zero.

5-3. FORCES AND TORQUES ON CHARGED CONDUCTORS

Let the geometrical configuration of a system of n charged conductors be specified by m parameters a_k ($k = 1, 2, \ldots, m$). The a_k may be either lengths or angles. Denote by F_k the force (torque) due to the electric field in the direction of increasing length (angle) a_k. Then the work done when the parameters change from a_k to $a_k + da_k$ is given by

$$d\mathscr{W} = \sum_{k=1}^{m} F_k \, da_k \tag{5-4}$$

When the conductors are insulated so that the charges are maintained constant, no energy is supplied to the system and the work must be done at the expense of the energy W in the electrostatic field. Then

$$d\mathscr{W} = \sum_{k=1}^{m} F_k \, da_k = -dW \tag{5-5}$$

and $$F_k = -\frac{\partial W}{\partial a_k} \tag{5-6}$$

The system tends to move so as to diminish the energy.

Substitution for W in (5-6) by means of

$$W(q,p) = \frac{1}{2} \sum_{i,j=1}^{n} p_{ji}q_j q_i \qquad (2\text{-}48)$$

where the coefficients of potential p_{ji} are functions of the a_k only, then yields

$$F_k = -\frac{\partial W(q,p)}{\partial a_k} = -\frac{1}{2} \sum_{i,j=1}^{n} \frac{\partial p_{ji}}{\partial a_k} q_j q_i \qquad (5\text{-}7)$$

If, on the other hand, the potentials are maintained constant, energy must be supplied from the outside (from a battery or equivalent device) and (5-6) no longer applies. To determine the force (torque) in terms of the potentials, we combine the relations

$$W(q,\phi) = \frac{1}{2} \sum_{i=1}^{n} \phi_i q_i \qquad (2\text{-}47)$$

$$W(\phi,c) = \frac{1}{2} \sum_{i,j=1}^{n} c_{ji}\phi_j \phi_i \qquad (2\text{-}49)$$

where the coefficients c_{ji} are functions of the a_k only, with (2-48) to form the function

$$\chi(q,\phi,a) = W(q,p) + W(\phi,c) - 2W(q,\phi) = 0 \qquad (5\text{-}8)$$

Then
$$d\chi = \sum_{i=1}^{n} \frac{\partial \chi}{\partial q_i} dq_i + \sum_{i=1}^{n} \frac{\partial \chi}{\partial \phi_i} d\phi_i + \sum_{k=1}^{m} \frac{\partial \chi}{\partial a_k} da_k = 0$$

$$= \sum_{j=1}^{n} p_{ji}q_j - \phi_i + \sum_{j=1}^{n} c_{ji}\phi_j - q_i + \sum_{k=1}^{m} \frac{\partial \chi}{\partial a_k} da_k = 0$$

$$= \sum_{k=1}^{m} \frac{\partial \chi}{\partial a_k} da_k = 0 \qquad (5\text{-}9)$$

where we have used (2-35) and (2-36). Since the da_k are arbitrary, it follows that

$$\frac{\partial \chi}{\partial a_k} = 0$$

so that, from (5-8),

$$\frac{\partial W(q,p)}{\partial a_k} + \frac{\partial W(\phi,c)}{\partial a_k} = 0$$

or
$$\frac{\partial W(\phi,c)}{\partial a_k} = -\frac{\partial W(q,p)}{\partial a_k} = F_k$$

by (5-7).   Hence

$$F_k = \frac{\partial W(\phi,c)}{\partial a_k} = \frac{1}{2} \sum_{i,j=1}^{m} \frac{\partial c_{ji}}{\partial a_k} \phi_j \phi_i \qquad (5\text{-}10)$$

and

$$dW(\phi,c) = \sum_{k=1}^{m} F_k \, da_k = d\mathcal{W} \qquad (5\text{-}11)$$

The system now tends to move so as to increase the energy, and the increase of energy is exactly equal to the work done by the electrical forces.

5-4. THOMSON'S THEOREM

Consider n conductors in a homogeneous isotropic medium of permittivity ϵ. Let each conductor receive a given fixed total charge q_i $(i = 1, 2, \ldots, n)$. Thomson's theorem states these charges will distribute themselves over the surfaces of the conductors in such a way that the energy of the resultant electrostatic field is a minimum. To verify the theorem, let $\mathbf{E}$ represent the actual field and $\mathbf{E} + \mathbf{E}'$ the field which arises when the charges are distributed differently over the surfaces of the conductors. Then, from the integral statement of Gauss' law

$$\iint_i \mathbf{E} \cdot d\mathbf{S} = \frac{q_i}{\epsilon} = \iint_i (\mathbf{E} + \mathbf{E}') \cdot d\mathbf{S}$$

so that

$$\iint_i \mathbf{E}' \cdot d\mathbf{S} = 0 \qquad (5\text{-}12)$$

where the subscript i on the integration sign indicates that the integration is over the surface of the ith conductor only.

If there is a density of charge ρ throughout the volume of the dielectric, the differential statement of Gauss' law yields

$$\operatorname{div} \mathbf{E} = \frac{\rho}{\epsilon} = \operatorname{div} (\mathbf{E} + \mathbf{E}')$$

or

$$\operatorname{div} \mathbf{E}' = 0 \qquad (5\text{-}13)$$

Let W represent the energy of the field $\mathbf{E}$ and $W + W'$ the energy of the field $\mathbf{E} + \mathbf{E}'$. Then, using (2-45),

$$\begin{aligned}
W' &= \tfrac{1}{2}\iiint\epsilon(\mathbf{E} + \mathbf{E}') \cdot (\mathbf{E} + \mathbf{E}') \, d\tau - \tfrac{1}{2}\iiint\epsilon\mathbf{E} \cdot \mathbf{E} \, d\tau \\
&= \tfrac{1}{2}\iiint\epsilon(\mathbf{E}' \cdot \mathbf{E}' + 2\mathbf{E} \cdot \mathbf{E}') \, d\tau \qquad (5\text{-}14)
\end{aligned}$$

where the integration is over the volume of the dielectric, i.e., over all space outside the conductors. The next step is to demonstrate that the integral of $\mathbf{E} \cdot \mathbf{E}'$ is identically zero. In this event (5-14) reduces to

$$W' = \tfrac{1}{2}\iiint\epsilon\mathbf{E}' \cdot \mathbf{E}' \, d\tau > 0$$

and the verification of Thomson's theorem is complete. To show that the integral of $\mathbf{E} \cdot \mathbf{E}'$ is identically zero, let ϕ be the potential due to $\mathbf{E}$. Then

$$\iiint\mathbf{E} \cdot \mathbf{E}' \, d\tau = -\iiint\nabla\phi \cdot \mathbf{E}' \, d\tau$$
$$= -\iiint(\operatorname{div} \phi\mathbf{E}' - \phi \operatorname{div} \mathbf{E}') \, d\tau$$
$$= -\iiint \operatorname{div} \phi\mathbf{E}' \, d\tau \qquad (5\text{-}15)$$

by reason of (5-13). Application of Gauss' theorem to (5-15) then gives

$$\iiint\mathbf{E} \cdot \mathbf{E}' \, d\tau = -\iint\phi\mathbf{E}' \cdot d\mathbf{S} \qquad (5\text{-}16)$$

where the surface integral is over a sphere at infinity and the surface of each of the n conductors. Since ϕ is constant on the surface of each conductor, it follows from (5-12) that the contribution of each conductor to (5-16) is zero. Since ϕ vanishes at infinity for any finite system of charges, the contribution of the sphere at infinity to (5-16) is also zero. Hence

$$\iiint\mathbf{E} \cdot \mathbf{E}' \, d\tau = 0$$

and the verification of Thomson's theorem is complete.

5-5. ENERGY CHANGE DUE TO INCREASE IN PERMITTIVITY

Let q_i be the charge on the ith of n conductors embedded in an isotropic medium of permittivity ϵ. Suppose that the volume charge distribution ρ in the system and the charge on each conductor are kept constant while the permittivity of the medium is changed from ϵ to $\epsilon + \delta\epsilon$ (or the medium is changed from one with permittivity ϵ to one with permittivity $\epsilon + \delta\epsilon$). The permittivities ϵ and $\epsilon + \delta\epsilon$ are not necessarily constant throughout the medium. We shall show that the energy of the system decreases (increases) with an increase (decrease) of the permittivity.

Let W represent the energy of the field $\mathbf{E}$ when the permittivity is ϵ and W' the energy of the field $\mathbf{E}'$ when the permittivity is $\epsilon + \delta\epsilon$. Then

$$W' - W = \tfrac{1}{2}\iiint(\epsilon + \delta\epsilon)\mathbf{E}' \cdot \mathbf{E}' \, d\tau - \tfrac{1}{2}\iiint\epsilon\mathbf{E} \cdot \mathbf{E} \, d\tau$$
$$= \tfrac{1}{2}\iiint(\mathbf{D}' \cdot \mathbf{E}' - \mathbf{D} \cdot \mathbf{E}) \, d\tau$$
$$= \tfrac{1}{2}\iiint(\mathbf{D} \cdot \mathbf{E}' - \mathbf{D}' \cdot \mathbf{E}) \, d\tau$$
$$+ \tfrac{1}{2}\iiint(\mathbf{D}' - \mathbf{D}) \cdot \mathbf{E}' \, d\tau + \tfrac{1}{2}\iiint(\mathbf{D}' - \mathbf{D}) \cdot \mathbf{E} \, d\tau \qquad (5\text{-}17)$$

where $\mathbf{D} = \epsilon\mathbf{E}$, $\mathbf{D}' = (\epsilon + \delta\epsilon)\mathbf{E}'$, and the integration is over all space outside the conductors.

From (4-34)

$$\iint_i \mathbf{D} \cdot d\mathbf{S} = q_i = \iint_i \mathbf{D}' \cdot d\mathbf{S}$$

so that
$$\iint_i (\mathbf{D}' - \mathbf{D}) \cdot d\mathbf{S} = 0 \tag{5-18}$$

where the integration is over the surface of the ith conductor only. From (4-32)

$$\text{div } \mathbf{D} = \rho = \text{div } \mathbf{D}'$$

so that
$$\text{div } (\mathbf{D}' - \mathbf{D}) = 0 \tag{5-19}$$

Now

$$\begin{aligned}
\iiint (\mathbf{D}' - \mathbf{D}) \cdot \mathbf{E} \, d\tau &= -\iiint (\mathbf{D}' - \mathbf{D}) \cdot \nabla \phi \, d\tau \\
&= \iiint [\phi \, \text{div } (\mathbf{D}' - \mathbf{D}) - \text{div } \phi(\mathbf{D}' - \mathbf{D})] \, d\tau \\
&= -\iiint \text{div } \phi(\mathbf{D}' - \mathbf{D}) \, d\tau
\end{aligned}$$

because of (5-19).   Similarly

$$\begin{aligned}
\iiint (\mathbf{D}' - \mathbf{D}) \cdot \mathbf{E}' \, d\tau &= -\iiint (\mathbf{D}' - \mathbf{D}) \cdot \nabla \phi' \\
&= -\iiint \text{div } \phi'(\mathbf{D}' - \mathbf{D}) \, d\tau
\end{aligned}$$

Hence (5-17) reduces to

$$\begin{aligned}
W' - W &= \tfrac{1}{2}\iiint (\mathbf{D} \cdot \mathbf{E}' - \mathbf{D}' \cdot \mathbf{E}) \, d\tau - \tfrac{1}{2}\iiint \text{div } (\phi' + \phi)(\mathbf{D}' - \mathbf{D}) \, d\tau \\
&= \tfrac{1}{2}\iiint (\mathbf{D} \cdot \mathbf{E}' - \mathbf{D}' \cdot \mathbf{E}) \, d\tau - \tfrac{1}{2}\iint (\phi' + \phi)(\mathbf{D}' - \mathbf{D}) \cdot d\mathbf{S}
\end{aligned} \tag{5-20}$$

where the surface integral is over a sphere at infinity and the surfaces of the n conductors. Since ϕ and ϕ' must be constant on the surface of each conductor, it follows from (5-18) that the contribution of each conductor to (5-20) is zero. The contribution of the sphere at infinity is also zero, since for any finite system of charges ϕ and ϕ' must vanish at infinity. Hence (5-20) becomes

$$\begin{aligned}
W' - W &= \tfrac{1}{2}\iiint (\mathbf{D} \cdot \mathbf{E}' - \mathbf{D}' \cdot \mathbf{E}) \, d\tau \\
&= -\tfrac{1}{2}\iiint \delta \epsilon \mathbf{E}' \cdot \mathbf{E} \, d\tau
\end{aligned} \tag{5-21}$$

For small $\delta\epsilon$, $\mathbf{E}' = \mathbf{E} + \delta\mathbf{E}$, where $\delta\mathbf{E}$ is also a small quantity.   Then, to a first approximation, (5-21) gives

$$\delta W = -\tfrac{1}{2}\iiint \delta\epsilon \mathbf{E} \cdot \mathbf{E} \, d\tau \tag{5-22}$$

for the change in field energy due to a change in the permittivity.

5-6. VOLUME FORCES IN THE ELECTROSTATIC FIELD

According to (2-45) the energy in an electrostatic field is

$$W = \tfrac{1}{2}\iiint \epsilon \mathbf{E} \cdot \mathbf{E} \, d\tau$$

where ϵ is the permittivity of the medium, $\mathbf{E}$ is the electrostatic field intensity, and the integration is over the entire volume τ of the field. Suppose now that every element of volume in the dielectric medium is subjected to an arbitrary infinitesimal displacement $d\mathbf{s}$. This results in a change $\delta\epsilon$ in the permittivity of the medium and, according to (5-22), a change

$$\delta W = -\tfrac{1}{2}\iiint \delta\epsilon \mathbf{E} \cdot \mathbf{E}\, d\tau$$

in the energy in the field.

If the permittivity is a function only of position $\mathbf{r}$ in the medium and of the density θ, then

$$\delta\epsilon = -\frac{\partial\epsilon}{\partial s}\, ds + \frac{\partial\epsilon}{\partial\theta}\, d\theta$$

$$= -\boldsymbol{\nabla}\epsilon \cdot d\mathbf{s} + \frac{\partial\epsilon}{\partial\theta}\, d\theta$$

where the minus sign in the first term of the right-hand member appears because the element which is found at the point $\mathbf{r}$ after the displacement was at the point $\mathbf{r} - d\mathbf{s}$ before the displacement. The second term can be transformed by use of the equation of continuity, so that

$$\delta\epsilon = -\boldsymbol{\nabla}\epsilon \cdot d\mathbf{s} - \theta\frac{\partial\epsilon}{\partial\theta}\boldsymbol{\nabla} \cdot d\mathbf{s} \qquad (5\text{-}23)$$

Hence the change in the electrostatic energy is

$$\delta W = \frac{1}{2}\iiint \mathbf{E} \cdot \mathbf{E}\left(\boldsymbol{\nabla}\epsilon + \theta\frac{\partial\epsilon}{\partial\theta}\boldsymbol{\nabla}\right) \cdot d\mathbf{s}\, d\tau$$

But $\quad \mathbf{E} \cdot \mathbf{E}\theta\frac{\partial\epsilon}{\partial\theta}\boldsymbol{\nabla} \cdot d\mathbf{s} = \boldsymbol{\nabla} \cdot \left(\mathbf{E} \cdot \mathbf{E}\theta\frac{\partial\epsilon}{\partial\theta}\, d\mathbf{s}\right) - \boldsymbol{\nabla}\left(\mathbf{E} \cdot \mathbf{E}\theta\frac{\partial\epsilon}{\partial\theta}\right) \cdot d\mathbf{s}$

Therefore

$$\delta W = \frac{1}{2}\iiint \left[\mathbf{E} \cdot \mathbf{E}\boldsymbol{\nabla}\epsilon - \boldsymbol{\nabla}\left(\mathbf{E} \cdot \mathbf{E}\theta\frac{\partial\epsilon}{\partial\theta}\right)\right] \cdot d\mathbf{s}\, d\tau$$

$$+ \frac{1}{2}\iiint \boldsymbol{\nabla} \cdot \left(\mathbf{E} \cdot \mathbf{E}\theta\frac{\partial\epsilon}{\partial\theta}\, d\mathbf{s}\right) d\tau$$

$$= \frac{1}{2}\iiint \left[\mathbf{E} \cdot \mathbf{E}\boldsymbol{\nabla}\epsilon - \boldsymbol{\nabla}\left(\mathbf{E} \cdot \mathbf{E}\theta\frac{\partial\epsilon}{\partial\theta}\right)\right] \cdot d\mathbf{s}\, d\tau$$

$$+ \frac{1}{2}\iint \mathbf{E} \cdot \mathbf{E}\theta\frac{\partial\epsilon}{\partial\theta}\, d\mathbf{s} \cdot d\mathbf{S} \qquad (5\text{-}24)$$

where $d\mathbf{S}$ is an element of the surface bounding the volume τ of the dielectric. This surface consists of the surfaces S_i of all the conductors in the medium plus a surface S_0 which encloses all the conductors and all parts of the dielectric in which $\mathbf{E}$ is different from zero.

Since $\mathbf{E}$ is zero on S_0, the contribution of the surface to the surface integral in (5-24) is clearly zero. If it is assumed that the conductors were held rigidly in place while the dielectric particles were subjected to the displacement ds, then $ds \cdot dS_i = 0$; i.e., the displacement of the dielectric adjacent to any conductor is necessarily tangential to the surface of the conductor. Hence (5-24) reduces to

$$\delta W = \frac{1}{2} \iiint \left[\mathbf{E} \cdot \mathbf{E} \nabla \epsilon - \nabla \left(\mathbf{E} \cdot \mathbf{E} \theta \frac{\partial \epsilon}{\partial \theta} \right) \right] \cdot d\mathbf{s} \, d\tau \qquad (5\text{-}25)$$

and the change δw in the energy density in the field is

$$\delta w = \left[\frac{1}{2} \mathbf{E} \cdot \mathbf{E} \nabla \epsilon - \frac{1}{2} \nabla \left(\mathbf{E} \cdot \mathbf{E} \theta \frac{\partial \epsilon}{\partial \theta} \right) \right] \cdot d\mathbf{s} \equiv -\mathbf{f} \cdot d\mathbf{s} \qquad (5\text{-}26)$$

where

$$\mathbf{f} = -\frac{1}{2} \mathbf{E} \cdot \mathbf{E} \nabla \epsilon + \frac{1}{2} \nabla \left(\mathbf{E} \cdot \mathbf{E} \theta \frac{\partial \epsilon}{\partial \theta} \right) \qquad (5\text{-}27)$$

is the force on a unit volume of the dielectric. If there is also a free charge ρ_F per unit volume distributed throughout the dielectric, (5-27) becomes

$$\mathbf{f} = \rho_F \mathbf{E} - \frac{1}{2} \mathbf{E} \cdot \mathbf{E} \nabla \epsilon + \frac{1}{2} \nabla \left(\mathbf{E} \cdot \mathbf{E} \theta \frac{\partial \epsilon}{\partial \theta} \right) \qquad (5\text{-}28)$$

The second term in (5-28) gives the contribution to the force per unit volume due to the inhomogeneity of the dielectric. The third term is known as the electrostriction term, since it gives the contribution to the force per unit volume due to the elastic deformation of the dielectric under the electric forces.

5-7. STRESSES IN A DIELECTRIC MEDIUM

For simplicity we limit the discussion in this section to homogeneous isotropic dielectric media. For such media the expression (5-28) for the force per unit volume reduces to

$$\mathbf{f} = \rho_F \mathbf{E} \qquad (5\text{-}29)$$

The total force on a volume τ of such a dielectric is then

$$\mathbf{F} = \iiint \mathbf{f} \, d\tau \qquad (5\text{-}30)$$

where the integration is over the entire volume τ. We shall show that the force $\mathbf{F}$ can be expressed as the surface integral of a vector $\mathbf{T}^{(e)}$:

$$\mathbf{F} = \iiint \mathbf{f} \, d\tau = \iint \mathbf{T}^{(e)} \, dS \qquad (5\text{-}31)$$

where dS is an element of the surface S which bounds the volume τ. To find the expression for $\mathbf{T}^{(e)}$ proceed as follows:

Since $\qquad\qquad\qquad \operatorname{div} \mathbf{D} = \rho_F \qquad\qquad\qquad (4\text{-}32)$

and $\qquad\qquad\qquad \operatorname{curl} \mathbf{E} = 0 \qquad\qquad\qquad (2\text{-}11)$

(5-29) can be written

$$\mathbf{f} = (\text{div } \mathbf{D})\mathbf{E} + (\text{curl } \mathbf{E}) \times \mathbf{D} \qquad (5\text{-}32)$$
$$\mathbf{f} = \epsilon[(\text{div } \mathbf{E})\mathbf{E} + (\text{curl } \mathbf{E}) \times \mathbf{E}] \qquad (5\text{-}33)$$

The x_1 component of (5-33) is

$$f_1 = \frac{\partial}{\partial x_1} \epsilon\left(E_1{}^2 - \frac{1}{2} E^2\right) + \frac{\partial}{\partial x_2} \epsilon(E_1 E_2) + \frac{\partial}{\partial x_3} \epsilon(E_1 E_3) \equiv \text{div } \mathbf{t}^{(1)}$$

Hence $\qquad \iiint f_1 \, d\tau = \iiint \text{div } \mathbf{t}^{(1)} \, d\tau = \iint \mathbf{t}^{(1)} \cdot \mathbf{n} \, dS \qquad (5\text{-}34)$

where $\qquad \mathbf{t}^{(1)} = \epsilon(E_1{}^2 - \tfrac{1}{2}E^2)\mathbf{i}_1 + \epsilon(E_1 E_2)\mathbf{i}_2 + \epsilon(E_1 E_3)\mathbf{i}_3 \qquad (5\text{-}35)$

Similarly $\qquad \iiint f_2 \, d\tau = \iint \mathbf{t}^{(2)} \cdot \mathbf{n} \, dS$

$$\iiint f_3 \, d\tau = \iint \mathbf{t}^{(3)} \cdot \mathbf{n} \, dS$$

where $\qquad \mathbf{t}^{(2)} = \epsilon(E_1 E_2)\mathbf{i}_1 + \epsilon(E_2{}^2 - \tfrac{1}{2}E^2)\mathbf{i}_2 + \epsilon(E_2 E_3)\mathbf{i}_3 \qquad (5\text{-}36)$

$$\mathbf{t}^{(3)} = \epsilon(E_1 E_3)\mathbf{i}_1 + \epsilon(E_2 E_3)\mathbf{i}_2 + \epsilon(E_3{}^2 - \tfrac{1}{2}E^2)\mathbf{i}_3 \qquad (5\text{-}37)$$

Therefore

$$\iiint \mathbf{f} \, d\tau = \iiint \epsilon[(\text{div } \mathbf{E})\mathbf{E} + (\text{curl } \mathbf{E}) \times \mathbf{E}] \, d\tau = \iint \mathbf{T}^{(e)} \, dS \qquad (5\text{-}38)$$

where $\qquad \mathbf{T}^{(e)} = (\mathbf{t}^{(1)} \cdot \mathbf{n})\mathbf{i}_1 + (\mathbf{t}^{(2)} \cdot \mathbf{n})\mathbf{i}_2 + (\mathbf{t}^{(3)} \cdot \mathbf{n})\mathbf{i}_3$

$$= \epsilon(\mathbf{E} \cdot \mathbf{n})\mathbf{E} - \frac{\epsilon}{2} E^2 \mathbf{n} \qquad (5\text{-}39)$$

or, in matrix notation,

$$\begin{pmatrix} T_1{}^{(e)} \\ T_2{}^{(e)} \\ T_3{}^{(e)} \end{pmatrix} = \begin{pmatrix} \epsilon(E_1{}^2 - \tfrac{1}{2}E^2) & \epsilon E_1 E_2 & \epsilon E_1 E_3 \\ \epsilon E_1 E_2 & \epsilon(E_2{}^2 - \tfrac{1}{2}E^2) & \epsilon E_2 E_3 \\ \epsilon E_1 E_3 & \epsilon E_2 E_3 & \epsilon(E_3{}^2 - \tfrac{1}{2}E^2) \end{pmatrix} \begin{pmatrix} n_1 \\ n_2 \\ n_3 \end{pmatrix} \qquad (5\text{-}40)$$

In more compact notation (5-40) can be written

$$\mathbf{T}^{(e)} = \underline{\underline{T}}^{(e)} \mathbf{n} \qquad (5\text{-}41)$$

where $\underline{\underline{T}}^{(e)}$ is the matrix

$$\underline{\underline{T}}^{(e)} = \begin{pmatrix} \epsilon(E_1{}^2 - \tfrac{1}{2}E^2) & \epsilon E_1 E_2 & \epsilon E_1 E_3 \\ \epsilon E_1 E_2 & \epsilon(E_2{}^2 - \tfrac{1}{2}E^2) & \epsilon E_2 E_3 \\ \epsilon E_1 E_3 & \epsilon E_2 E_3 & \epsilon(E_3{}^2 - \tfrac{1}{2}E^2) \end{pmatrix} \qquad (5\text{-}42)$$

The matrix is the representative in the given coordinate system of the second-rank tensor $\mathfrak{T}^{(e)}$ known as the *electric stress* tensor. Since the matrix is symmetric, it follows from Sec. 1-25 that a coordinate system exists in which the matrix representing the tensor $\mathfrak{T}^{(e)}$ is diagonal.

EXERCISES

5-1. Show that, if a new uncharged or grounded conductor is introduced into the electric field produced by a system of charged conductors while the charges on all the conductors are maintained constant, the energy of the system is decreased.

5-2. The assumption that the permittivity ϵ of a dielectric medium can be expressed as a function of position and density alone is valid for liquids and gases but not necessarily for solids. To a very good approximation the relationship between permittivity and density in gases, liquids, and some solids is the Clausius-Mosotti law (4-43a). Show that the force exerted by an electric field on a unit volume of a gas or liquid is

$$\mathbf{f} = -\frac{1}{2} \mathbf{E} \cdot \mathbf{E} \nabla \epsilon + \frac{1}{6\epsilon_0} \nabla[\mathbf{E} \cdot \mathbf{E}(\epsilon - \epsilon_0)(\epsilon + 2\epsilon_0)]$$

5-3. The equilibrium condition in an uncharged gas or liquid is

$$\nabla p = -\frac{1}{2} \mathbf{E} \cdot \mathbf{E} \nabla \epsilon + \frac{1}{2} \nabla \left(\mathbf{E} \cdot \mathbf{E} \theta \frac{\partial \epsilon}{\partial \theta} \right)$$

where p denotes the pressure. Verify that

$$\frac{1}{\theta} \nabla p = \frac{1}{2} \nabla \left(\mathbf{E} \cdot \mathbf{E} \frac{\partial \epsilon}{\partial \theta} \right)$$

Show that, in the case of a nearly incompressible liquid, the difference in pressure between two points 0 and 1 is given by

$$p_1 - p_0 = \frac{1}{2} \mathbf{E}_1 \cdot \mathbf{E}_1 \theta \frac{\partial \epsilon}{\partial \theta}$$

when $\mathbf{E}_0 = 0$. Use the Clausius-Mosotti law to verify that

$$p_1 - p_0 = \frac{1}{6\epsilon_0} \mathbf{E}_1 \cdot \mathbf{E}_1(\epsilon - \epsilon_0)(\epsilon + 2\epsilon_0)$$

5-4. Show that in the case of an ideal gas

$$\frac{RT}{M} \ln \frac{p_1}{p_0} = \frac{1}{2} \mathbf{E}_1 \cdot \mathbf{E}_1 \frac{d\epsilon}{d\theta}$$

where R is the gas content, T the absolute temperature, and M the molecular weight. Then show that

$$\frac{RT}{M} \ln \frac{p_1}{p_0} = \frac{1}{2} \mathbf{E}_1 \cdot \mathbf{E}_1 \frac{\epsilon - \epsilon_0}{\theta}$$

when the electric susceptibility is proportional to the density.

REFERENCES

Abraham, M., and R. Becker: "The Classical Theory of Electricity and Magnetism," chap. 5, Hafner Publishing Company, Inc., New York, 1950.

Panofsky, W. K. H., and M. Phillips: "Classical Electricity and Magnetism," chap. 6, Addison-Wesley Publishing Company, Inc., Cambridge, Mass., 1955.

Smythe, W. R.: "Static and Dynamic Electricity," 2d ed., chap. 2, McGraw-Hill Book Company, Inc., New York, 1950.

Sommerfeld, A.: "Electrodynamics," paragraph 11, Academic Press, Inc., New York, 1952.

Stratton, J. A.: "Electromagnetic Theory," chap. 2, McGraw-Hill Book Company, Inc., New York, 1941.

CHAPTER 6

Solutions of the Equations of Laplace and Poisson

6-1. INTRODUCTION

We began our study of electrostatics by presenting the experimentally verifiable Coulomb law of force (Sec. 2-2). The next step was to define the electrostatic field intensity $\mathbf{E}$ and to verify that the electrostatic field was a conservative field. This permitted us to define a potential ϕ such that $\mathbf{E} = -\text{grad } \phi$. We then took the divergence of both sides of this equation and made use of the differential statement of Gauss' law [Eq. (2-20)] to obtain Poisson's equation

$$\nabla^2\phi = -\frac{\rho}{\epsilon} \qquad (2\text{-}21)$$

For a region in which there is no charge, (2-21) reduces to Laplace's equation

$$\nabla^2\phi = 0 \qquad (2\text{-}22)$$

Now the procedure which we have followed could have as easily been reversed. That is, we could have begun the study of electrostatics with Poisson's equation, solved for the potential, and then by means of the relation $\mathbf{E} = -\text{grad } \phi$ introduced the electrostatic field intensity. The purpose of the present chapter is to present solutions of the equations of Laplace and Poisson. General solutions of Laplace's equation are found in several coordinate systems. These are then used to determine the potential and electric field intensity for a number of illustrative cases, some of which have already been considered using other methods. Green's functions and solutions of Poisson's equation are considered in Sec. 6-8.

6-2. LAPLACE'S EQUATION IN CARTESIAN COORDINATES

When the potential ϕ is a function of the three cartesian coordinates x_1, x_2, x_3, Laplace's equation takes the form

$$\nabla^2\phi(x_1,x_2,x_3) \equiv \frac{\partial^2}{\partial x_1{}^2}\phi + \frac{\partial^2}{\partial x_2{}^2}\phi + \frac{\partial^2}{\partial x_3{}^2}\phi = 0 \qquad (6\text{-}1)$$

To solve this equation we make the assumption that ϕ can be written as the product†

$$\phi(x_1,x_2,x_3) = X_1(x_1)X_2(x_2)X_3(x_3) \tag{6-2}$$

where X_i is a function of x_i only.   Substitution of (6-2) into (6-1) followed by division by ϕ yields

$$\frac{1}{X_1}\frac{d^2}{dx_1^2}X_1 + \frac{1}{X_2}\frac{d^2}{dx_2^2}X_2 = -\frac{1}{X_3}\frac{d^2}{dx_3^2}X_3 \tag{6-3}$$

The left-hand member of (6-3) is a function of x_1 and x_2, while the right-hand member is a function of x_3 alone.   Consequently, if (6-3) is to have a solution at all, each side of the equation must be equal to the same constant.   For convenience we write this constant, which may have any value, as k_3^2.   Then (6-3) leads to

$$\frac{d^2}{dx_3^2}X_3 + k_3^2X_3 = 0 \tag{6-4}$$

and $\qquad\qquad \dfrac{1}{X_1}\dfrac{d^2}{dx_1^2}X_1 = -\dfrac{1}{X_2}\dfrac{d^2X_2}{dx_2^2} + k_3^2 \qquad\qquad\qquad$ (6-5)

The left-hand member of (6-5) is a function of x_1 only, while the right-hand member is a function of x_2 alone.   Consequently, each side of the equation must be equal to a constant, say k_1^2.   Then

$$\frac{d^2}{dx_1^2}X_1 + k_1^2X_1 = 0 \tag{6-6}$$

$$\frac{d^2}{dx_2^2}X_2 + k_2^2X_2 = 0 \qquad k_2^2 = k_1^2 - k_3^2 \tag{6-7}$$

In the special case when $k_i = 0$ $(i = 1, 2, 3)$ Eqs. (6-4), (6-6), and (6-7) have solutions of the form

$$X_i(x_i) = a_ix_i + b_i \qquad k_i = 0 \qquad i = 1, 2, 3 \tag{6-8}$$

where the a_i and b_i are arbitrary constants of integration.   When $k_1 \neq 0$, the solution of (6-6) is of the form

$$X_1(x_1) = c_1(k_1)e^{k_1x_1} \qquad k_1 \neq 0 \qquad -\infty < k_1 < +\infty \tag{6-9}$$

where c_1 is an arbitrary function of k_1.   It is convenient to take k_1 as positive and to rewrite (6-9) as

$$X_1(x_1) = c_1(k_1)e^{k_1x_1} + c_1'(k_1)e^{-k_1x_1} \qquad k_1 \neq 0 \qquad 0 < k_1 < +\infty \tag{6-10}$$

† The *method of separation of variables.*

Similarly, the solutions of (6-4) and (6-7) when $k_i \neq 0$ are of the form

$$X_2(x_2) = c_2(k_2)e^{ik_2x_2} + c_2'(k_2)^{-ik_2x_2} \qquad k_2 \neq 0 \qquad 0 < k_2 < +\infty \qquad (6\text{-}11)$$
$$X_3(x_3) = c_3(k_3)e^{ik_3x_3} + c_3'(k_3)e^{-ik_3x_3} \qquad k_3 \neq 0 \qquad 0 < k_3 < +\infty \qquad (6\text{-}12)$$

Substitution of (6-10), (6-11), and (6-12) into (6-2) yields

$$\phi(x_1,x_2,x_3) = [c_1(k_1)e^{k_1x_1} + c_1'(k_1)e^{-k_1x_1}] \prod_{i=2}^{3} [c_i(k_i)e^{ik_ix_i} + c_i'(k_i)e^{-ik_ix_i}]$$
$$k_i \neq 0 \qquad 0 < k_i < +\infty \qquad (6\text{-}13)$$

as the solution of (6-1). If any $k_i = 0$, the potential ϕ is obtained by replacing the corresponding factor in (6-13) by $a_i x_i + b_i$.

The general solution of (6-1) when $k_i \neq 0$ is obtained by integrating (6-13) over all the permissible values of the k_i. Thus

$$\phi(x_1,x_2,x_3) = \int\int\int_0^\infty \left\{ [c_1(k_1)e^{k_1x_1} + c_1'(k_1)e^{-k_1x_1}] \right.$$
$$\left. \prod_{i=2}^{3} [c_i(k_i)e^{ik_ix_i} + c_i'(k_i)e^{-ik_ix_i}] \right\} dk_1\, dk_2\, dk_3 \qquad (6\text{-}14)$$

6-3. APPLICATION OF THE SOLUTIONS OF LAPLACE'S EQUATION IN CARTESIAN COORDINATES

We consider two simple problems which have already been solved by other methods (cf. example 3 of Sec. 2-6 and example 1 of Sec. 3-7). The first problem is to find the potential at a point P a distance h from a uniformly charged infinite plane in a dielectric of permittivity ϵ. Let σ represent the charge per unit area of the plane. Take the origin of coordinates in the plane and the x_1 axis perpendicular to the plane. Clearly, the potential is a function of x_1 only. Of the two types of solutions,

$$\phi(x_1) = c_1(k_1)e^{k_1x_1} + c_1'(k_1)e^{-k_1x_1} \qquad (6\text{-}15)$$
and
$$\phi(x_1) = a_1x_1 + b_1 \qquad (6\text{-}16)$$

only (6-16) can satisfy both the boundary condition that the plane is an equipotential, that is, $\phi(0) =$ constant, and the second "boundary" condition that, for all x_1, $E = -\partial\phi/\partial x_1 = \sigma/2\epsilon$. Hence $b_1 = \phi(0)$, $a_1 = -\sigma/2\epsilon$, and (6-16) becomes

$$\phi(x_1) = -\frac{\sigma}{2\epsilon} x_1 + \phi(0) \qquad (6\text{-}17)$$

As the second example consider two semi-infinite perpendicular planes OX_1 and OX_2 at potential ϕ_0. The problem is to find the potential at any point within the quadrant X_1OX_2. Of the two types of solutions to Laplace's equation, only

$$\phi(x_1,x_2) = \prod_{i=1}^{2} (a_i x_i + b_i)$$
$$= a_1a_2x_1x_2 + a_1b_2x_1 + b_1a_2x_2 + b_1b_2 \qquad (6\text{-}18)$$

can satisfy the boundary conditions

$$\phi(x_1,0) = \phi(0,x_2) = \phi_0$$

Application of these boundary conditions shows that $b_1a_2 = a_1b_2 = 0$ and $b_1b_2 = \phi_0$. Hence (6-18) reduces to

$$\phi(x_1,x_2) = a_1a_2x_1x_2 + \phi_0 \qquad (6\text{-}19)$$

The components of the electric intensity are

$$E_1 = -a_1a_2x_2 \qquad \text{and} \qquad E_2 = -a_1a_2x_1$$

If the quadrant X_1OX_2 is filled with a dielectric of permittivity ϵ, the charges on the planes $x_1 = 0$ and $x_2 = 0$ are

$$\sigma_1 = -2a_1a_2\epsilon x_2 \qquad \text{and} \qquad \sigma_2 = -2a_1a_2\epsilon x_1$$

respectively. The density of charge is consequently zero along the line of intersection of the two planes and increases linearly with distance from this line.

6-4. LAPLACE'S EQUATION IN CYLINDRICAL COORDINATES

To solve Laplace's equation in cylindrical coordinates, namely,

$$\nabla^2\phi(r,\theta,x_3) \equiv \frac{1}{r}\frac{\partial}{\partial r}\left(r\frac{\partial\phi}{\partial r}\right) + \frac{1}{r^2}\frac{\partial^2\phi}{\partial\theta^2} + \frac{\partial^2\phi}{\partial x_3^2} = 0 \qquad (6\text{-}20)$$

we assume that

$$\phi(r,\theta,x_3) = R(r)\Theta(\theta)X_3(x_3) \qquad (6\text{-}21)$$

Substitution into (6-20) followed by division by ϕ yields

$$\frac{1}{rR}\frac{d}{dr}\left(r\frac{dR}{dr}\right) + \frac{1}{r^2\Theta}\frac{d^2\Theta}{d\theta^2} = -\frac{1}{X_3}\frac{d^2X_3}{dx_3^2} \qquad (6\text{-}22)$$

Clearly, both sides of (6-22) must be equal to a constant, say $-k^2$. Hence

$$\frac{d^2X_3}{dx_3^2} - k^2X_3 = 0$$

which has for solution

$$X_3(x_3) = c(k)e^{kx_3} + c'(k)e^{-kx_3} \qquad k \neq 0 \qquad 0 < k < +\infty$$
$$= ax_3 + b \qquad\qquad\qquad k = 0 \qquad\qquad\qquad (6\text{-}23)$$

and
$$\frac{r}{R}\frac{d}{dr}\left(r\frac{dR}{dr}\right) + k^2r^2 = -\frac{1}{\Theta}\frac{d^2\Theta}{d\theta^2}$$

Both sides of this last equation must be equal to a constant, say l^2. Then

$$\frac{d^2}{d\theta^2}\Theta + l^2\Theta = 0 \qquad\qquad (6\text{-}24)$$

and
$$\frac{1}{r}\frac{d}{dr}\left(r\frac{dR}{dr}\right) + \left(k^2 - \frac{l^2}{r^2}\right)R = 0 \qquad\qquad (6\text{-}25)$$

Equation (6-24) has solutions of the form

$$\Theta(\theta) = d(l)e^{il\theta} \qquad l \neq 0 \qquad -\infty < l < +\infty$$
$$= e\theta + f \qquad l = 0$$

where $d(l)$ is an arbitrary function of l and e and f are arbitrary constants of integration. The single-valuedness condition on the potential ϕ requires that $\Theta(\theta) = \Theta(\theta + 2n\pi)$, where n is an integer. It follows from this that l must be an integer or zero and that $e = 0$. Then if l is taken as positive, the solutions of (6-24) reduce to

$$\Theta(\theta) = d(l)e^{il\theta} + d'(l)e^{-il\theta} \qquad l \neq 0 \qquad l = \text{positive integer}$$
$$= f \qquad l = 0 \qquad\qquad\qquad\qquad (6\text{-}26)$$

In the special case when $k = 0$, Eq. (6-25) has solutions of the form

$$R(r) = g(l)r^l + g'(l)r^{-l} \qquad l \neq 0$$
$$= h \ln r + m \qquad\qquad l = 0 \qquad k = 0 \qquad (6\text{-}27)$$

where g and g' are arbitrary functions of l and h and m are arbitrary constants of integration.

When $k \neq 0$, Eq. (6-25) is just like Bessel's equation, except that it has the constant k^2 in place of unity. A simple change of variable removes this discrepancy, however. Let $x = kr$. Then (6-25) becomes

$$\frac{d^2R}{dx^2} + \frac{1}{x}\frac{dR}{dx} + \left(1 - \frac{l^2}{x^2}\right)R = 0 \qquad\qquad (6\text{-}28)$$

the well-known equation of Bessel. To solve this equation we first note that $x = 0$ is a regular singular point and that all other finite points are ordinary points.† The change of variable $y = x^{-1}$ shows that $y = 0$, that is, $x = \infty$, is an irregular singular point. We then seek the general solution of (6-28) in the neighborhood of $x = 0$ expressed as a power series

$$R(x) = \sum_{n=0}^{\infty} a_n x^{n+s} \qquad (6\text{-}29)$$

where the a_n and s are constants to be determined. Substitution of (6-29) into (6-28) yields

$$\sum_{n=0}^{\infty} a_n \{[(n+s)^2 - l^2]x^{n+s-2} + x^{n+s}\} = 0 \qquad (6\text{-}30)$$

The fact that the smallest difference in the exponents of x in (6-30) is 2 indicates that the power series (6-29) proceeds in powers of x^2.

The value of the constant s is determined as follows: Since the relation (6-30) is an identity in x (i.e., an equation which is true for all values of x), the coefficient of each power of x must be equal to zero. The coefficient of the lowest power of x in (6-30) is $(s^2 - l^2)a_0$. Hence the equation

$$(s^2 - l^2)a_0 = 0 \qquad (6\text{-}31)$$

known as the *indicial equation*, must hold. There are thus two possible values of s, $s = \pm l$.‡ Since we have already determined that l is an

---

† A function $f(x)$ is called *analytic* at a point α if it can be expanded in a Taylor's series in powers of $x - \alpha$ which is valid near α. Consider the equation

$$\frac{d^2y}{dx^2} + P(x)\frac{dy}{dx} + Q(x)y = 0$$

A point α at which the coefficients $P(x)$ and $Q(x)$ are analytic is called an *ordinary point* of the equation. A point at which one or both of them fails to be analytic is called a *singular point*. A singular point α is called a *regular singular point* if $(x - \alpha)P(x)$ and $(x - \alpha)^2 Q(x)$ are analytic. About such a point the equation has, as we shall see below, a special type of series solution.

‡ Consider again the general equation

$$\frac{d^2y}{dx^2} + P(x)\frac{dy}{dx} + Q(x)y = 0$$

A singular point α of the equation is, as stated above, a regular singular point if $(x - \alpha)P(x)$ and $(x - \alpha)Q(x)$ are analytic. The indicial equation is quadratic. In general, then, one obtains two formal independent series solutions, say y_1 and y_2. If the roots of the indicial equation are unequal but differ by an integer, one of the series solutions, say y_2, may break down or it may coincide with y_1. If the roots are equal, there is, of course, but one series. If α_1 and α_2 are singular points ($\alpha_1 \leq \alpha \leq \alpha_2$), then the series converges in the region $\alpha_1 \leq x \leq \alpha_2$.

If there is no indicial equation at the point β, there is no solution in $(x - \beta)$.

integer, the two roots of the indicial equation differ by an integer, so that one of the series solutions may break down or the two solutions may coincide. We consider first the root $s = +l$, $l \geq 0$.

The next step in obtaining the series solutions of (6-28) is to determine the relation between the coefficients a_n in (6-30). It is seen that the complete coefficient of the term in x^{n+l} in (6-30) is

$$[(n + l + 2)^2 - l^2]a_{n+2} + a_n$$

Since this must vanish for every value of n, it follows that

$$a_{n+2} = \frac{a_n}{l^2 - (n + l + 2)^2} \tag{6-32}$$

This relation, which enables us to calculate the coefficients a_2, a_4, a_6, etc., in terms of the coefficient a_0, is known as the *recursion* or *recurrence formula*. The series solution (6-29) then becomes

$$R(x) = a_0 x^l \left[1 - \frac{x^2}{2^2(l + 1)} + \frac{x^4}{2^4 \cdot 2!(l + 1)(l + 2)} \cdots \right] \tag{6-33}$$

The test ratio readily establishes the convergence of this series. As $n \to \infty$, we find that

$$\left| \frac{a_{n+2}x^{n+2}}{a_n x^n} \right| = \left| \frac{x^2}{(n + l + 2)^2 - l^2} \right| \to 0$$

Thus, the series converges for all values of x (in agreement with the theory, since the nearest singular point to $x = 0$ is at infinity).

When a_0 is taken equal to $1/2^l l!$, the function R is designated $J_l(x)$. Then (6-33) becomes

$$J_l(x) = \sum_{n=0}^{\infty} \frac{(-1)^n (x/2)^{l+2n}}{n!(n + l)!} \tag{6-34}$$

If $s = -l$, the series solution is

$$J_{-l}(x) = \sum_{n=l}^{\infty} \frac{(-1)^n (x/2)^{2n-l}}{n!(n - l)!}$$

$$= \sum_{m=0}^{\infty} \frac{(-1)^{m+l} (x/2)^{l+2m}}{m!(m + l)!}$$

$$= (-1)^l J_l(x) \tag{6-35}$$

Hence the two series solutions coincide. The function $J_l(x)$, which has now been defined for all integral values of l, positive and negative, is called the *Bessel function of integral order l*.

Since (6-28) is a second-order differential equation, there must be a second solution. This solution is†

$$R(x) = J_l(x) \left\{ A + B \int \frac{dx}{x[J_l(x)]^2} \right\} \tag{6-36}$$

where A and B are constants. When they are taken to be

$$A = \frac{2}{\pi}(\gamma - \ln 2) \quad\text{and}\quad B = \frac{2}{\pi}$$

where $\gamma = 0.5772157$ is Euler's constant, the second solution is called a *Neumann function of the lth order* and designated by $N_l(x)$.

The general solution (6-25) when $k \neq 0$ is, therefore,

$$R(r) = p(l)J_l(kr) + q(l)N_l(kr) \quad k \neq 0 \tag{6-37}$$

where p and q are arbitrary functions of l.

The Bessel function $J_l(kr)$ is regular and the Neumann function $N_l(kr)$ is irregular at the origin $r = 0$. Since $J_l(kr)$ and $N_l(kr)$ are both solutions of (6-25), the functions

$$H_l^{(1)}(kr) = J_l(kr) + iN_l(kr) \tag{6-38}$$
$$H_l^{(2)}(kr) = J_l(kr) - iN_l(kr) \tag{6-39}$$

are also solutions. $H_l^{(1)}$ and $H_l^{(2)}$ are known, respectively, as the *Hankel functions of the first and second kinds* of the *l*th order.

---

† Consider again the equation

$$\frac{d^2y}{dx^2} + P(x)\frac{dy}{dx} + Q(x)y = 0$$

Suppose that $y = y_1$ is a particular solution. The substitution $y = y_1 z$ yields

$$y_1 \frac{d^2}{dx^2} z + \left[2\frac{dy_1}{dx} + P(x)y_1 \right] \frac{dz}{dx} = 0$$

Hence

$$\frac{d/dx(dz/dx)}{dz/dx} = -\frac{2}{y_1}\frac{dy_1}{dx} - P(x)$$

$$\ln \frac{dz}{dx} = -\ln y_1{}^2 - \int P(x)\, dx + \ln B$$

$$\frac{dz}{dx} = \frac{B}{y_1{}^2} e^{-\int P(x)\, dx}$$

$$z - A = B \int \frac{e^{-\int P(x)\, dx}}{y_1{}^2}\, dx$$

so that

$$y = y_1 z = y_1 \left(A + B \int \frac{e^{-\int P(x)\, dx}}{y_1{}^2}\, dx \right)$$

where A and B are arbitrary constants of integration.

The functions J_l, N_l, $H_l^{(1)}$, and $H_l^{(2)}$ which are solutions of (6-25) are known as *cylindrical functions of integral order* l and denoted by $Z_l(kr)$. The properties of these functions are well known.† Only the Bessel function remains finite for all r.

The solution of Laplace's equation (6-20) can now be written

$$
\begin{aligned}
\phi(r,\theta,x_3) &= (ax_3 + b)(h \ln r + m) \qquad k = 0 \qquad l = 0 \\
&= (ax_3 + b)[g(l)r^l + g'(l)r^{-l}][d(l)e^{il\theta} + d'(l)e^{-il\theta}] \\
&\qquad\qquad\qquad\qquad\qquad\qquad\qquad k = 0 \qquad l \neq 0 \\
&= [c(k)e^{kx_3} + c'(k)e^{-kx_3}]Z_0(kr) \qquad k \neq 0 \qquad l = 0 \\
&= [c(k)e^{kx_3} + c'(k)e^{-kx_3}]Z_l(kr)[d(l)e^{il\theta} + d'(l)e^{-il\theta}] \\
&\qquad\qquad\qquad\qquad\qquad\qquad\qquad k \neq 0 \qquad l \neq 0 \qquad (6\text{-}40)
\end{aligned}
$$

The general solution of (6-20) is obtained by summing (6-40) over the appropriate values of l and integrating over k.

6-5. APPLICATION OF THE SOLUTIONS OF LAPLACE'S EQUATION IN CYLINDRICAL COORDINATES

As a first example consider an infinitely long cylindrical conductor with radius a and charge per unit length λ. Take the origin of coordinates on the axis of the cylinder. The problem is to find the potential at a point P a distance $r > a$ from the axis of the cylinder (cf. example 2 of Sec. 2-6). Since the cylinder is an equipotential, one boundary condition is that

$$
\phi = \text{constant} = \phi(a) \qquad \text{for } r = a \text{ and all } \theta \text{ and } x_3
$$

The second boundary condition is that

$$
E = -\frac{\partial \phi}{\partial r} - \frac{\lambda}{2\pi a \epsilon} \qquad \text{for } r = a \text{ and all } \theta \text{ and } x_3
$$

Of the four types of solutions (6-40) to Laplace's equation in cylindrical coordinates only the first can satisfy these boundary conditions. Hence

$$
\phi(r) = b(h \ln r + m) = -\frac{\lambda}{2\pi\epsilon} \ln \frac{r}{a} + \phi(a) \qquad (6\text{-}41)
$$

As the next example consider an infinitely long uncharged conducting cylinder of radius a in a uniform electric field E_0 directed at right angles to the axis of the cylinder. The problem is to find the potential at a

† See, for example, E. Jahnke, F. Emde, and F. Losch, "Tables of Higher Functions," 6th ed., McGraw-Hill Book Company, Inc., 1960, and W. Magnus and F. Oberhettinger, "Formulas and Theorems for the Special Functions of Mathematical Physics," Chelsea Publishing Company, New York, 1949.

point $r > a$ from the axis of the cylinder. The boundary conditions are

$$\phi(r,\theta) = -E_0 r \cos\theta = -E_0 x_1 \quad \text{for } r \to \infty \quad (6\text{-}42)$$
$$\phi(r,\theta) = 0 \quad \text{for } r = a \quad (6\text{-}43)$$

where the x_1 axis has been taken in the direction of the uniform field. Of the four types of solutions (6-40) only the second,

$$\phi(r,\theta,x_3) = (ax_3 + b)[g(l)r^l + g'(l)r^{-l}][d(l)e^{il\theta} + d'(l)e^{-il\theta}]$$

can satisfy the boundary conditions. Since the potential must be independent of x_3, this solution reduces to

$$\begin{aligned}\phi(r,\theta) &= b[g(l)r^l + g'(l)r^{-l}][d(l)e^{il\theta} + d'(l)e^{-il\theta}] \\ &= [g(l)r^l + g'(l)r^{-l}][D(l)\cos l\theta + D'(l)\sin l\theta] \quad (6\text{-}44)\end{aligned}$$

where $D(l) = b[d(l) + d'(l)]$ and $D'(l) = ib[d(l) - d'(l)]$. To satisfy the boundary condition (6-42), we must have $l = 1$ and $D'(l) = 0$. Then (6-44) becomes

$$\phi(r,\theta) = \left(Gr + \frac{G'}{r}\right)\cos\theta \quad (6\text{-}45)$$

where $G = g(1)D(1)$ and $G' = g'(1)D(1)$. From (6-42)

$$-E_0 r\cos\theta = \left(Gr + \frac{G'}{r}\right)\cos\theta \quad \text{as } r \to \infty$$

Hence

$$G = -E_0$$

At $r = a$,

$$\phi(a,\theta) = 0 = \left(-E_0 a + \frac{G'}{a}\right)\cos\theta$$

so that

$$G' = E_0 a^2$$

Hence

$$\phi(r,\theta) = -E_0\left(1 - \frac{a^2}{r^2}\right)r\cos\theta \quad (6\text{-}46)$$

The components of the field intensity are

$$E_r = -\frac{\partial\phi}{\partial r} = \left(1 + \frac{a^2}{r^2}\right)E_0\cos\theta$$

$$E_\theta = -\frac{1}{r}\frac{\partial\phi}{\partial\theta} = -\left(1 - \frac{a^2}{r^2}\right)E_0\sin\theta$$

The charge per unit area of the cylinder is

$$\sigma = \epsilon E_r\Big|_{r=a} = 2\epsilon E_0\cos\theta$$

The charge per unit length is

$$\int_0^{2\pi} \sigma a \, d\theta = 2\epsilon E_0 a \int_0^{2\pi} \cos \theta \, d\theta = 0$$

as it should be.

As the last example consider a long cylindrical rod of radius a and permittivity ϵ_i in a uniform electric field E_0 which is perpendicular to the axis of the cylinder. The problem is to find the potential both inside, ϕ_i, and outside, ϕ_o, the rod. The boundary condition at infinity is

$$\phi_o(r,\theta) = -E_0 r \cos \theta = -E_0 x_1 \qquad \text{for } r \to \infty \qquad (6\text{-}47)$$

The boundary conditions at $r = a$ are

$$\phi_i(a,\theta) = \phi_o(a,\theta) \qquad \text{or} \qquad E_{\theta i} = E_{\theta o} \qquad (6\text{-}48)$$

and
$$D_{ri} = D_{ro} \qquad (6\text{-}49)$$

where the subscripts θ and r denote, respectively, the tangential and normal components. The boundary condition at $r = 0$ is

$$\phi_i(r,\theta) \text{ remains finite as } r \to 0 \qquad (6\text{-}50)$$

As in the preceding example of the conducting cylinder, the outside potential must have the form

$$\phi_o(r,\theta) = \left(Gr + \frac{G''}{r} \right) \cos \theta$$

in order to satisfy the boundary condition at infinity. Then

$$\phi_o(r,\theta) = \left(-E_0 r + \frac{G'}{r} \right) \cos \theta \qquad (6\text{-}51)$$

and
$$E_{ro} = -\frac{\partial \phi_o}{\partial r} = \left(E_0 + \frac{G'}{r^2} \right) \cos \theta$$

$$(6\text{-}52)$$

$$E_{\theta o} = -\frac{1}{r} \frac{\partial \phi_o}{\partial \theta} = \left(-E_0 + \frac{G'}{r^2} \right) \sin \theta$$

Since there is no volume distribution of polarization charge, the potential inside the cylinder also satisfies Laplace's equation. In order to satisfy the boundary conditions, this potential must also be of the form

$$\phi_i(r,\theta) = \left(Hr + \frac{H'}{r} \right) \cos \theta$$

To satisfy the boundary condition at $r = 0$, H' must be zero. Then

$$\phi_i(r,\theta) = Hr \cos \theta$$
$$E_{ri} = -H \cos \theta$$
$$E_{\theta i} = H \sin \theta$$

Application of the boundary conditions (6-48) and (6-40) then yields

$$Ha \cos \theta = \left(-E_o a + \frac{G'}{a} \right) \cos \theta \qquad (6\text{-}53)$$

$$-\epsilon_i H \cos \theta = \epsilon_o \left(E_0 + \frac{G'}{a^2} \right) \cos \theta \qquad (6\text{-}54)$$

Hence
$$G' = \frac{\epsilon_i - \epsilon_o}{\epsilon_i + \epsilon_o} a^2 E_0$$

$$H = -\frac{2\epsilon_o}{\epsilon_i + \epsilon_o} E_0$$

so that
$$\phi_o(r,\theta) = -\left(1 + \frac{\epsilon_o - \epsilon_i}{\epsilon_o + \epsilon_i} \frac{a^2}{r^2} \right) E_0 r \cos \theta \qquad r \geq a$$

$$\phi_i(r,\theta) = -\frac{2\epsilon_o}{\epsilon_o + \epsilon_i} E_0 r \cos \theta \qquad r \leq a$$

6-6. LAPLACE'S EQUATION IN SPACE POLAR COORDINATES

Laplace's equation in space polar coordinates is

$$\nabla^2 \phi(r,\theta,\varphi) \equiv \frac{1}{r} \frac{\partial}{\partial r} \left(r^2 \frac{\partial \phi}{\partial r} \right) + \frac{1}{r^2 \sin \theta} \frac{\partial}{\partial \theta} \left(\sin \theta \frac{\partial \phi}{\partial \theta} \right) + \frac{1}{r^2 \sin^2 \theta} \frac{\partial^2 \phi}{\partial \varphi^2} = 0$$
$$(6\text{-}55)$$

To solve, we assume that

$$\phi(r,\theta,\varphi) = R(r)\Theta(\theta)\Phi(\varphi) \qquad (6\text{-}56)$$

substitute into (6-55), and divide by ϕ. Then

$$\frac{\sin^2 \theta}{R} \frac{d}{dr} \left(r^2 \frac{dR}{dr} \right) + \frac{\sin \theta}{\Theta} \frac{d}{d\theta} \left(\sin \theta \frac{d\Theta}{d\theta} \right) = -\frac{1}{\Phi} \frac{d^2}{d\varphi^2} \Phi$$

For a solution, both sides of this equation must be equal to a constant, say m^2. Consequently

$$\frac{d^2\Phi}{d\varphi^2} + m^2\Phi = 0$$

which has for solution [cf. solution of Eq. (6-24)]

$$\Phi = a(m)e^{im\varphi} + a'(m)e^{-im\varphi} \qquad m \neq 0 \qquad m = \text{positive integer}$$
$$= b \qquad\qquad\qquad m = 0 \qquad\qquad\qquad\qquad (6\text{-}57)$$

and
$$\frac{1}{\Theta \sin \theta} \frac{d}{d\theta} \left(\sin \theta \frac{d\Theta}{d\theta} \right) - \frac{m^2}{\sin^2 \theta} = -\frac{1}{R} \frac{d}{dr} \left(r^2 \frac{dR}{dr} \right)$$

This last equation also will have a solution only if both sides equal a constant, say $-\beta$. Then

$$\frac{1}{\Theta \sin \theta} \frac{d}{d\theta}\left(\sin \theta \frac{d\Theta}{d\theta}\right) - \frac{m^2}{\sin^2 \theta} = -\beta \qquad (6\text{-}58)$$

and

$$\frac{1}{R} \frac{d}{dr}\left(r^2 \frac{dR}{dr}\right) = \beta \qquad (6\text{-}59)$$

where β is to be determined.

To solve (6-58) we first make the substitution $x = \cos \theta$ and set $P(x) = \Theta(\theta)$. The equation then becomes

$$\frac{d}{dx}\left[(1 - x^2)\frac{dP}{dx}\right] + \left(\beta - \frac{m^2}{1 - x^2}\right)P = 0$$

or

$$\frac{d^2P}{dx^2} - \frac{2x}{1 - x^2}\frac{dP}{dx} + \left[\frac{\beta}{1 - x^2} - \frac{m^2}{(1 - x^2)^2}\right]P = 0 \qquad (6\text{-}60)$$

We note that the points $x = \pm 1$ are regular singular points of the equation. In order to study the behavior of the solution near $x = +1$, it is convenient to make the substitution $u = 1 - x$, $U(u) = P(x)$, bringing the point to the origin of u. The resulting equation is

$$\frac{d}{du}\left[u(2 - u)\frac{dU}{du}\right] + \left[\beta - \frac{m^2}{u(2 - u)}\right]U = 0$$

When we make the substitution $U = \sum_{n=0}^{\infty} a_n u^{n+s}$ in this equation, we find that the indicial equation leads to the values $\pm m/2$ for s.

Similarly, if we investigate the point $x = -1$ by making the substitution $v = 1 + x$ and study the indicial equation at the origin of v, we find the same values, $\pm m/2$, for the index there.

We consider first the value $+m/2$, $m \geq 0$, corresponding to the regular solutions which are finite everywhere. The above considerations lead us to assume as the solution of (6-60)

$$P(x) = (1 - x)^{m/2}(1 + x)^{m/2}y(x) = (1 - x^2)^{m/2}y(x) \qquad m \geq 0 \quad (6\text{-}61)$$

where the function $y(x)$ satisfies the differential equation

$$(1 - x^2)\frac{d^2}{dx^2}y - 2(m + 1)x\frac{dy}{dx} + [\beta - m(m + 1)]y = 0 \quad (6\text{-}62)$$

which should be directly soluble by a power series. The assumption

$$y(x) = \sum_{n=0}^{\infty} c_n x^{n+s}$$

leads to the indicial equation $s(s - 1) = 0$, so that the solution can be rewritten

$$y(x) = \sum_{n \text{ even}} c_n x^n + \sum_{n \text{ odd}} c_n x^n$$

The recursion formula is

$$c_{n+2} = \frac{(n + m)(n + m + 1) - \beta}{(n + 1)(n + 2)} c_n \qquad (6\text{-}63)$$

It is readily verified that an infinite series with this relation between coefficients converges for $-1 < x < +1$ but diverges for $x = \pm 1$. A solution which converges for all x can be obtained by breaking either the even or odd series off at the term in x^j. This is done by setting the so-far arbitrary constant β equal to

$$\beta = (j + m)(j + m + 1) = l(l + 1)$$

where $\qquad l = m, m + 1, m + 2, \ldots$

or equivalently,

$$m = 0, 1, 2, \ldots, l$$

The solutions of (6-60) so obtained are designated by $P_l{}^m(x)$ and are known as the *associated Legendre functions of the first kind of degree l and order m* where l and m take on the values $l = 0, 1, 2, \ldots$ and $m = 0, 1, 2, \ldots, l$.

The second solution of (6-60) is given by

$$P(x) = P_l{}^m(x) \left\{ A + B \int \frac{dx}{(1 - x^2)[P_l{}^m(x)]^2} \right\}$$

where A and B are arbitrary constants. When they are taken as

$$A = 0 \qquad \text{and} \qquad B = 1$$

the second solution is called an *associated Legendre function of the second kind of degree l and order m* and designated by $Q_l{}^m(x)$.

The general solution of (6-60) for $m \geq 0$ is therefore

$$P(x) = d_1 P_l{}^m(x) + d_2 Q_l{}^m(x)$$
$$\Theta(\theta) = d_1 P_l{}^m(\cos \theta) + d_2 Q_l{}^m(\cos \theta) \qquad (6\text{-}64)$$

or

where d_1 and d_2 are arbitrary constants, $l = 0, 1, 2, \ldots$, and $m = 0, 1, 2, \ldots, l$. The properties of the associated Legendre functions are well known.† Only the associated Legendre function of the first kind, $P_l{}^m(\cos \theta)$, remains finite over the entire range of θ, $0 \leq \theta \leq \pi$.

---

† See, for instance, Jahnke, Emde, and Losch, *op. cit.*, and Magnus and Oberhettinger, *op. cit.*

Since $\beta = l(l + 1)$, Eq. (6-59) for $R(r)$ becomes

$$\frac{d}{dr}\left(r^2 \frac{dR}{dr}\right) - l(l + 1)R = 0 \tag{6-65}$$

When $l = 0$, the solution of (6-65) is

$$R(r) = \frac{e}{r} + f \qquad l = 0 \tag{6-66}$$

where e and f are arbitrary constants. When $l \neq 0$, the solution is

$$R(r) = g(l)r^l + g'(l)r^{-l-1} \qquad l \neq 0 \tag{6-67}$$

The solution of Laplace's equation (6-55) can now be written

$$\begin{aligned}
\phi(r,\theta,\varphi) &= [g(l)r^l + g'(l)r^{-l-1}][P_l{}^m(\cos\theta) + dQ_l{}^m(\cos\theta)] \\
&\qquad [a(m)e^{im\varphi} + a(m)e^{-im\varphi}] \qquad l \neq 0 \qquad m \neq 0 \\
&= [g(l)r^l + g'(l)r^{-l-1}][P_l(\cos\theta) + dQ_l(\cos\theta)] \qquad l \neq 0 \qquad m = 0 \\
&= \left(\frac{e}{r} + f\right)[P_0(\cos\theta) + dQ_0(\cos\theta)] \qquad l = m = 0 \tag{6-68}
\end{aligned}$$

where $P_l \equiv P_l{}^0$ and $Q_l \equiv Q_l{}^0$ are known as the *Legendre functions of degree l of the first and second kinds*, respectively.

The general solution of (6-55) is obtained by summing (6-68) over the appropriate values of l and m.

It is sometimes convenient to introduce the *normalized spherical harmonics* denoted by $Y_l{}^m(\theta,\varphi)$ and defined by the relations

$$Y_l{}^m(\theta,\varphi) = \Theta_l{}^m(\theta)\frac{e^{im\varphi}}{\sqrt{2\pi}}$$

$$\Theta_l{}^m(\theta) = (-1)^{\frac{1}{2}(m+|m|)}\sqrt{\frac{(2l+1)(l-|m|)!}{2(l+|m|)!}}\,P_l{}^{|m|}(\cos\theta)$$

$$Y_l{}^m(\theta,\varphi) = (-1)^m Y_l{}^{-m*}(\theta,\varphi)$$

where m may be positive or negative and the asterisk denotes the complex conjugate. The *modified normalized spherical harmonics* $\mathcal{Y}_l{}^m(\theta,\varphi)$ are defined by the similar relations in which $Q_l{}^{|m|}(\cos\theta)$ replaces $P_l{}^{|m|}(\cos\theta)$. In terms of these functions the solutions (6-68) become

$$\begin{aligned}
\phi(r,\theta,\varphi) &= [g(l)r^l + g'(l)r^{-l-1}][Y_l{}^m(\theta,\varphi) + d\mathcal{Y}_l{}^m(\theta,\varphi)] \qquad l \neq 0 \qquad m \neq 0 \\
&= [g(l)r^l + g'(l)r^{-l-1}][Y_l{}^0(\theta) + d\mathcal{Y}_l{}^0(\theta)] \qquad l \neq 0 \qquad m = 0 \\
&= \left(\frac{e}{r} + f\right)[Y_0{}^0(\theta) + d\mathcal{Y}_0{}^0(\theta)] \qquad l = m = 0 \tag{6-69}
\end{aligned}$$

6-7. APPLICATION OF THE SOLUTIONS OF LAPLACE'S EQUATION IN SPACE POLAR COORDINATES

As a first example consider a conducting spherical shell with center at the origin of coordinates, radius a, and charge σ per unit area. The problem is to find the potential at a point P a distance $r > a$ from the center of the shell (cf. example 1 of Sec. 2-6). Since the shell is an equipotential, one boundary condition is that

$$\phi = \text{constant} = \phi(a) \qquad \text{for } r = a \text{ and all } \theta \text{ and } \varphi \qquad (6\text{-}70)$$

The second boundary condition is that

$$\phi \to 0 \qquad \text{for } r \to \infty \text{ and all } \theta \text{ and } \varphi \qquad (6\text{-}71)$$

Of the three types of solutions (6-68) to Laplace's equation in space polar coordinates only the last can satisfy the boundary conditions. Thus

$$\phi(r,\theta,\varphi) = \left(\frac{e}{r} + f\right)[P_0(\cos\theta) + dQ_0(\cos\theta)] \qquad (6\text{-}72)$$

Since $\qquad P_0(\cos\theta) = 1 \qquad$ and $\qquad Q_0(\cos\theta) = \dfrac{1}{2}\ln\dfrac{1+\cos\theta}{1-\cos\theta}$

boundary condition (6-70) can be satisfied only if $d = 0$. Then

$$\phi(a) = \frac{e}{a} + f$$

In order to satisfy the boundary condition (6-71), f must be equal to zero. Hence $e = a\phi(a)$ and the potential is

$$\phi(r) = \frac{a\phi(a)}{r} \qquad (6\text{-}73)$$

The electric field intensity is

$$E(r) = -\frac{\partial\phi}{\partial r} = a\frac{\phi(a)}{r^2}$$

If the sphere is embedded in a dielectric of permittivity ϵ,

$$E(a) = \frac{\phi(a)}{a} = \frac{\sigma}{\epsilon} = \frac{Q}{4\pi a^2\epsilon}$$

where Q is the total charge on the spherical shell. Then (6-73) can be written

$$\phi(r) = \frac{Q}{4\pi\epsilon r}$$

As the next example consider a grounded conducting sphere of radius a in a uniform field E_0. If the origin of coordinates is taken at the center of the sphere and the x_3 axis in the direction of the uniform field, the potential at a great distance from the sphere is

$$\phi = -E_0 x_3 = -E_0 r \cos \theta$$

that is, the field at a great distance from the sphere retains its uniform character. The problem is to find the potential at any point (r,θ), $r > a$. Hence we must look for a solution of Laplace's equation in space polar coordinates which satisfies the two boundary conditions

$$\phi(r,\theta) = -E_0 r \cos \theta \qquad \text{for } r \rightarrow \infty \tag{6-74}$$
$$\phi(r,\theta) = 0 \qquad \text{for } r = a \tag{6-75}$$

Since the potential is independent of the azimuthal angle φ, the solution of Laplace's equation which applies here is either the second or third of (6-68). Since $Q_0(\cos \theta) = \frac{1}{2} \ln [(1 + \cos \theta)/(1 - \cos \theta)]$, the solution for $l = m = 0$ cannot satisfy the boundary condition (6-74). Hence the applicable solution is

$$\psi(r,\theta) - [y(l)r^l + y'(l)r^{l-1}][P_l(\cos \theta) + dQ_l(\cos \theta)] \tag{6-76}$$

In order to satisfy the r dependence of boundary condition (6-74), we must take $l = 1$. Then, since

$$P_1(\cos \theta) = \cos \theta \qquad \text{and} \qquad Q_1(\cos \theta) = \frac{1}{2} \cos \theta \ln \frac{1 + \cos \theta}{1 - \cos \theta} - 1$$

in order to satisfy the θ dependence we set $d = 0$. Consequently, the solution (6-76) reduces to

$$\phi(r,\theta) = \left(gr + \frac{g'}{r^2} \right) \cos \theta \tag{6-77}$$

Application of boundary condition (6-74) then yields $g = -E_0$, while application of (6-75) gives $g' = E_0 a^3$. Hence,

$$\phi(r,\theta) = -\left(1 - \frac{a^3}{r^3} \right) E_0 r \cos \theta \tag{6-78}$$

The components of the electric field intensity are

$$E_r = -\frac{\partial \phi}{\partial r} = \left(1 + 2\frac{a^3}{r^3} \right) E_0 \cos \theta$$
$$E_\theta = -\frac{1}{r}\frac{\partial \phi}{\partial \theta} = -\left(1 - \frac{a^3}{r^3} \right) E_0 \sin \theta \tag{6-79}$$

The charge per unit area of the surface of the sphere is

$$\sigma = \epsilon \frac{\partial \phi}{\partial r}\Big|_{r=a} = 3\epsilon E_0 \cos \theta \tag{6-80}$$

As the last example consider a sphere of radius a and permittivity ϵ_i in a uniform field E_0. The problem is to find the potential inside, ϕ_i, and outside, ϕ_o, the sphere. The boundary condition at infinity is

$$\phi_o(r,\theta) = -E_0 r \cos \theta = -E_0 x_3 \qquad \text{for } r \to \infty \tag{6-81}$$

The boundary conditions at $r = a$ are

$$\phi_i(a,\theta) = \phi_o(a,\theta) \qquad \text{or} \qquad E_{\theta i} = E_{\theta o} \tag{6-82}$$
and
$$D_{ri} = D_{ro} \tag{6-83}$$

The boundary condition at $r = 0$ is

$$\phi_i(r,\theta) \text{ remains finite as } r \to 0 \tag{6-84}$$

As in the preceding example of the conducting sphere, the outside potential must have the form

$$\phi_o(r,\theta) = \left(gr + \frac{g'}{r^2} \right) \cos \theta$$

in order to satisfy the boundary condition at infinity. Then

$$\phi_o(r,\theta) = \left(-E_0 r + \frac{g'}{r^2} \right) \cos \theta \tag{6-85}$$
and
$$E_{ro} = \left(E_0 + 2\frac{g'}{r^3} \right) \cos \theta$$
$$\tag{6-86}$$
$$E_{\theta o} = \left(-E_0 + \frac{g'}{r^3} \right) \sin \theta$$

Since there is no volume distribution of polarization charge, the potential inside the sphere also satisfies Laplace's equation. In order to satisfy the boundary conditions it also must be of the form

$$\phi_i(r,\theta) = \left(hr + \frac{h'}{r^2} \right) \cos \theta$$

The boundary condition at $r = 0$ requires that $h' = 0$. Then

$$\phi_i(r,\theta) = hr \cos \theta$$
$$E_{ri} = -h \cos \theta$$
$$E_{\theta i} = h \sin \theta$$

Application of the boundary conditions (6-82) and (6-83) then yields

$$ha \cos \theta = \left(-E_0 a + \frac{g'}{a^2}\right) \cos \theta$$

$$-\epsilon_i h \cos \theta = \epsilon_0 \left(E_0 + 2\frac{g'}{a^3}\right) \cos \theta$$

Hence

$$g' = \frac{\epsilon_i - \epsilon_0}{\epsilon_i + 2\epsilon_0} a^3 E_0$$

$$h = -\frac{3\epsilon_0}{\epsilon_i + 2\epsilon_0} E_0$$

so that

$$\phi_0(r,\theta) = -\left(1 + \frac{\epsilon_0 - \epsilon_i}{2\epsilon_0 + \epsilon_i}\frac{a^3}{r^3}\right) E_0 r \cos \theta \tag{6-87}$$

$$\phi_i(r,\theta) = -\frac{3\epsilon_0}{2\epsilon_0 + \epsilon_i} E_0 r \cos \theta \tag{6-88}$$

6-8. SOLUTION OF POISSON'S EQUATION. GREEN'S FUNCTIONS

It is easily shown that the solution of Poisson's equation

$$\nabla^2 \phi(\mathbf{r}) = -\frac{1}{\epsilon}\rho(\mathbf{r}) \tag{2-21}$$

can be expressed in terms of Green's function $G(\mathbf{r};\mathbf{r}')$, which, by definition, is the solution of

$$\nabla^2 G(\mathbf{r};\mathbf{r}') = \delta(\mathbf{r} - \mathbf{r}') \tag{6-89}$$

satisfying the same boundary conditions as specified for the potential ϕ. In (2-21), ρ denotes the density of charge and ϵ the permittivity of the medium. In (6-89), $\delta(\mathbf{r} - \mathbf{r}')$ is the Dirac delta function (cf. Sec. 1-14).

To obtain the desired expression for the potential ϕ, first multiply (6-89) by ϕ and (2-21) by G. Subtraction of the resulting equations then yields

$$\phi(\mathbf{r})\nabla^2 G(\mathbf{r};\mathbf{r}') - G(\mathbf{r};\mathbf{r}')\nabla^2\phi(r) = \phi(\mathbf{r})\delta(\mathbf{r} - \mathbf{r}') + \frac{1}{\epsilon}G(\mathbf{r};\mathbf{r}')\rho(\mathbf{r})$$

or, on interchange of $\mathbf{r}$ and $\mathbf{r}'$,

$$\phi(\mathbf{r}')\delta(\mathbf{r}' - \mathbf{r}) = -\frac{1}{\epsilon}G(\mathbf{r};\mathbf{r}')\rho(\mathbf{r}') + \phi(\mathbf{r}')\nabla'^2 G(\mathbf{r};\mathbf{r}') - G(\mathbf{r};\mathbf{r}')\nabla'^2\phi(\mathbf{r}')$$

where the prime on ∇ signifies that differentiations are with respect to the primed coordinates, and we have used the symmetry property of Green's function. Next, integrate this relation over all $\mathbf{r}'$ within and on the surface S' which encloses all charge. Then, because of the property (1-55) of the delta function,

$$\phi(\mathbf{r}) = -\frac{1}{\epsilon} \int G(\mathbf{r};\mathbf{r}')\rho(\mathbf{r}') \, d\mathbf{r}' + \int [\phi(\mathbf{r}')\nabla'^2 G(\mathbf{r};\mathbf{r}') - G(\mathbf{r};\mathbf{r}')\nabla'^2\phi(\mathbf{r}')] \, d\mathbf{r}'$$

$$(6\text{-}90)$$

if $\mathbf{r}$ is within or on S'.   Finally, use Green's theorem (1-72) to transform the second term in the right-hand member of (6-90):

$$\phi(\mathbf{r}) = -\frac{1}{\epsilon} \int G(\mathbf{r};\mathbf{r}')\rho(\mathbf{r}') \, d\mathbf{r}' + \int [\phi(\mathbf{r}')\nabla' G(\mathbf{r};\mathbf{r}') - G(\mathbf{r};\mathbf{r}')\nabla'\phi(\mathbf{r}')] \cdot d\mathbf{S}'$$

$$(6\text{-}91)$$

or

$$\phi(\mathbf{r}) = -\frac{1}{\epsilon} \int G(\mathbf{r};\mathbf{r}')\rho(\mathbf{r}') \, d\mathbf{r}'$$

$$+ \int \left[\phi(\mathbf{r}') \frac{\partial}{\partial n'} G(\mathbf{r};\mathbf{r}') - G(\mathbf{r};\mathbf{r}') \frac{\partial}{\partial n'} \phi(\mathbf{r}') \right] dS' \quad (6\text{-}91a)$$

where $\mathbf{n}'$ is the outward drawn normal to dS'.   This is the desired expression for the solution of Poisson's equation.

There are two cases of special interest:

1. If on the surface S' the potential ϕ vanishes or $\partial\phi/\partial n'$ vanishes or ϕ equals a function $f(\mathbf{r}')$ times $\partial\phi/\partial n'$, then because Green's function satisfies the same boundary conditions as the potential, (6-91a) reduces to

$$\phi(\mathbf{r}) = -\frac{1}{\epsilon} \int G(\mathbf{r};\mathbf{r}')\rho(\mathbf{r}') \, d\mathbf{r}' \qquad (6\text{-}92)$$

2. If the surface S' encloses no charge, then $\nabla^2\phi = 0$ and (6-91a) reduces to

$$\phi(\mathbf{r}) = \int \left[\phi(\mathbf{r}') \frac{\partial}{\partial n'} G(\mathbf{r};\mathbf{r}') - G(\mathbf{r};\mathbf{r}') \frac{\partial}{\partial n'} \phi(\mathbf{r}') \right] dS' \qquad (6\text{-}93)$$

Let us consider first those problems in which the potential ϕ is a function of three variables.   Then $\rho(\mathbf{r})$ in (2-21) represents the charge per unit volume at the point specified by the position vector $\mathbf{r}$.   If the medium is unbounded, the Green's function is (cf. Sec. 1-14)

$$G(\mathbf{r};\mathbf{r}') = -\frac{1}{4\pi} \frac{1}{|\mathbf{r} - \mathbf{r}'|} \qquad (6\text{-}94)$$

namely, *the potential at a field point $\mathbf{r}$ due to a point charge $-\epsilon$ located at the point $\mathbf{r}'$.*   In a cartesian coordinate system, (6-94) takes the form

$$G(x_1,x_2,x_3;x_1',x_2',x_3') = -\frac{1}{4\pi} [(x_1 - x_1')^2 + (x_2 - x_2')^2 + (x_3 - x_3')^2]^{-\frac{1}{2}}$$

$$(6\text{-}94a)$$

where (x_1, x_2, x_3) and (x_1', x_2', x_3') are, respectively, the coordinates of the field and source points.   In the case of space polar coordinates, (6-94) becomes

$$G(r, \theta, \varphi; r', \theta', \varphi') = -\frac{1}{4\pi} (r^2 + r'^2 - 2rr' \cos \alpha)^{-\frac{1}{2}} \qquad (6\text{-}94b)$$

where (r, θ, φ) and (r', θ', φ') are, respectively, the coordinates of the field and source points and

$$\cos \alpha = \cos \theta \cos \theta' + \sin \theta \sin \theta' \cos (\varphi - \varphi') \qquad (6\text{-}95)$$

where α is the angle between the vectors $\mathbf{r}$ and $\mathbf{r}'$.

If the medium is bounded, the Green's function can be obtained by direct solution of (6-89) subject to the appropriate boundary conditions. However, the fact that the Green's function is the potential at a field point $\mathbf{r}$ due to a point charge $-\epsilon$ located at the point $\mathbf{r}'$ permits one to obtain the Green's function by other methods, such as the method of images or the method of conformal representation.   As examples consider the following problems:

1. A dielectric of permittivity ϵ fills the space on both sides of a grounded conducting plane of infinite extent.   Let $\rho(\mathbf{r})$ denote the density of charge in the dielectric.   Find the potential at any point in the dielectric.

From the results of Sec. 3-2 Green's function is

$$G(\mathbf{r}; \mathbf{r}') = -\frac{1}{4\pi} \left(\frac{1}{R} - \frac{1}{R'} \right) \qquad (6\text{-}96)$$

where R and R' are, respectively, the distances of the field point from the charge $-\epsilon$ and its image charge $+\epsilon$.   If the conducting plane is taken at $x_1 = 0$ and (x_1', x_2', x_3'), $(-x_1', x_2', x_3')$, and (x_1, x_2, x_3) denote, respectively, the coordinates of the charge $-\epsilon$, its image charge $+\epsilon$, and the field point, (6-96) becomes

$$G(x_1, x_2, x_3; x_1', x_2', x_3') = -\frac{1}{4\pi} \{ [(x_1 - x_1')^2 + (x_2 - x_2')^2 + (x_3 - x_3')^2]^{-\frac{1}{2}}$$
$$- [(x_1 + x_1')^2 + (x_2 - x_2')^2 + (x_2 - x_3')^2]^{-\frac{1}{2}} \} \quad (6\text{-}96a)$$

and, from (6-92), the solution of Poisson's equation is

$$\phi(x_1, x_2, x_3) = \frac{1}{4\pi\epsilon} \int\!\!\!\int\!\!\!\int_{-\infty}^{+\infty} G(x_1, x_2, x_3; x_1', x_2', x_3') \rho(x_1', x_2', x_3') \, dx_1' \, dx_2' \, dx_3'$$

2. The potential ϕ is given over the surface of a plane of infinite extent which is surrounded by a dielectric of permittivity ϵ.   The density of

charge is zero everywhere in the dielectric. Find the potential at any point in the dielectric.

Take the plane to be at $x_1' = 0$, let the potential on the plane be specified by $f(x_2',x_3')$, and let (x_1,x_2,x_3) be the coordinates of the field point. Then, according to (6-93), the potential is given by

$$\phi(x_1,x_2,x_3) = \int\int_{-\infty}^{+\infty} \left[f(x_2',x_3') \frac{\partial G}{\partial n'} - G \frac{\partial}{\partial n'} f(x_2',x_3') \right] dx_2'\, dx_3'$$

Since $\partial/\partial n' = -\partial/\partial x_1'$ and f is independent of x_1', this expression reduces to

$$\phi(x_1,x_2,x_3) = - \int\int_{-\infty}^{+\infty} f(x_2',x_3') \frac{\partial G}{\partial x_1'} dx_2'\, dx_3'$$

From (6-96a),

$$\frac{\partial G}{\partial x_1'}\bigg|_{x_1'=0} = -\frac{1}{2\pi} x_1[x_1^2 + (x_2 - x_2')^2 + (x_3 - x_3')^2]^{-\frac{3}{2}}$$

Hence $$\phi(x_1,x_2,x_3) = \frac{1}{2\pi} \int\int_{-\infty}^{+\infty} \frac{x_1 f(x_2',x_3')\, dx_2'\, dx_3'}{[x_1^2 + (x_2 - x_2')^2 + (x_3 - x_3')^2]^{\frac{3}{2}}}$$

3. Let $\rho(\mathbf{r})$ denote the charge density in a dielectric of permittivity ϵ which surrounds a grounded conducting sphere of radius a. Find the potential at a field point in the dielectric.

If the center of the sphere is taken as the origin of coordinates and (r',θ',φ'), $(a^2/r',\theta',\varphi')$, and (r,θ,φ) denote, respectively, the coordinates of the charge $-\epsilon$, its image charge $a\epsilon/r'$, and the field point, the results of Sec. 3-3 give

$$G = -\frac{1}{4\pi} \left[(r^2 + r'^2 - 2rr' \cos\alpha)^{-\frac{1}{2}} - \frac{a}{r'} \left(r^2 + \frac{a^4}{r'^2} - 2r\frac{a^2}{r'} \cos\alpha \right)^{-\frac{1}{2}} \right]$$
$$(6\text{-}97)$$

where $\cos\alpha$ is given by (6-95), as the expression for Green's function. The solution of Poisson's equation is then

$$\phi(r,\theta,\varphi) = \frac{1}{4\pi\epsilon} \int_a^\infty \int_0^\pi \int_0^{2\pi} G\rho(r',\theta',\varphi')r'^2 \sin\theta'\, dr'\, d\theta'\, d\varphi'$$

4. Let the potential ϕ be given over the surface of a sphere of radius a which is surrounded by a dielectric of permittivity ϵ. The density of charge in the dielectric is everywhere zero. Find the potential at any point in the dielectric.

Take the center of the sphere as origin of coordinates, let the potential on the surface of the sphere be denoted by $f(a,\theta',\varphi')$, and let (r,θ,φ) be the coordinates of the field point. Then, according to (6-93), the potential is given by

$$\phi(r,\theta,\varphi) = \int_0^\pi \int_0^{2\pi} \left[f(a,\theta',\varphi') \frac{\partial G}{\partial n'} - G \frac{\partial}{\partial n'} f(a,\theta',\varphi') \right] a^2 \sin\theta' \, d\theta' \, d\varphi'$$

Since $\partial/\partial n' = -\partial/\partial r'$ and f is independent of r', this expression reduces to

$$\phi(r,\theta,\varphi) = - \int_0^\pi \int_0^{2\pi} f(a,\theta',\varphi') \frac{\partial G}{\partial r'} a^2 \sin\theta' \, d\theta' \, d\varphi'$$

From (6-97),

$$\frac{\partial G}{\partial r'}\bigg|_{r'=a} = \frac{1}{4\pi} \frac{a^2 - r^2}{a(r^2 + a^2 - 2ra\cos\alpha)^{3/2}}$$

Hence $$\phi(r,\theta,\varphi) = \frac{a(r^2 - a^2)}{4\pi} \int_0^\pi \int_0^{2\pi} \frac{f(a,\theta',\varphi') \sin\theta' \, d\theta' \, d\varphi'}{(r^2 + a^2 - 2ra\cos\alpha)^{3/2}}$$

Let us now consider problems in which the potential ϕ and the charge density ρ are functions of only two variables. If the medium is unbounded, the Green's function is given by [cf. Eqs. (2-24) and (3-21)]

$$G(\mathbf{r};\mathbf{r}') = \frac{1}{2\pi} \ln |\mathbf{r} - \mathbf{r}'| \tag{6-98}$$

namely, the potential at a field point $\mathbf{r}$ due to a charge $-\epsilon$ per unit length located at the point $\mathbf{r}'$. In a cartesian coordinate system, (6-98) takes the form

$$G(x_1,x_2;x_1',x_2') = \frac{1}{4\pi} \ln [(x_1 - x_1')^2 + (x_2 - x_2')^2] \tag{6-98a}$$

where (x_1,x_2) and (x_1',x_2') are, respectively, the coordinates of the field and source points. In the case of plane polar coordinates, (6-98) becomes

$$G(r,\theta;r',\theta') = \frac{1}{4\pi} \ln [r^2 + r'^2 - 2rr' \cos(\theta - \theta')] \tag{6-98b}$$

where (r,θ) and (r',θ') are, respectively, the coordinates of the field and source points.

As examples of the use of Green's functions in two-dimensional problems, consider the following:

1. Let $\rho(\mathbf{r})$ denote the charge density in a dielectric of permittivity ϵ which surrounds a grounded conducting cylinder of radius a. Find the potential at a field point in the dielectric.

Take the origin of coordinates on the axis of the cylinder, and let (r',θ') and (r,θ) denote, respectively, the coordinates of the charge $-\epsilon$ per unit length and the field point. The Green's function is [cf. Sec. 3-4 and Eq. (3-24)]

$$G(r,\theta;r',\theta') = \frac{1}{4\pi} \ln \frac{r^2 + r'^2 - 2rr' \cos (\theta - \theta')}{r^2 + a^4/r'^2 - 2r(a^2/r') \cos (\theta - \theta')}$$
$$- \frac{1}{4\pi} \ln \frac{a^2 + r'^2 - 2ar' \cos (\theta - \theta')}{a^2 + a^4/r'^2 - 2(a^3/r') \cos (\theta - \theta')}$$
$$= \frac{1}{4\pi} \ln \frac{a^2[r^2 + r'^2 - 2rr' \cos (\theta - \theta')]}{r'^2 r^2 + a^4 - 2rr'a^2 \cos (\theta - \theta')} \qquad (6\text{-}99)$$

and the solution to Poisson's equation is

$$\phi(r,\theta) = -\frac{1}{\epsilon} \int_a^\infty \int_0^{2\pi} G(r,\theta;r',\theta')\rho(r',\theta')r'\,dr'\,d\theta'$$

2. Let the potential ϕ be given over the surface of a cylinder of radius a which is surrounded by a dielectric of permittivity ϵ. The density of charge in the dielectric is everywhere zero. If the potential on the cylinder is $f(a,\theta')$, find the potential on any line (r,θ) in the dielectric.

According to (6-93), the potential is given by

$$\phi(r,\theta) = \int_0^{2\pi} \left[f(a,\theta') \frac{\partial G}{\partial n'} - G \frac{\partial}{\partial n'} f(a,\theta') \right] a\,d\theta'$$
$$= - \int_0^{2\pi} f(a,\theta') \frac{\partial G}{\partial r'} a\,d\theta'$$

since $\partial/\partial n' = -\partial/\partial r'$ and f is independent of r'. From (6-99),

$$\frac{\partial G}{\partial r'}\bigg|_{r'=a} = \frac{1}{2\pi a} \frac{a^2 - r^2}{r^2 + a^2 - 2ra \cos (\theta - \theta')}$$

Hence
$$\phi(r,\theta) = \frac{1}{2\pi} \int_0^{2\pi} \frac{f(a,\theta')(r^2 - a^2)\,d\theta'}{r^2 + a^2 - 2ra \cos (\theta - \theta')}$$

Finally, let us consider the case when the potential ϕ and the charge density ρ are functions of but a single variable, say x_1. If the medium is unbounded, the Green's function is [cf. Eqs. (2-26) and (6-17)]

$$G(x_1;x_1') = \tfrac{1}{2}|x_1 - x_1'| \qquad (6\text{-}100)$$

namely, the potential at a field point x_1 due to a charge $-\epsilon$ per unit area on the plane at x_1'.

The Green's function is of little practical use in one-dimensional potential problems. We consider one (trivial) example:

A grounded conducting plane of infinite extent is located at $x_1 = 0$ and is surrounded by a dielectric of permittivity ϵ. Let $\rho(x_1)$ denote the charge distribution in the region to the right of the plane. Find the potential at any point x_1 in this region.

Let x_1' denote the location of the charge $-\epsilon$ and $-x_1'$ the location of the image charge ϵ. Then the Green's function is

$$G(x_1;x_1') = \tfrac{1}{2}|x_1 - x_1'| - \tfrac{1}{2}|x_1 + x_1'| \qquad (6\text{-}101)$$

and the solution to Poisson's equation is

$$\phi(x_1) = -\frac{1}{\epsilon} \int_0^\infty G(x_1;x_1')\rho(x_1')\, dx_1' \qquad (6\text{-}102)$$

An interesting case is that when $\rho(x_1') = -\sigma\delta(x_1' - d)$, which corresponds to a plane at $x_1 = d$ with charge $-\sigma$ per unit area. Then (6-102) becomes

$$\phi(x_1) = \frac{\sigma}{\epsilon} G(x_1;d) = \frac{\sigma}{2\epsilon}\,(|x_1 - d| - |x_1 + d|)$$

or

$$\phi(x_1) = -\frac{\sigma}{\epsilon} x_1 \qquad \text{for } d \geq x_1$$

$$= -\frac{\sigma}{\epsilon} d \qquad \text{for } d < x_1$$

so that

$$E(x_1) = \frac{\sigma}{\epsilon} \qquad \text{for } d \geq x_1$$

$$= 0 \qquad \text{for } d < x_1$$

Thus, the electric field at any point between two infinite plane conductors is $1/\epsilon$ times the charge per unit area and is zero elsewhere.

Thus far we have seen how Green's functions can be obtained by the use of the method of images or the method of conformal representation. In many cases it is convenient to obtain the Green's function by direct solution of (6-89). We demonstrate this *direct method* for determining Green's functions in the following illustrative examples.

1. Find the Green's function satisfying the equation

$$\frac{d^2G}{dx_1^2} = \delta(x_1 - x_1') \qquad (6\text{-}103)$$

and the boundary conditions $G = 0$ when $x_1 = 0$ and G remains bounded when x_1 approaches infinity. This Green's function is the potential due to a surface charge $-\epsilon$ per unit area on a plane of infinite extent situated at $x_1 = x_1'$ in a dielectric of permittivity ϵ when a grounded conducting plane of infinite extent is located at $x_1 = 0$.

When $x_1 \neq x_1'$, (6-103) reduces to

$$\frac{d^2G}{dx_1^2} = 0 \qquad (6\text{-}104)$$

which has for solution

$$G = Ax_1 + B \qquad (6\text{-}105)$$

where A and B are constants to be determined.

The conditions that the Green's function vanish when $x_1 = 0$ and remain finite when x_1 approaches infinity cannot be satisfied simultaneously by either of the terms in (6-105). The condition that $G = 0$ when $x_1 = 0$ can be satisfied by taking $B = 0$, while the condition that G remain bounded as x_1 approaches infinity can be satisfied by setting $A = 0$. Consequently, we write

$$\begin{aligned} G &= Ax_1 & \text{for } x_1 < x_1' \\ &= B & \text{for } x_1 > x_1' \end{aligned}$$

The condition that G be a single-valued function requires that $Ax_1' = B$. Hence

$$\begin{aligned} G &= Ax_1 & \text{for } x_1 \leq x_1' \\ &= Ax_1' & \text{for } x_1 \geq x_1' \end{aligned} \qquad (6\text{-}106)$$

It is convenient to introduce the *Heaviside unit function* $\eta(x - x')$, which will enable us to combine Eqs. (6-106) into a single relation. This function is defined by

$$\begin{aligned} \eta(x - x') &= 1 & \text{for } x > x' \\ &= 0 & \text{for } x < x' \end{aligned} \qquad (6\text{-}107)$$

It is related to the Dirac delta function $\delta(x - x')$ by

$$\delta(x - x') = \frac{d}{dx}\,\eta(x - x') \qquad (6\text{-}108)$$

The verification of this relation proceeds as follows: For any $f(x)$ such that $\int_{-\infty}^{+\infty} f(x)\,dx$ converges absolutely

$$\int_{-\infty}^{+\infty} f(x')\eta(x - x')\,dx' = \int_{-\infty}^{x} f(x')\,dx'$$

Hence
$$f(x) = \frac{d}{dx} \int_{-\infty}^{+\infty} f(x')\eta(x - x')\,dx'$$

$$= \int_{-\infty}^{+\infty} f(x')\,\frac{d}{dx}\,\eta(x - x')\,dx'$$

which verifies (6-108).

With the use of the Heaviside unit function (6-106) becomes

$$G = A[x_1\eta(x_1' - x_1) + x_1'\eta(x_1 - x_1')] \qquad (6\text{-}106a)$$

Then
$$\frac{dG}{dx_1} = A[\eta(x_1' - x_1) - (x_1 - x_1')\delta(x_1 - x_1')]$$

$$= A\eta(x_1' - x_1)$$

$$\frac{d^2G}{dx_1^2} = -A\delta(x_1 - x_1')$$

Comparison of this result with (6-103) shows that $A = -1$. Thus, the Green's function is completely determined and (6-106a) becomes

$$G = -[x_1\eta(x_1' - x_1) + x_1'\eta(x_1 - x_1')]$$

2. Find the Green's function satisfying the equation

$$\frac{\partial^2 G}{\partial x_1^2} + \frac{\partial^2 G}{\partial x_2^2} = \delta(x_1 - x_1')\delta(x_2 - x_2') \qquad (6\text{-}109)$$

and the boundary conditions $G = 0$ when $x_1 = 0$, $x_1 = a$, and $x_2 = 0$ and G remains bounded when x_2 approaches infinity. This Green's function is the potential due to a line source of density $-\epsilon$ per unit length located at (x_1', x_2') inside a rectangular trough which is formed by the orthogonal intersection of three grounded conducting planes $x_1 = 0$, $x_1 = a$, and $x_2 = 0$.

For $x_1 \neq x_1'$ and $x_2 \neq x_2'$, (6-109) reduces to Laplace's equation

$$\frac{\partial^2 G}{\partial x_1^2} + \frac{\partial^2 G}{\partial x_2^2} = 0 \qquad (6\text{-}110)$$

We solve by the method of separation of variables. Substitution of

$$G = X_1(x_1)X_2(x_2) \qquad (6\text{-}111)$$

into (6-110) leads to

$$\frac{1}{X_1}\frac{d^2X_1}{dx_1^2} = -\frac{1}{X_2}\frac{d^2X_2}{dx_2^2} = \text{constant}$$

Depending on the choice for the sign of this separation constant, one can obtain two different expressions for the (same) Green's function. We first take the constant to be negative, say $-b^2$. Then

$$X_1 = A\sin bx_1 + B\cos bx_1$$
$$X_2 = Ce^{bx_2} + De^{-bx_2}$$

where A, B, C, and D are constants to be determined.

The condition that $G = 0$ when $x_1 = 0$ and $x_1 = a$ can be satisfied by setting $B = 0$ and $b = n\pi/a$, where $n = 1, 2, 3, \ldots$. Hence

$$X_{1n} = A_n \sin \frac{n\pi x_1}{a} \tag{6-112}$$

and
$$X_{2n} = C_n e^{n\pi x_2/a} + D_n e^{-n\pi x_2/a}$$

The conditions that $G = 0$ when $x_2 = 0$ and that G remain bounded as x_2 approaches infinity cannot be satisfied simultaneously by either of the terms in X_{2n}. Consequently, we write

$$
\begin{aligned}
X_{2n} &= 2C_n \sinh \frac{n\pi x_2}{a} & x_2 < x_2' \\
&= D_n e^{-n\pi x_2/a} & x_2 > x_2'
\end{aligned} \tag{6-113}
$$

The single-valuedness condition at $x_2 = x_2'$ requires that

$$2C_n \sinh \frac{n\pi x_2'}{a} = D_n e^{-n\pi x_2'/a}$$

Hence
$$2C_n = E_n e^{-n\pi x_2'/a}$$

$$D_n = E_n \sinh \frac{n\pi x_2'}{a}$$

where E_n is an undetermined constant. Equations (6-113) then become

$$
\begin{aligned}
X_{2n} &= E_n e^{-n\pi x_2'/a} \sinh \frac{n\pi x_2}{a} & x_2 \leq x_2' \\
&= E_n e^{-n\pi x_2/a} \sinh \frac{n\pi x_2'}{a} & x_2 \geq x_2'
\end{aligned}
$$

or, using the Heaviside unit function,

$$X_{2n} = E_n \left[e^{-n\pi x_2'/a} \sinh \frac{n\pi x_2}{a} \, \eta(x_2' - x_2) \right.$$
$$\left. + e^{-n\pi x_2/a} \sinh \frac{n\pi x_2'}{a} \, \eta(x_2 - x_2') \right] \tag{6-114}$$

Then
$$G = \sum_{n=0}^{\infty} G_n = \sum_{n=0}^{\infty} X_{1n} X_{2n}$$

where

$$G_n = X_{1n} X_{2n} = F_n \sin \frac{n\pi x_1}{a} \left[e^{-n\pi x_2'/a} \sinh \frac{n\pi x_2}{a} \, \eta(x_2' - x_2) \right.$$
$$\left. + e^{-n\pi x_2/a} \sinh \frac{n\pi x_2'}{a} \, \eta(x_2 - x_2') \right] \tag{6-115}$$

in which $F_n = A_n E_n$.

To determine the F_n we substitute for G in (6-109).   Thus

$$\frac{\partial^2 G}{\partial x_1{}^2} = -\sum_n \left(\frac{n\pi}{a}\right)^2 G_n$$

$$\frac{\partial G}{\partial x_2} = \sum_n \frac{n\pi}{a} F_n \sin \frac{n\pi x_1}{a} \left[e^{-n\pi x_2'/a} \cosh \frac{n\pi x_2}{a} \eta(x_2' - x_2) \right.$$

$$\left. - \sinh \frac{n\pi x_2'}{a} e^{-n\pi x_2/a} \eta(x_2 - x_2') \right]$$

$$\frac{\partial^2 G}{\partial x_2{}^2} = \sum_n \left\{ \left(\frac{n\pi}{a}\right)^2 G_n - \frac{n\pi}{a} F_n \sin \frac{n\pi x_1}{a} \left[e^{-n\pi x_2'/a} \cosh \frac{n\pi x_2}{a} \right.\right.$$

$$\left.\left. + \sinh \frac{n\pi x_2'}{a} e^{-n\pi x_2/a} \right] \delta(x_2 - x_2') \right\}$$

and (6-109) becomes

$$-\sum_n \frac{n\pi}{a} F_n \sin \frac{n\pi x_1}{a} \left[e^{-n\pi x_2'/a} \cosh \frac{n\pi x_2}{a} + \sinh (n\pi x_2') e^{-n\pi x_2/a} \right] \delta(x_2 - x_2')$$

$$= \delta(x_1 - x_1')\delta(x_2 - x_2')$$

Multiply both sides of this equation by $\sin (m\pi x_1/a)$, and integrate from $x_1 = 0$ to $x_1 = a$.   Since

$$\int_0^a \sin \frac{n\pi x}{a} \sin \frac{m\pi x}{a} dx = 0 \qquad \text{if } n \neq m$$

$$= \frac{a}{2} \qquad \text{if } n = m$$

there results

$$-\frac{m\pi F_m}{2} \left(e^{-m\pi x_2'/a} \cosh \frac{m\pi x_2}{a} + \sinh \frac{m\pi x_2'}{a} e^{-m\pi x_2/a} \right) \delta(x_2 - x_2')$$

$$= \sin \frac{m\pi x_1'}{a} \delta(x_2 - x_2')$$

Next integrate both sides of this equation over all values of x_2 to obtain

$$F_m = -\frac{2}{m\pi} \sin \frac{m\pi x_1'}{a}$$

This completely determines Green's function.

Let us now find the form of the solution when the separation constant in the equation immediately following (6-111) is taken as positive, say k^2. Then

$$X_1 = Ae^{kx_1} + Be^{-kx_1}$$
$$X_2 = C \sin kx_2 + D \cos kx_2$$

The conditions that $G = 0$ when $x_2 = 0$ and that G remains finite as x_2 approaches infinity can be satisfied by taking $D = 0$ and k as a continuous variable with the range $0 < k < \infty$. Then

$$X_2(x_2,k) = C(k) \sin kx_2 \qquad (6\text{-}116)$$

The conditions that $G = 0$ when $x_1 = 0$ and $x_1 = a$ cannot be satisfied simultaneously by either of the terms in X_1. Hence we write

$$
\begin{aligned}
X_1(x_1,k) &= 2A(k) \sinh kx_1 && \text{for } x_1 < x_1' \\
&= -2B(k)e^{-ka} \sinh k(x_1 - a) && \text{for } x_1 > x_1'
\end{aligned}
$$

Because of the single-valuedness condition at $x_1 = x_1'$, these relations can be written

$$
\begin{aligned}
X_1(x_1,k) &= E(k) \sinh k(x_1' - a) \sinh kx_1 && \text{for } x_1 \le x_1' \\
&= E(k) \sinh kx_1' \sinh k(x_1 - a) && \text{for } x_1 \ge x_1'
\end{aligned}
$$

or, using the Heaviside unit function,

$$
\begin{aligned}
X_1(x_1,k) = E(k)[&\sinh k(x_1' - a) \sinh kx_1 \eta(x_1' - x_1) \\
&+ \sinh kx_1' \sinh k(x_1 - a)\eta(x_1 - x_1')] \quad (6\text{-}117)
\end{aligned}
$$

Then
$$G = \int_0^\infty G(k)\, dk = \int_0^\infty X_1(x_1,k)X_2(x_2,k)\, dk$$

where

$$
\begin{aligned}
G(k) &= X_1(x_1,k)X_2(x_2,k) \\
&= F(k) \sin kx_2[\sinh k(x_1' - a) \sinh kx_1\eta(x_1' - x_1) \\
&\qquad\qquad + \sinh kx_1' \sinh k(x_1 - a)\eta(x_1 - x_1')] \quad (6\text{-}118)
\end{aligned}
$$

in which $F(k) = C(k)E(k)$.

To determine the $F(k)$ we substitute for G in (6-109), obtaining

$$
\begin{aligned}
\int_0^\infty kF(k) \sin kx_2[&\sinh kx_1' \cosh k(x_1 - a) \\
&- \sinh k(x_1' - a) \cos kx_1]\delta(x_1 - x_1')\, dk = \delta(x_1 - x_1')\delta(x_2 - x_2')
\end{aligned}
$$

Multiplication of both sides of this equation by $\sin lx_2$ followed by integration over x_2 from zero to infinity then yields

$$
\begin{aligned}
\int_0^\infty \frac{\pi k}{2} F(k)\delta(k - l)[&\sinh kx_1' \cosh k(x_1 - a) \\
&- \sinh k(x_1' - a) \cosh kx_1]\delta(x_1 - x_1')\, dk = \sin lx_2'\delta(x_1 - x_1')
\end{aligned}
$$

since
$$\frac{2}{\pi} \int_0^\infty \sin kx \sin lx = \delta(k - l)$$

Integration over k then gives

$$\frac{\pi l}{2} F(l)[\sinh lx_1' \cosh l(x_1 - a) - \sinh l(x_1' - a) \cosh lx_1]\delta(x_1 - x_1')$$
$$= \sin lx_2'\delta(x_1 - x_1')$$

Finally, integration over x_1 yields

$$F(l) = \frac{2}{\pi l} \frac{\sin lx_2'}{\sinh la}$$

This completely determines the Green's function.

Three-dimensional problems are solved in the same manner.

EXERCISES

6-1. Two infinite plane conductors are separated by a distance d. The first is at potential ϕ_1; the second at potential ϕ_2. Find the potential and field intensity at any point between the conductors.

6-2. Three conducting planes intersect orthogonally to form a rectangular trough of width $2a$. Let the planes be grounded and be represented by $x_1 = \pm a$ and $x_2 = 0$. Find the potential and field intensity at a field point (x_1, x_2) where $-a < x_1 < +a$ and $0 < x_2 < +\infty$.

6-3. Consider two concentric spherical shells. Let the first be of radius r_a and at potential ϕ_a. Let the second be of radius $r_b > r_a$ and at potential ϕ_b. The region between the shells is filled with dielectric of permittivity ϵ. Find the potential and field intensity at any point in this region.

6-4. Consider two coaxial cylinders. Let the first be of radius r_a and at potential ϕ_a. Let the second be of radius $r_b > r_a$ and at potential ϕ_b. The region between the cylinders is filled with a dielectric of permittivity ϵ. Find the potential and field intensity at any point in this region.

6-5. A conducting sphere of radius R with charge Q is placed in a uniform field E_0. Find the potential and field intensity at any point outside the sphere.

6-6. An infinite conducting plane with a hemispherical boss of radius a is at potential ϕ_o. Find the potential and field intensity at any point in the region on the boss side of the plane. Find the charge density on the boss and the plane.

6-7. An infinite plane with a cylindrical ridge of radius a is at potential ϕ_o. Find the potential and field intensity at any point in the region on the ridge side of the plane. Find the charge density on the ridge and the plane.

6-8. A dielectric of permittivity ϵ is placed in a uniform field of intensity $\mathbf{E}$. Show that the field intensity inside a spherical cavity in the dielectric is $[3\epsilon/(2\epsilon + \epsilon_0)] \mathbf{E}$.

6-9. A dielectric of permittivity ϵ is placed in a uniform field of intensity $\mathbf{E}$. A cylindrical cavity of radius a with its axis perpendicular to $\mathbf{E}$ is cut out of the dielectric. Verify that the electric field intensity inside the cavity is $[2\epsilon/(\epsilon + \epsilon_0)] \mathbf{E}$.

6-10. Given the potential over the surface of a sphere of radius a, find the potential at any interior point. Take the center of the sphere as origin of coordinates, and let $f(a, \theta', \varphi')$ denote the potential on the surface of the sphere.

6-11. Use the answer to Exercise 6-10 to show that the mean value of a potential function over a spherical surface is equal to its value at the center.

6-12. Given the potential over the surface of a cylinder of radius a, find the potential at any interior point. Take the origin of coordinates on the axis of the cylinder, and let $f(a, \theta')$ denote the potential on the surface of the cylinder.

6-13. Show that Green's function (6-94b) can be written

$$G = -\frac{1}{4\pi r} \sum_{l=0}^{\infty} \left(\frac{r'}{r}\right)^l P_l(\cos\alpha) \qquad r > r'$$

$$= -\frac{1}{4\pi r'} \sum_{l=0}^{\infty} \left(\frac{r}{r'}\right)^l P_l(\cos\alpha) \qquad r < r'$$

where P_l denotes the Legendre function of degree l. Then use the addition theorem for spherical harmonics† to show that

$$G = -\frac{1}{r} \sum_{l=0}^{\infty} \sum_{m=-l}^{+l} \frac{1}{2l+1} \left(\frac{r'}{r}\right)^l \overline{Y_l^m(\theta',\varphi')} Y_l^m(\theta,\varphi) \qquad r > r'$$

$$= -\frac{1}{r'} \sum_{l=0}^{\infty} \sum_{m=-l}^{+l} \frac{1}{2l+1} \left(\frac{r}{r'}\right)^l \overline{Y_l^m(\theta',\varphi')} Y_l^m(\theta,\varphi) \qquad r < r'$$

6-14. Find by the direct method the Green's function which satisfies

$$\frac{\partial^2 G}{\partial r^2} + \frac{1}{r}\frac{\partial G}{\partial r} + \frac{1}{r^2}\frac{\partial^2 G}{\partial \theta^2} = \frac{1}{r}\delta(r-r')\delta(\theta-\theta')$$

and the boundary conditions that $G = 0$ when $\theta = 0$ and $\theta = \alpha$ and that G goes to zero as r approaches infinity. This Green's function is the potential at a field point (r,θ) due to a line charge $-\epsilon$ per unit length situated at (r',θ'), both between two intersecting grounded planes of infinite extent located at $\theta = 0$ and $\theta = \alpha$.

6-15. Find by the direct method the Green's function which satisfies

$$\frac{\partial^2 G}{\partial x_1^2} + \frac{\partial^2 G}{\partial x_2^2} = \delta(x_1 - x_1')\delta(x_2 - x_2')$$

and the boundary conditions $G = 0$ when $x_2 = 0$, $x_2 = a$ and $x_1 = \pm\infty$. This Green's function is the potential at a field point (x_1,x_2) due to a line charge $-\epsilon$ per unit length situated at (x_1',x_2'), both between two parallel grounded planes of infinite extent located at $x_2 = 0$ and $x_2 = a$.

REFERENCES

Goertzel, G., and N. Tralli: "Some Mathematical Methods of Physics," chaps. 10 and 11 and Appendix 2C, McGraw-Hill Book Company, Inc., New York, 1960.

Jahnke, E., F. Emde, and F. Losch: "Tables of Higher Functions," 6th ed., chaps. 8 and 9, McGraw-Hill Book Company, Inc., New York, 1960.

Jeffreys, H., and B. S. Jeffreys: "Methods of Mathematical Physics," 3d ed., chaps. 6 and 18, Cambridge University Press, London, 1956.

Magnus, W., and F. Oberhettinger: "Formulas and Theorems for the Special Functions of Mathematical Physics," chaps. 3 and 4, Chelsea Publishing Company, New York, 1949.

† See, for instance, G. Goertzel and N. Tralli, "Some Mathematical Methods of Physics," p. 161, McGraw-Hill Book Company, Inc., 1960.

Margenau, H., and G. M. Murphy: "The Mathematics of Physics and Chemistry," 2d ed., chap. 7, D. Van Nostrand Company, Inc., Princeton, N.J., 1956.

Morse, P. M., and H. Feshback: "Methods of Theoretical Physics," chap. 10, McGraw-Hill Book Company, Inc., New York, 1953.

Panofsky, W. K. H., and M. Phillips: "Classical Electricity and Magnetism," chaps. 4 and 5, Addison-Wesley Publishing Company, Inc., Cambridge, Mass., 1955.

Smythe, W. R.: "Static and Dynamic Electricity," 2d ed., chaps. 4 and 5, McGraw-Hill Book Company, Inc., New York, 1950.

Sommerfeld, A.: "Partial Differential Equations in Physics," Academic Press, Inc., New York, 1949.

CHAPTER 7

The Special Theory of Relativity

7-1. INTRODUCTION

Thus far we have considered only electrostatics, that branch of electricity which deals with stationary configurations of charge and the associated fields. With the present chapter we begin our study of electrodynamics, which deals with charges in motion and their associated fields. The major part of the chapter is devoted to presenting the fundamentals of the special theory of relativity. The reason for this is to lead naturally to the concept of magnetic induction (Sec. 7-10) and to its origin in moving electric charges. Thus in Sec. 7-10 are defined electric current, permeability of free space, and magnetic induction. Ampère's law is discussed in Sec. 7-11 and magnetic media in Sec. 7-12.

7-2. THE FUNDAMENTAL POSTULATES

The special theory of relativity was formulated to explain the negative result of the Michelson-Morley experiment,† namely, the velocity of light relative to the earth is independent of the direction of propagation. The theory is based on the following two postulates:

1. The principle of relativity of uniform motion: Physical laws or the mathematical equations defining them have the same form in all cartesian coordinate systems which have a uniform motion of translation relative to one another.

2. The principle of the constancy of the velocity of light: The velocity of light in a vacuum in any given frame of reference is independent of the velocity of the source.

As a consequence of postulate 1 an observer in any arbitrary coordinate system cannot detect the motion of the system by any observation confined to the system. Combination of postulate 2 with postulate 1 yields

---

† For a discussion of this experiment as well as a general review of measurements of the velocity of light the reader is referred to Determination of the Velocity of Light by E. Bergstrand in "Handbuch der Physik," Band XXIV, Springer-Verlag OHG, Berlin, 1956.

the result that the velocity of light in a vacuum is independent of the relative velocity of the source and the observer. In the following sections we shall examine some additional implications of the fundamental postulates.

7-3. THE LORENTZ TRANSFORMATION

Consider two cartesian coordinate systems $OX_1X_2X_3$ and $O'X_1'X_2'X_3'$ with coincident X_1 and X_1' axes (Fig. 7-1). Let the primed system be moving with a uniform velocity v in the X_1 direction with respect to the unprimed system. Furthermore, let two observers, A and A', make

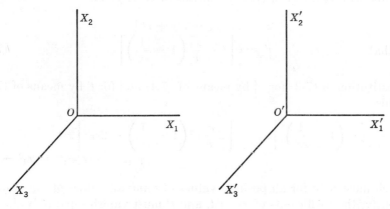

FIGURE 7-1

observations of the laws of nature in the unprimed and primed system, respectively. Suppose that at the instant $t = t' = 0$ the two origins of coordinates coincide and that at this instant a light pulse leaves the common origin. The fundamental postulates require that both A and A' observe a spherical wave diverging from the common origin with a velocity c. Consequently, at any time $t > 0$ observer A observes a spherical wave, the front of which is given by

$$x_1{}^2 + x_2{}^2 + x_3{}^2 - c^2t^2 = 0 \qquad (7\text{-}1)$$

Similarly, for A' the equation of the wavefront is

$$x_1'{}^2 + x_2'{}^2 + x_3'{}^2 - c^2t^2 = 0 \qquad (7\text{-}2)$$

Because of the symmetry of the situation we assume that

$$x_2 = x_2'$$
$$x_3 = x_3'$$

Then Eqs. (7-1) and (7-2) will be satisfied if

$$x_1{}^2 - c^2t^2 = x_1'{}^2 - c^2t'{}^2 \tag{7-3}$$

For A, O' has the coordinates $x_1 = vt$, $x_2 = x_3 = 0$, at time t. For A', O has the coordinates $x_1' = -vt'$, $x_2' = x_3' = 0$, at time t'. The simplest relations which will give this result are

$$x_1' = \kappa(x_1 - vt) \tag{7-4}$$
$$x_1 = \kappa'(x_1' + vt') \tag{7-5}$$

where κ and κ' are quantities to be determined.

Substitution for x_1' in (7-5) by means of (7-4) yields

$$x = \kappa'[\kappa(x_1 - vt) + vt']$$

so that

$$t' = \kappa\left[t - \frac{x_1}{v}\left(1 - \frac{1}{\kappa\kappa'}\right)\right] \tag{7-6}$$

Substitution in (7-3) for x_1' by means of (7-4) and for t' by means of (7-6) yields

$$\left[\kappa^2 - \frac{c^2}{v^2}\kappa^2\left(1 - \frac{1}{\kappa\kappa'}\right)^2\right]x_1{}^2 + \left[2\frac{c^2}{v}\kappa^2\left(1 - \frac{1}{\kappa\kappa'}\right) - 2v\kappa^2\right]x_1t$$
$$+ [\kappa^2v^2 - c^2\kappa^2]t^2 = x_1{}^2 - c^2t^2$$

which must hold for all positive values of t and all values of x_1. Consequently, the coefficients of $x_1{}^2$, x_1t, and t^2 must vanish separately; i.e.,

$$\kappa^2 - \frac{c^2}{v^2}\kappa^2\left(1 - \frac{1}{\kappa\kappa'}\right)^2 = 1 \tag{7-7}$$

$$2\frac{c^2}{v}\kappa^2\left(1 - \frac{1}{\kappa\kappa'}\right) - 2v\kappa^2 = 0 \tag{7-8}$$

$$\kappa^2v^2 - c^2\kappa^2 = -c^2 \tag{7-9}$$

From (7-9) it follows that

$$\kappa = \left(1 - \frac{v^2}{c^2}\right)^{-\frac{1}{2}} \tag{7-10}$$

From (7-8),

$$\frac{1}{\kappa\kappa'} = 1 - \frac{v^2}{c^2} = \frac{1}{\kappa^2}$$

so that

$$\kappa = \kappa' \tag{7-11}$$

Consequently, the transformation equations (7-4) and (7-5) become

$$x_1' = \kappa(x_1 - vt) \tag{7-12}$$
$$x_1 = \kappa(x_1' + vt') \tag{7-13}$$

Substitution for κ and κ' in (7-6) yields

$$t' = \kappa\left(t - \frac{v}{c^2}x_1\right) \qquad (7\text{-}14)$$

Then
$$t = \kappa\left(t' + \frac{v}{c^2}x_1'\right) \qquad (7\text{-}15)$$

7-4. THE LORENTZ-FITZGERALD CONTRACTION

Let a rod whose length is to be determined be placed along the X_1' axis. At a given instant determined by observer A in the unprimed coordinate system, observer A' notes the positions of the ends of the rod. Let the values be $x_1'(1)$ and $x_1'(2)$. Since observer A' is "at rest" with respect to the primed coordinate system, the "rest" length l_0 of the rod is

$$l_0 = x_1'(1) - x_1'(2) \qquad (7\text{-}16)$$

In order for observer A in the unprimed coordinate system to know the length of the rod which is moving with respect to him with velocity v, he must transform $x_1'(1)$ and $x_1'(2)$ by means of (7-12). Thus

$$\begin{aligned} l_0 &= \kappa[x_1(1) - vt(1)] - \kappa[x_1(2) - vt(2)] \\ &= \kappa[x_1(1) - x_1(2)] \end{aligned} \qquad (7\text{-}17)$$

since $t(1)$ and $t(2)$ are identical by the conditions of the observation. The length of the moving rod as determined by observer A with respect to his coordinate system is then

$$\begin{aligned} l &= x_1(1) - x_1(2) \\ &= \frac{l_0}{\kappa} \end{aligned} \qquad (7\text{-}18)$$

i.e., observer A finds that the length l is shorter than the "rest" length l_0 in the ratio $1:\kappa$.

7-5. THE EXPANSION OF TIME INTERVALS

Let observer A', from a given point in the moving (according to observer A) system, send two signals at instants t_1' and t_2' to observer A in the fixed (according to him) system. The time interval $\Delta t'$ between the two signals will be

$$\Delta t' = t_1' - t_2'$$

according to A'. The corresponding time interval as determined by A

is, from (7-15),

$$\Delta t = t_1 - t_2$$
$$= \kappa \left(t_1' + \frac{v}{c^2} x_1' \right) - \kappa \left(t_2' + \frac{v}{c^2} x_1' \right)$$
$$= \kappa (t_1' - t_2') = \kappa \, \Delta t' \tag{7-19}$$

i.e., observer A finds that the time interval Δt is longer then $\Delta t'$ in the ratio $\kappa : 1$.

7-6. THE COMPOSITION OF VELOCITIES

Let a body have a velocity $u_1' = dx_1'/dt'$ in the primed coordinate system. The velocity $u_1 = dx_1/dt$ as measured by observer A in the unprimed system can be obtained as follows: From (7-13),

$$dx_1 = \kappa (dx_1' + v \, dt') \tag{7-20}$$

From (7-15),

$$dt = \kappa \left(dt' + \frac{v}{c^2} \, dx_1' \right) \tag{7-21}$$

Division of (7-20) by (7-21) then gives

$$u_1 = \frac{dx_1}{dt} = \frac{dx_1' + v \, dt'}{dt' + (v/c^2) \, dx_1'}$$
$$= \frac{u_1' + v}{1 + vu_1'/c^2} \tag{7-22}$$

Although $x_2 = x_2'$, it does not follow that $dx_2/dt = dx_2'/dt'$, because of the difference in the time scales in the primed and unprimed systems. Thus

$$dx_2 = dx_2'$$
$$dt = \kappa \left(dt' + \frac{v}{c^2} \, dx_1' \right)$$

so that
$$u_2 = \frac{dx_2}{dt} = \frac{1}{\kappa} \frac{u_2'}{1 + vu_1'/c^2} \tag{7-23}$$

where $u_2' = dx_2'/dt'$. Similarly,

$$u_3 = \frac{dx_3}{dt} = \frac{1}{\kappa} \frac{u_3'}{1 + vu_1'/c^2} \tag{7-24}$$

where $u_3' = dx_3'/dt'$.

From (7-22) it is easily demonstrated that the velocity of light in a vacuum c is the upper limit of possible velocities. Thus, suppose

$v/c \leq 1$ and $u_1'/c \leq 1$.   Then

$$1 - \frac{v}{c} \geq 0$$

$$1 - \frac{u_1'}{c} \geq 0$$

so that

$$\left(1 - \frac{v}{c}\right)\left(1 - \frac{u_1'}{c}\right) \geq 0$$

or

$$1 + \frac{v}{c^2}u_1' \geq \frac{v + u_1'}{c}$$

from which it follows from (7-22) that

$$u_1 \leq c \qquad (7\text{-}25)$$

Thus, even if the relative velocity v of the two systems is equal to c and a body in the primed system has a velocity $u_1' = c$, the velocity u_1 in the unprimed system is still c.

7-7. THE VARIATION OF MASS WITH VELOCITY

Consider two equal masses m in the primed coordinate system in which their velocities are u_1' and $-u_1'$.   Let their velocities in the unprimed system be $u_1^{(a)}$ and $u_1^{(b)}$ and the corresponding masses $m^{(a)}$ and $m^{(b)}$. (If $m^{(a)} = m^{(b)}$, we shall find this out.)   Then the law of conservation of momentum requires that

$$m^{(a)}u_1^{(a)} + m^{(b)}u_1^{(b)} = (m^{(a)} + m^{(b)})v \qquad (7\text{-}26)$$

in the unprimed system.   From (7-26) it follows that

$$\frac{m^{(a)}}{m^{(b)}} = \frac{v - u_1^{(b)}}{u_1^{(a)} - v} \qquad (7\text{-}27)$$

But from (7-22),

$$u_1^{(a)} = \frac{u_1' + v}{1 + vu_1'/c^2} \qquad u_1^{(b)} = \frac{-u_1' + v}{1 - vu_1'/c^2}$$

Hence

$$\frac{m^{(a)}}{m^{(b)}} = \frac{1 + vu_1'/c^2}{1 - vu_1'/c^2} \qquad (7\text{-}28)$$

Also

$$u_1^{(a)2} = \frac{u_1'^2 + 2u_1'v + v^2}{(1 + vu_1'/c^2)^2}$$

$$1 - \frac{u_1^{(a)2}}{c^2} = \frac{(1 - v^2/c^2)(1 - u'^2/c^2)}{(1 + vu_1'/c^2)^2}$$

Similarly

$$1 - \frac{u_1^{(b)2}}{c^2} = \frac{(1 - v^2/c^2)(1 - u'^2/c^2)}{(1 - vu_1'/c^2)^2}$$

Hence, (7-28) becomes

$$\frac{m^{(a)}}{m^{(b)}} = \frac{\sqrt{1 - u_1^{(b)2}/c^2}}{\sqrt{1 - u_1^{(a)2}/c^2}}$$

so that

$$m^{(a)} \sqrt{1 - \frac{u_1^{(a)2}}{c^2}} = m^{(b)} \sqrt{1 - \frac{u_1^{(b)2}}{c^2}} \tag{7-29}$$

In order for (7-29) to hold for all values of $u_1^{(a)}$ and $u_1^{(b)}$ it is necessary that both sides of the equation be equal to a constant, say m_0. Then, in general,

$$m = \frac{m_0}{\sqrt{1 - u^2/c^2}} \tag{7-30}$$

Note that, when $u = 0$, $m = m_0$. For this reason m_0 is known as the *rest mass* of the body whose mass m, when moving with velocity u, is given by (7-30). Since $u \leq c$, $m \geq m_0$; the mass of a body increases with increasing velocity.

7-8. THE RELATION BETWEEN MASS AND ENERGY

The momentum p of a body of mass m moving with velocity u is given by

$$p = mu = \frac{m_0 u}{\sqrt{1 - u^2/c^2}} \tag{7-31}$$

Hence

$$dp = m \, du + u \, dm \tag{7-32}$$

$$dp = \frac{m_0 \, du}{(1 - u^2/c^2)^{3/2}} \tag{7-33}$$

Equating the right-hand members of (7-32) and (7-33) to each other, we obtain

$$m \, du = \frac{c^2}{u} \left(1 - \frac{u^2}{c^2}\right) dm$$

Substitution into (7-32) then yields

$$dp = \frac{c^2}{u} \, cm$$

Therefore

$$dW \equiv u \, dp \equiv c^2 \, dm \tag{7-34}$$

which gives on integration

$$W = mc^2 + \text{constant} \tag{7-35}$$

Since experimentally one measures only differences in energy, the value of the constant is of little importance and can be taken as zero. Then

$$W = mc^2 \tag{7-36}$$

which is the well-known Einstein relation expressing the equivalence of mass and energy.

If one defines a "rest energy" W_0 by means of the relation

$$W_0 = m_0c^2 \tag{7-37}$$

the kinetic energy T is given by

$$T = W - W_0 = (m - m_0)c^2 \tag{7-38}$$

which states that the kinetic energy of a body is equal to c^2 times the mass it gained owing to its motion. Substitution for m in (7-38) by means of (7-35) yields

$$T = m_0c^2 \left(\frac{1}{\sqrt{1 - u^2/c^2}} - 1 \right) \tag{7-39}$$

Now

$$\frac{u^2}{c^2} = \frac{p^2}{m^2c^2} = \frac{p^2}{m_0^2c^2}\left(1 - \frac{u^2}{c^2} \right)$$

$$\frac{u^2}{c^2}\left(1 + \frac{p^2}{m_0^2c^2} \right) = \frac{p^2}{m_0^2c^2}$$

$$\frac{u^2}{c^2} = \frac{p^2}{m_0^2c^2 + p^2}$$

so that

$$1 - \frac{u^2}{c^2} = \frac{m_0^2c^2}{m_0^2c^2 + p^2}$$

Substitution into (7-39) then gives

$$T = m_0c^2 \left(\frac{\sqrt{m_0^2c^2 + p^2}}{m_0c} - 1 \right)$$

$$= c\sqrt{m_0^2c^2 + p^2} - m_0c^2 \tag{7-40}$$

Comparison of (7-40) with (7-38) yields

$$W = mc^2 = c\sqrt{m_0^2c^2 + p^2} \tag{7-41}$$

as the expression for the total energy in terms of the momentum p.

Expansion of (7-39) by means of the binomial theorem gives

$$T = \frac{1}{2} m_0u^2 + \frac{3}{8} m_0\frac{u^4}{c^2} + \cdots \tag{7-42}$$

Clearly, if $u \ll c$, the kinetic energy T reduces approximately to the non-relativistic value $\frac{1}{2}m_0u^2$.

7-9. THE TRANSFORMATION EQUATIONS FOR FORCE

Consider a body which has mass m when moving with a velocity $\mathbf{u}$ in the unprimed coordinate system. Since, by definition, force is the time rate of change of momentum,

$$\mathbf{F}_0 = \frac{d}{dt}\mathbf{p} = \frac{d}{dt}(m\mathbf{u}) = m_0 \frac{d}{dt}\left(\frac{1}{\sqrt{1 - u^2/c^2}}\mathbf{u}\right) \qquad (7\text{-}43)$$

The observer A' in the primed coordinate system will observe a force $\mathbf{F}_0'$ given by

$$\mathbf{F}_0' = \frac{d}{dt'}\mathbf{p}' = \frac{d}{dt'}(m'\mathbf{u}') = m_0 \frac{d}{dt'}\left(\frac{1}{\sqrt{1 - u'^2/c^2}}\mathbf{u}'\right) \qquad (7\text{-}44)$$

The X_1 component of $\mathbf{F}_0$ is

$$\begin{aligned}
F_{01} &= m_0 \frac{d}{dt}\left(\frac{1}{\sqrt{1 - u^2/c^2}}u_1\right) \\
&= m_0 \frac{d}{dt'}\left(\frac{1}{\sqrt{1 - u^2/c^2}}u_1\right)\frac{dt'}{dt} \qquad (7\text{-}45)
\end{aligned}$$

From (7-14) and (7-22),

$$\frac{dt'}{dt} = \frac{1}{\kappa(1 + vu_1'/c^2)} \qquad (7\text{-}46)$$

From (7-22) through (7-24)

$$\frac{d}{dt'}\left(\frac{1}{\sqrt{1 - u^2/c^2}}u_1\right) = \kappa\frac{d}{dt'}\left(\frac{u_1' + v}{\sqrt{1 - u'^2/c^2}}\right) \qquad (7\text{-}47)$$

Substitution of (7-46) and (7-47) into (7-45) gives

$$\begin{aligned}
F_{01} &= \frac{m_0}{1 + vu_1'/c^2}\frac{d}{dt'}\left(\frac{u_1' + v}{\sqrt{1 - u'^2/c^2}}\right) \\
&= F_{01}' + \frac{m_0}{1 + vu_1'/c^2}\left[v\frac{d}{dt'}\left(\frac{1}{\sqrt{1 - u'^2/c^2}}\right) - v\frac{u_1}{c^2}\frac{d}{dt'}\left(\frac{u_1'}{\sqrt{1 - u'^2/c^2}}\right)\right] \\
&= F_{01}' + \frac{m_0 v}{c^2 + vu_1'}\left[c^2\frac{d}{dt'}\left(\frac{1}{\sqrt{1 - u'^2/c^2}}\right) - u_1'\frac{d}{dt'}\left(\frac{u_1'}{\sqrt{1 - u'^2/c^2}}\right)\right] \\
&= F_{01}' + \frac{u_2'v}{c^2 + vu_1'}F_{02}' + \frac{u_3'v}{c^2vu_1'}F_{03}' \qquad (7\text{-}48)
\end{aligned}$$

Similarly, it can be shown that

$$F_{02} = \frac{c^2}{\kappa(c^2 vu_1')}F_{02}' \qquad (7\text{-}49)$$

$$F_{03} = \frac{c^2}{\kappa(c^2 + vu_1')}F_{03}' \qquad (7\text{-}50)$$

7-10. THE MAGNETIC INDUCTION

Consider two point charges q and Q in vacuum, and assume that the magnitudes of the charges are the same for all observers.† Let the charges be fixed in the primed coordinate system. At a given instant determined by observer A in the unprimed coordinate system, say $t = 0$, so that by (7-14) $t' = -\kappa v x_1/c^2$, observer A' notes the positions of the charges. Let the coordinates be $(0,x_2',0)$ and $(X_1',0,0)$ for q and Q, respectively. Then (cf. Sec. 7-3 or 7-4) the coordinates for q and Q as determined by A are $(0,x_2,0)$ and $(\kappa X_1,0,0)$, respectively.

The force on q measured by the observer A' in the primed system is given by Coulomb's law:

$$F_{01}' = -\frac{qQX_1'}{4\pi\epsilon_0(X_1'^2 + x_2'^2)^{3/2}} \qquad F_{02}' = \frac{qQx_2'}{4\pi\epsilon_0(X_1'^2 + x_2'^2)^{3/2}} \qquad F_{03}' = 0 \quad (7\text{-}51)$$

where ϵ_0 is the permittivity of free space.

Since the charges are fixed in this coordinate system, Eqs. (7-48) through (7-50) give

$$F_{01} = -\frac{qQX_1'}{4\pi\epsilon_0(X_1'^2 + x_2'^2)^{3/2}} \qquad F_{02} = \frac{qQx_2'}{4\pi\epsilon_0\kappa(X_1'^2 + x_2'^2)^{3/2}} \qquad F_{03} = 0 \quad (7\text{-}52)$$

for the components of the force on q in the unprimed system. Substituting for X_1' and x_2', the force components (7-52) become

$$F_{01} = -\frac{qQ\kappa X_1}{4\pi\epsilon_0(\kappa^2 X_1^2 + x_2^2)^{3/2}} \qquad F_{02} = \frac{qQx_2}{4\pi\epsilon_0\kappa(\kappa^2 X_1^2 + x_2^2)^{3/2}} \qquad F_{03} = 0$$
$$(7\text{-}53)$$

The force on a charge q located at a distance x_2 from an infinite line of charges uniformly spaced along the X_1 axis both moving with speed v in the positive X_1 direction is easily obtained from (7-53). Let‡

$$Q = \lambda \, dX_1 = \lambda' \, dX_1' \qquad (7\text{-}54)$$

Then substitution of (7-54) into (7-53) followed by integration from

---

† This assumption is, of course, consistent with experiment. For example, the results of experimental determinations of e/m, the ratio of the charge to the mass of beta particles, are completely explained by the variation of mass with velocity (cf. J. D. Stranathan, "The 'Particles' of Modern Physics," pp. 138–145, McGraw-Hill Book Company, Inc., Blakiston Division, New York, 1948).

‡ Note that, since the elements of length in the two coordinate systems are unequal: that is, $dX_1' = \kappa \, dX_1$, the charge densities observed by A and A' will be different, $\lambda = \kappa\lambda'$.

$X_1 = -\infty$ to $X_1 = +\infty$ yields

$$F_{01} = 0 \qquad F_{02} = \frac{q(1 - v^2/c^2)\lambda}{2\pi\epsilon_0 x_2} \qquad F_{03} = 0 \qquad (7\text{-}55)$$

When $v = 0$, (7-55) reduces to

$$F_{02s} = qE_0 = q\,\frac{\lambda}{2\pi\epsilon_0 x_2} \qquad (7\text{-}56)$$

which is the electrostatic force on q due to a line with charge λ per unit length (cf. Sec. 2-6). The additional force, due to the motion, is

$$F_{02m} = -qv\,\frac{\lambda v}{2\pi c^2 \epsilon_0 x_2} \qquad (7\text{-}57)$$

We define an *electric current* i_1 in the positive X_1 direction by the relation

$$i_1 = \lambda v \qquad (7\text{-}58)$$

Since the units of λ are coulombs/meter and those of v are meters/second, the units of i_1 are *amperes*, where, by definition,

$$1 \text{ ampere} = 1\,\frac{\text{coulomb}}{\text{second}} \qquad (7\text{-}59)$$

We further define the *permeability of free space* μ_0 by the relation

$$\mu_0 = \frac{1}{\epsilon_0 c^2} \qquad (7\text{-}60)$$

Since $\epsilon_0 = (10^7/4\pi c^2)$ farads/meter and the dimensions of c are meters/second,

$$\mu_0 = 4\pi \times 10^{-7}\,\frac{\text{henry}}{\text{meter}} \qquad (7\text{-}61)$$

where, by definition,

$$1 \text{ henry} = 1\,\frac{(\text{second})^2}{\text{farad}} = 1\,\frac{\text{volt}}{\text{coulomb}}\,(\text{second})^2$$

$$= 1\,\frac{\text{neutron meter}}{(\text{coulomb})^2}\,(\text{second})^2 = 1\,\frac{\text{kilogram}(\text{meter})^2}{(\text{coulomb})^2} \qquad (7\text{-}62)$$

in which use has been made of Eqs. (2-7) and (2-8) and the definition of the newton.

Using the definitions (7-58) and (7-60), the expression (7-57) for the additional force on q due to the motion can be written

$$F_{02m} = -qv\,\frac{\mu_0 i_1}{2\pi x_2} \qquad (7\text{-}63)$$

In this form F_{02m} represents the force on a charge q moving in free space with uniform velocity v parallel to and at a distance x_2 from a current i_1 flowing in an infinitely long straight path.

We note that the force F_{02m} is in the X_2 direction while the direction of motion of the charge q is in the positive X_1 direction. One way to relate the direction of the force to that of the motion of the charge is to interpret (7-63) as a vector relation and introduce a vector $\mathbf{B}_0$ such that

$$\mathbf{F}_{0m} = q(\mathbf{v} \times \mathbf{B}_0) \tag{7-64}$$

in which

$$F_{01m} = 0 \qquad F_{02m} = -qvB_{03} \qquad F_{03m} = 0$$
$$v_1 = v \qquad v_2 = v_3 = 0 \tag{7-65}$$
$$B_{01} = B_{02} = 0 \qquad B_{03} = \frac{\mu_0 i_1}{2\pi x_2}$$

From either (7-64) or (7-65) it follows that the units of $\mathbf{B}_0$ are webers/(meter)^2 where, by definition,

$$1 \text{ weber} = 1 \frac{\text{kilogram (meter)}^2}{\text{coulomb second}} \tag{7-66}$$

Thus, according to the last of Eqs. (7-65), observer A interprets the additional force due to the motion of the charges as being due to the infinitely long straight-line current. He states that a current i_1 flowing in an infinitely long straight path produces a field of strength

$$B_{03} = \frac{\mu_0 i_1}{2\pi x_2} \tag{7-67}$$

at a distance x_2 from it. Equation (7-67) is the well-known *law of Biot and Savart* for the *magnetic induction* $\mathbf{B}_0$ at a point x_2 distant from an infinitely long straight conductor bearing a current i_1. In accordance with the experimental results of Biot and Savart, the direction of the magnetic induction is that of a circle of radius x_2 with center on the conductor bearing the current i_1 and lying in the plane passing through the field point and perpendicular to the current (Fig. 7-2). The sense in which the circle is described is that of rotation of a right-hand screw advancing in the direction of the current.

According to (7-56) and (7-64) the force experienced by a charge q moving with velocity v in a field of electric intensity $\mathbf{E}_0$ and magnetic induction $\mathbf{B}_0$ is

$$\mathbf{F}_0 = q(\mathbf{E}_0 + \mathbf{v} \times \mathbf{B}_0) \tag{7-68}$$

This force is known as the *Lorentz force*.

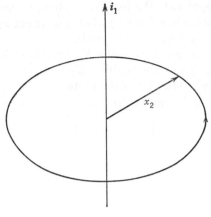

FIGURE 7-2

7-11. AMPÈRE'S LAW

The law of Biot and Savart is a special case of Ampère's law, which states that the magnetic induction in vacuum at a field point P which is $\mathbf{r}$ distant from an element $d\mathbf{s}$ of a linear conductor bearing a current i is

$$d\mathbf{B}_0 = \mu_0 i \frac{d\mathbf{s} \times \mathbf{r}}{4\pi r^3} \tag{7-69}$$

That the law of Biot and Savart is indeed a special case of Ampère's law is easily verified. Application of (7-69) to the current in an infinitely long straight wire (Fig. 7-3) yields

$$|d\mathbf{B}_0| = \frac{\mu_0 i}{4\pi} \frac{\sin \alpha}{r^2} ds$$

$$= \frac{\mu_0 i}{4\pi} \frac{a \csc^2 \alpha \sin \alpha}{a^2 \csc^2 \alpha} d\alpha = \frac{\mu_0 i}{4\pi a} \sin \alpha \, d\alpha$$

where a is the perpendicular distance from the field point P to the wire, $s = -a \cot \alpha$, and $r = a \csc \alpha$. Then

$$B_0 = \frac{\mu_0 i}{4\pi a} \int_0^\pi \sin \alpha \, d\alpha = \frac{\mu_0 i}{2\pi a} \tag{7-70}$$

in agreement with (7-67).

The line integral of B_0 over the circle of radius a is then

$$\oint \mathbf{B}_0 \cdot d\mathbf{s} = \oint B_0 \, ds = \int_0^{2\pi} \frac{\mu_0 i}{2\pi a} a \, d\theta = \mu_0 i \tag{7-71}$$

since the direction of $\mathbf{B}_0$ is that of the circle. Although derived in a special case, this result is generally valid: The line integral of $\mathbf{B}_0$ about a

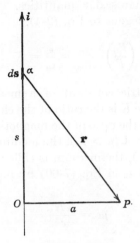

FIGURE 7-3

closed contour is equal to μ_0 times the total current flowing through the contour of integration. A general derivation is given in Sec. 8-3.

7-12. MAGNETIC MEDIA

According to Eq. (7-63), the force on a charge q moving in vacuum with uniform velocity v parallel to and at a distance a from a current i flowing in an infinitely long straight path is given by

$$F_0 = -qv\,\frac{\mu_0 i}{2\pi a} \tag{7-72}$$

where μ_0 is the permeability of free space. In the case of a material medium the force F on the charge q is given by

$$F = -qv\,\frac{\mu i}{2\pi a} \tag{7-73}$$

where μ is the *permeability* of the medium.

Division of (7-73) by (7-72) yields

$$\frac{F}{F_0} = \frac{\mu}{\mu_0} = K_m \tag{7-74}$$

where K_m, the ratio of the force in the medium to that in vacuum, is known as the *relative permeability* of the medium.

The reader is reminded that we are considering here only a special case, namely, a homogeneous isotropic medium. In anisotropic media, K_m and μ are tensor rather than scalar quantities.

Equation (7-74) is analogous to Eq. (2-4),

$$\left(\frac{F_0}{F}\right)_{\text{electric}} = \frac{\epsilon}{\epsilon_0} = K \qquad (2\text{-}4)$$

which defines the dielectric constant of a medium of permittivity ϵ. Note, however, that, while K is the ratio of the electric force in vacuum to that in the medium, K_m is the ratio of the magnetic force in the medium to that in vacuum. If $K_m > 1$ ($\mu > \mu_0$), the medium is said to be *paramagnetic*. If $K_m < 1$ ($\mu < \mu_0$), the medium is called *diamagnetic*.

Substitution for μ_0 and ϵ_0 in Eq. (7-60) by means of Eqs. (7-74) and (2-4) yields the relation

$$\mu\epsilon = \frac{KK_m}{c^2} \qquad (7\text{-}75)$$

for the product of the permeability and the permittivity of a medium.

It is clear that Ampère's law, Eq. (7-69); the law of Biot and Savart, Eq. (7-70); and the integral $\oint \mathbf{B} \cdot d\mathbf{s}$, Eq. (7-71), become, respectively,

$$d\mathbf{B} = \mu i\, \frac{d\mathbf{s} \times \mathbf{r}}{4\pi r^3} \qquad (7\text{-}76)$$

$$B = \frac{\mu i}{2\pi a} \qquad (7\text{-}77)$$

$$\oint \mathbf{B} \cdot d\mathbf{s} = \mu i \qquad (7\text{-}78)$$

in the case of a medium with permeability μ.

EXERCISES

7-1. Let two point masses m_0 and M_0 be fixed in the primed coordinate system. At time $t = 0$, determined by observer A in the unprimed coordinate system, observer A' notes the positions of the masses. Let the coordinates for m_0 and M_0 be $(0,x_2',0)$ and $(X_1',0,0)$, respectively. The force on m_0 measured by observer A' in the primed coordinate system is given by Newton's law of universal gravitation:

$$F_{01}' = -G\frac{m_0 M_0 X_1'}{(X_1'^2 + x_2'^2)^{3/2}} \qquad F_{02}' = G\frac{m_0 M_0 x_2'}{(X_1'^2 + x_2'^2)^{3/2}} \qquad F_{03}' = 0$$

where G is the gravitational constant. Find the force on the mass m_0 measured by observer A in the unprimed system, and comment on the result.

7-2. Let a point mass m_0 and an infinite line of uniformly spaced point masses M_0 be fixed in the primed coordinate system. At time $t = 0$, determined by observer A in the unprimed coordinate system, observer A' notes the positions of the masses. Let the coordinates for m_0 be $(0,x_2',0)$, and let the infinite line of uniformly spaced masses M_0 be along the X_1' axis. Find the force on m_0 measured by both observer A' and observer A.

7-3. A particle with charge q and mass m moves in a uniform magnetic field of induction **B**. Let the velocity of the particle at time $t = 0$ be **v**, and let the angle between **v** and **B** be α. Find the path in which the particle travels.

7-4. A particle with charge q and mass m is moving in a plane normal to a uniform field **B** in a medium which opposes the motion of the particle with a force proportional to its velocity. Find the path.

7-5. A particle with charge q and mass m moves in a region in which there are uniform electric and magnetic fields **E** and **B**. Find the path of the particle in the case when $\mathbf{E} \cdot \mathbf{B} = 0$.

REFERENCES

Bergmann, P. G.: "Introduction to the Theory of Relativity," Prentice-Hall, Inc., Englewood Cliffs, N.J., 1942.

Goldstein, H.: "Classical Mechanics," chap. 6, Addison-Wesley Publishing Company, Inc., Cambridge, Mass., 1950.

Landau, L., and E. Lifshitz: "The Classical Theory of Fields," chaps. 1 and 2, Addison-Wesley Publishing Company, Inc., Cambridge, Mass., 1951.

Panofsky, W. K. H., and M. Phillips: "Classical Electricity and Magnetism," chaps. 14, 15, and 16, Addison-Wesley Publishing Company, Inc., Cambridge, Mass., 1955.

Smythe, W. R.: "Static and Dynamic Electricity," 2d ed., chap. 14, McGraw-Hill Book Company, Inc., New York, 1950.

CHAPTER 8

The Magnetic Field

8-1. INTRODUCTION

In the preceding chapter it was shown that a steady or stationary current, i.e., a flow of charge which is independent of the time, produces a magnetic field. The purpose of the present chapter is to study in detail steady currents and their associated magnetic fields. As far as possible the treatment parallels that of Chap. 4 on the electric field in dielectrics so as to indicate clearly the similarities and dissimilarities of the electric and magnetic fields.

8-2. THE MAGNETIC DIPOLE AND SHELL

Consider any closed circuit $\mathbf{s}$ in which a current i is flowing. Let S be the area of an arbitrary surface bounded by the circuit $\mathbf{s}$. According to Ampère's law the magnetic induction at a field point $\mathbf{r}$ distant from a circuit element $d\mathbf{s}$ is

$$\mathbf{B} = \frac{\mu i}{4\pi} \oint \frac{d\mathbf{s} \times \mathbf{r}}{r^3} \tag{8-1}$$

By use of the theorem of Tait and McAulay (Sec. 1-18), Eq. (8-1) can be written

$$\mathbf{B} = \frac{\mu i}{4\pi} \iint \left[\boldsymbol{\nabla}_s \left(\frac{\mathbf{r}}{r^3} \cdot \mathbf{n} \right) - \left(\boldsymbol{\nabla}_s \cdot \frac{\mathbf{r}}{r^3} \right) \mathbf{n} \right] dS \tag{8-2}$$

where $\mathbf{n}$ is the normal to the element dS of the arbitrary surface S. The direction of the normal $\mathbf{n}$ and the currency of the circuit $\mathbf{s}$ are related to each other as the direction of advance of a right-hand screw is related to its rotation. The subscript s on the del operator indicates that the differentiation is with respect to the source coordinates. Since $\boldsymbol{\nabla} \cdot (\mathbf{r}/r^3) = 0$ and $\boldsymbol{\nabla}_s = -\boldsymbol{\nabla}$, where the omission of the subscript indicates differentiation with respect to the field coordinates, (8-2) reduces to

$$\mathbf{B} = -\frac{\mu i}{4\pi} \iint \nabla \left(\frac{\mathbf{r}}{r^3} \cdot \mathbf{n} \right) dS$$

or
$$\mathbf{B} = -\frac{\mu}{4\pi} \iint \nabla \left(\frac{\tau_m \cdot \mathbf{r}}{r^3} \right) dS \qquad (8\text{-}3)$$

where
$$\tau_m \equiv i\mathbf{n} \qquad (8\text{-}4)$$

If the circuit **s** is allowed to approach zero and the current to approach infinity in such a way that the product iS remains constant, the result

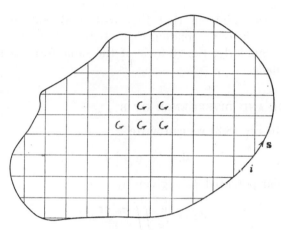

FIGURE 8-1

is, by definition, a magnetic dipole of moment $\mathbf{p}_m = \tau_m S$. From (8-3) the magnetic induction at a point r distant from such a dipole is given by

$$\mathbf{B} = -\frac{\mu}{4\pi} \nabla \left(\frac{\mathbf{p}_m \cdot \mathbf{r}}{r^3} \right) \qquad (8\text{-}5)$$

$$\mathbf{B} = \frac{\mu}{4\pi} \nabla \left[\mathbf{p}_m \cdot \nabla \left(\frac{1}{r} \right) \right] \qquad (8\text{-}6)$$

It is then convenient to think of the original circuit **s** bearing the current i as being equivalent to a magnetic shell of area S with boundary coincident with the circuit **s** and moment per unit area of magnitude $\tau_m = i$. Physically this can be seen as follows: Let wires be laid across the circuit **s** as indicated in Fig. 8-1. The envelope of these wires is the surface S. The wires divide S up into a multitude of elementary areas. The edge of each element of area not situated on the circuit **s** will be shared by two elements. Consequently, if for each of the elements we form the line integral

$$\oint \frac{d\mathbf{s} \times \mathbf{r}}{r^3}$$

and then add, the contributions from the edges of the elements of area not situated on the circuit s will be zero, since each of these edges is traversed twice, first in one direction for the line integral around a particular element and second in the opposite direction for the line integral around the adjacent element. Hence, after addition only the line integral over the circuit s remains and the magnetic induction is given by (8-1).

In passing, we point out that Eqs. (8-1) and (8-3) are of precisely the same form as the corresponding Eqs. (4-20) and (4-19) for the electric dipole sheet. Similarly, Eq. (8-6) is of the same form as Eq. (4-8) for the electric dipole.

8-3. THE CURL AND DIVERGENCE OF B

According to Eq. (8-3) we can write

$$\mathbf{B} = -\operatorname{grad} \phi_m \qquad (8\text{-}7)$$

where the scalar potential ϕ_m is given by

$$\phi_m = \frac{\mu}{4\pi} \iint \frac{\boldsymbol{\tau}_m \cdot \mathbf{r}}{r^3} \, dS \qquad (8\text{-}8)$$

Note that the scalar potential is defined at all points except $\mathbf{r} = 0$. It therefore follows that the magnetic induction $\mathbf{B}$ is derivable from a scalar potential in all regions in which there are no currents. Furthermore, in such regions

$$\operatorname{curl} \mathbf{B} = 0 \qquad (8\text{-}9)$$

Note further that Eq. (8-8) is of precisely the same form as Eq. (4-15) for the potential due to an electric dipole sheet. Consequently, the difference in potential between points 1 and 2 just on either side of the arbitrary surface S bounded by the circuit s (i.e., the equivalent magnetic shell) is

$$\phi_m(1) - \phi_m(2) = \mu i$$

Since the magnetic shell is merely an artifice, the points can be taken as close together as desired. Hence the line integral of $\mathbf{B}$ about a closed contour which links the current once is

$$\oint \mathbf{B} \cdot d\mathbf{s} = \mu i \qquad (8\text{-}10)$$

Application of Stokes' theorem to (8-10) yields

$$\iint \operatorname{curl} \mathbf{B} \cdot d\mathbf{S} = \mu i \qquad (8\text{-}11)$$

where the surface over which the curl is to be integrated is that bounded by the path taken in determining $\oint \mathbf{B} \cdot d\mathbf{s}$. However, curl $\mathbf{B}$ is zero except inside the wire in which the current i is flowing. Consequently, in integrating, we can choose as the surface of integration the cross section of the wire. This same conclusion can be reached in a different manner: The right-hand member of (8-11) contains no term in r. Hence r is arbitrary (except that it cannot be less than the radius of the wire, since in that case the current flowing in the cross section bounded by the path would be less then i) and we can choose r equal to the radius of the wire.

Let $\mathbf{j}$ represent the current density in the wire, so that the current i is given by

$$i = \iint \mathbf{j} \cdot d\mathbf{S} \qquad (8\text{-}12)$$

where the integration is over the cross section of the wire. Then substitution into (8-9) yields

$$\iint \operatorname{curl} \mathbf{B} \cdot d\mathbf{S} = \mu \iint \mathbf{j} \cdot d\mathbf{S}$$
or
$$\operatorname{curl} \mathbf{B} = \mu \mathbf{j} \qquad (8\text{-}13)$$

Thus, the magnetic induction in a region containing currents is not derivable from a scalar potential. Equation (8-13) is known as the *differential formulation of Ampère's law*. That it holds only in the case of steady currents is easily seen. Thus

$$\operatorname{div} \operatorname{curl} \mathbf{B} = \operatorname{div} (\mu \mathbf{j}) = \mu \operatorname{div} \mathbf{j}$$

for a homogeneous isotropic medium. Since the divergence of the curl of any vector is zero, it follows that div $\mathbf{j}$ must be zero. But div $\mathbf{j} = 0$ only in the case of a steady current in which there is no piling up or depletion of charge. A more general relation for curl $\mathbf{B}$ will be derived in Sec. 9-6.

The divergence of $\mathbf{B}$ is easily shown to be zero. For example, from (8-1)

$$\operatorname{div} \mathbf{B} = \frac{\mu i}{4\pi} \oint \boldsymbol{\nabla} \cdot \left(d\mathbf{s} \times \frac{\mathbf{r}}{r^3} \right)$$
$$= \frac{\mu i}{4} \oint \left(\operatorname{curl} d\mathbf{s} \cdot \frac{\mathbf{r}}{r^3} - d\mathbf{s} \cdot \operatorname{curl} \frac{\mathbf{r}}{r^3} \right)$$

The first term in the integrand is zero because $d\mathbf{s}$ is a constant and hence curl $d\mathbf{s} = 0$. The second term is zero because curl $\mathbf{r}/r^3 = 0$. Hence

$$\operatorname{div} \mathbf{B} = 0 \qquad (8\text{-}14)$$

8-4. MAGNETIC FIELDS OF SIMPLE CIRCUITS

In this section the magnetic induction due to two simple circuits is calculated.

The circular circuit. Consider a circular circuit of radius a bearing a current i as shown in Fig. 8-2. The problem is to find the magnetic

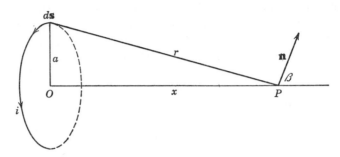

FIGURE 8-2

induction at a point P on the axis of the circle at a distance x from its center O. In this case Ampère's law,

$$d\mathbf{B} = \frac{\mu i}{4\pi} \frac{d\mathbf{s} \times \mathbf{r}}{r^3} \qquad (7\text{-}71)$$

reduces to

$$d\mathbf{B} = \frac{\mu i}{4\pi} \frac{ds}{r^2} \mathbf{n} \qquad (8\text{-}15)$$

where $\mathbf{n}$ is a unit vector perpendicular to both $d\mathbf{s}$ and $\mathbf{r}$. Since diametrically opposite circuit elements give rise to magnetic inductions whose components normal to the axis of the circle cancel each other, the resultant magnetic induction is along the axis and is given by

$$B = \frac{\mu i}{4\pi r^2} \cos \beta \oint ds = \frac{\mu i}{4\pi r^2} \cos \beta \, a \int_0^{2\pi} d\alpha$$

$$= \frac{\mu i a}{2r^2} \cos \beta = \frac{\mu i a^2}{2r^3} = \frac{\mu i a^2}{2(a^2 + x^2)^{3/2}} \qquad (8\text{-}16)$$

If the field point P is allowed to approach the center O of the circle, i.e., if x is allowed to approach zero, one obtains the result

$$B = \frac{\mu i}{2a} \qquad (8\text{-}17)$$

for the magnetic induction at the center of the circle.

The solenoidal current. From the expression (8-16) one can determine the magnetic induction along the axis of a solenoidal current. By definition, a solenoidal current is one which flows in a cylindrical tube, its direction being everywhere perpendicular to the axis of the cylinder. A current flowing in a wire wound upon a cylindrical form is for all practical purposes solenoidal provided that the wire is very closely wound and the thickness of the wire is small compared with the radius of the cylinder. Let n be the number of turns per unit length. The number of turns in a length ds is then $n\,dx$. From (8-16) the magnetic

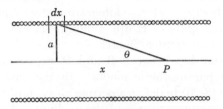

FIGURE 8-3

induction at a field point P on the axis of the cylinder due to an element dx of the solenoid is

$$dB - \frac{\mu i a^2}{2(a^2 + x^2)^{3/2}}\,n\,dx$$

where a is the radius of the solenoid. From Fig. 8-3 it is clear that $x = a \cot \theta$, so that $dx = -a \csc^2\theta\,d\theta$. Therefore

$$B = -\frac{\mu n i}{2}\int_{\theta_1}^{\theta_2} \sin \theta\,d\theta$$

$$= \frac{\mu n i}{2}(\cos \theta_2 - \cos \theta_1) \tag{8-18}$$

If the length of the solenoid is large compared with its radius, the magnetic induction at a field point far from the ends is

$$B = \mu n i \tag{8-19}$$

since $\cos \theta_1 = -1$ and $\cos \theta_2 = +1$. Since $\oint \mathbf{B}\cdot d\mathbf{s} = \mu i$ for any closed contour which links the current i once, it follows from (8-18) that the magnetic induction at a field point far from the ends of the solenoid and outside the solenoid is zero.

8-5. THE MAGNETIC FIELD INTENSITY AND THE MAGNETIZATION

In analogy with the relation

$$\mathbf{D} = \epsilon \mathbf{E} \tag{4-31}$$

between the electric induction $\mathbf{D}$ and the electric field intensity $\mathbf{E}$, it is customary to write

$$\mathbf{H} = \mu^{-1}\mathbf{B} \qquad (8\text{-}20)$$

where the vector $\mathbf{H}$ defined by (8-20) is known as the *magnetic field intensity*. As the results of Sec. 7-10 clearly indicate, $\mathbf{B}$ is the magnetic vector which is analogous to $\mathbf{E}$. It will be demonstrated below that, in accordance with the definition (8-20), $\mathbf{H}$ is analogous to $\mathbf{D}$. The unfortunate nomenclature in use for $\mathbf{H}$ and $\mathbf{B}$ is to be regretted.

Since the units of $\mathbf{B}$ are webers/(meter)^2 = kilogram/coulomb second and those of μ are henrys/meter = kilogram meter/(coulomb)^2, it follows from (8-20) that the units of $\mathbf{H}$ are coulomb/second meter or, as more commonly stated, ampere-turns/meter.

The linear relationship between $\mathbf{B}$ and $\mathbf{H}$ expressed by (8-20) holds only for dia- and paramagnetic media. In the case of ferromagnetic media, one can use (8-20) to define a permeability, but it will be a function of $\mathbf{H}$ and the absolute temperature of the medium rather than a constant. The discussion which follows is limited to dia- and paramagnetic media.

Consider now a solenoid whose length is large compared with its radius (cf. Sec. 8-4). Let it be connected to a battery or other source of steady current through an ammeter which indicates the current flowing in the circuit. If the solenoid is in vacuum, the magnitude of the magnetic induction at a field point inside the solenoid and far from the ends is given by

$$B_0 = \mu_0 n i_t = \mu_0 H \qquad (8\text{-}21)$$

where μ_0 is the permeability of free space, n is the number of turns per unit length of the solenoid, and i_t is the current flowing in the circuit. The directions of $\mathbf{B}$ and current flow are related by the right-hand-screw rule. The significance of the subscript t on i will become clear from the discussion below.

If the solenoid is filled with a homogeneous isotropic medium of permeability μ, one observes that, aside from a momentary deflection of the ammeter pointer, the current flowing in the circuit is still i_t. Hence the magnetic induction at the field point inside the solenoid is

$$B = \mu n i_t = \mu H = \mu_0 K_m H \qquad (8\text{-}22)$$

Subtraction of (8-21) from (8-22) yields

$$(\mu - \mu_0)n i_t \equiv \mu_0 n i_M = \mu_0(K_m - 1)H \qquad (8\text{-}23)$$

where

$$i_M \equiv (K_m - 1)i_t \qquad (8\text{-}24)$$

is known as the *magnetization current*.

Since the current through the solenoid remained the same while the magnetic induction changed, we are led to assume that when the medium of permeability μ was placed inside the solenoid, it developed a solenoidal current ni_M per unit length of its surface adjacent to the solenoid and, consequently, a magnetic moment per unit length of magnitude

$$ni_MS = (K_m - 1)HS$$

The magnetic moment per unit volume, called the *magnetization* and denoted by **M**, is then

$$\mathbf{M} = (K_m - 1)\mathbf{H} = \chi_m\mathbf{H} \tag{8-25}$$

where
$$\chi_m = K_m - 1 \tag{8-26}$$

is called the *magnetic susceptibility*.

By the use of Eq. (8-20), Eq. (8-25) can be rewritten

$$\mathbf{M} = \mu_0^{-1}\mathbf{B} - \mathbf{H}$$

or
$$\mathbf{H} = \mu_0^{-1}\mathbf{B} - \mathbf{M} \tag{8-27}$$

If one introduces the vector $\mathbf{M'} = -\mathbf{M}$, Eqs. (8-25) and (8-27) can be written

$$\mathbf{M'} = \mu_0^{-1}(K_m^{-1} - 1)\mathbf{B} \tag{8-28}$$
$$\mathbf{H} = \mu_0^{-1}\mathbf{B} + \mathbf{M'} \tag{8-29}$$

in analogy with the corresponding electrostatic equations

$$\mathbf{P} = \epsilon_0(K - 1)\mathbf{E} \tag{4-24}$$
$$\mathbf{D} = \epsilon_0\mathbf{E} + \mathbf{P} \tag{4-31}$$

There is one difference between Eqs. (8-28) and (4-24); namely, K_m may be greater than or less than unity, while K is never less than unity. Thus, while **P** is always in the same direction as **E**, **M'** may be either in the same direction as **B** or in the opposite direction.

From (8-29) it follows that

$$\text{div } \mathbf{H} = \text{div } \mathbf{M'} = -\text{div } \mathbf{M} \tag{8-30}$$

since div **B** = 0. Furthermore, from (8-20)

$$\text{div } \mathbf{B} = \text{div } (\mu\mathbf{H}) = \mu \text{ div } \mathbf{H} + \mathbf{H} \cdot \text{grad } \mu = 0$$

For homogeneous isotropic media grad $\mu = 0$ and, consequently,

$$\text{div } \mathbf{H} = 0$$

On the other hand, grad $\mu \neq 0$ in nonhomogeneous or anisotropic media. For such media

$$\text{div } \mathbf{H} = -\mathbf{H} \cdot \frac{1}{\mu} \text{ grad } \mu = -\mathbf{H} \cdot \text{grad } (\ln \mu) \tag{8-31}$$

One can then define a *magnetic density* ρ_m by the relation

$$\rho_m = -\mathbf{H} \cdot \text{grad} \, (\ln \mu) \tag{8-32}$$

so that (8-31) becomes

$$\text{div} \, \mathbf{H} = \rho_m \tag{8-33}$$

which is analogous to the electrostatic relation

$$\text{div} \, \mathbf{D} = \rho_F \tag{4-32}$$

From (8-30) and (8-33) it follows that

$$\text{div} \, \mathbf{M}' = - \, \text{div} \, \mathbf{M} = \rho_m \tag{8-34}$$

which is analogous to the electrostatic relation

$$- \, \text{div} \, \mathbf{P} = \rho_P \tag{4-30}$$

8-6. THE VECTOR POTENTIAL

It was demonstrated in Sec. 8-3 that the magnetic induction $\mathbf{B}$ cannot be expressed in terms of a scalar potential in regions containing currents. One can, however, introduce a vector potential which is generally useful.

Since div $\mathbf{B} = 0$ and the divergence of the curl of any vector is also zero, we can introduce a vector $\mathbf{A}$ such that

$$\mathbf{B} = \text{curl} \, \mathbf{A} \tag{8-35}$$

Then, using (8-13),

$$\text{curl} \, \mathbf{B} = \text{curl} \, \text{curl} \, \mathbf{A} = \nabla(\nabla \cdot \mathbf{A}) - \nabla^2 \mathbf{A} = \mu \mathbf{j} \tag{8-36}$$

Since (8-35) does not completely specify the vector $\mathbf{A}$, we complete the specification by requiring that

$$\text{div} \, \mathbf{A} = 0 \tag{8-37}$$

so that (8-36) reduces to

$$\nabla^2 \mathbf{A} = -\mu \mathbf{j} \tag{8-38}$$

The solution of (8-38) is

$$\mathbf{A} = \iiint \frac{\mu \mathbf{j}}{4\pi r} \, d\tau \tag{8-39}$$

and the vector $\mathbf{A}$ is known as the *vector potential*.

8-7. THE MUTUAL ENERGY OF TWO CIRCUITS

The force $\mathbf{F}_m$ on a charge q moving with velocity v in a field of magnetic induction $\mathbf{B}$ is, according to (7-64),

$$\mathbf{F}_m = q(\mathbf{v} \times \mathbf{B}) \tag{8-40}$$

If the induction $\mathbf{B}$ is due to a current i_1 flowing in a circuit $\mathbf{s}_1$, then (8-40) becomes

$$\mathbf{F}_m = q\left(\mathbf{v} \times \frac{\mu i_1}{4\pi} \oint_1 \frac{d\mathbf{s}_1 \times \mathbf{r}}{r^3}\right) \qquad (8\text{-}41)$$

where $\mathbf{r}$ is the vector from the circuit element $d\mathbf{s}_1$ to the charge q.   Now let

$$\mathbf{v} = \frac{d\mathbf{s}_2}{dt}$$

and

$$q = \lambda \, d\mathbf{s}_2$$

so that

$$q\mathbf{v} = \lambda\mathbf{v} \, ds_2 = \lambda v \, d\mathbf{s}_2 \equiv i_2 \, d\mathbf{s}_2 \qquad (8\text{-}42)$$

Substitution of (8-42) into (8-41) yields

$$\mathbf{F}_m \equiv d\mathbf{F}_{m_2} = \frac{\mu i_1 i_2}{4\pi}\left(d\mathbf{s}_2 \times \oint_1 \frac{d\mathbf{s}_1 \times \mathbf{r}}{r^3}\right) \qquad (8\text{-}43)$$

as the force on the current element $i_2 \, d\mathbf{s}_2$ due to the current i_1 flowing in the circuit $\mathbf{s}_1$.   Integration of (8-43) over the circuit $\mathbf{s}_2$ gives

$$\mathbf{F}_{m_2} = \frac{\mu i_1 i_2}{4\pi}\left(\oint_2 d\mathbf{s}_2 \times \oint_1 \frac{d\mathbf{s}_1 \times \mathbf{r}}{r^3}\right) \qquad (8\text{-}44)$$

as the force on the circuit $\mathbf{s}_2$ due to the current i_1 in the circuit $\mathbf{s}_1$.   But by expanding the triple vector product

$$
\begin{aligned}
\mathbf{F}_{m_2} &= \frac{\mu i_1 i_2}{4\pi}\oint_2\oint_1\left[\frac{d\mathbf{s}_2 \cdot \mathbf{r}}{r^3}\,d\mathbf{s}_1 - (d\mathbf{s}_1 \cdot d\mathbf{s}_2)\frac{\mathbf{r}}{r^3}\right]\\
&= -\frac{\mu i_1 i_2}{4\pi}\oint_2\oint_1 (d\mathbf{s}_1 \cdot d\mathbf{s}_2)\frac{\mathbf{r}}{r^3}\\
&= -\frac{\mu i_1 i_2}{4\pi}\oint_2\oint_1 \nabla\frac{d\mathbf{s}_1 \cdot d\mathbf{s}_2}{r} \qquad (8\text{-}45)
\end{aligned}
$$

since $\nabla = -\nabla_1$ and

$$\oint_2 \frac{d\mathbf{s}_2 \cdot \mathbf{r}}{r^3} = \oint_2 \nabla\frac{1}{r} \cdot d\mathbf{s}_2 = 0$$

It then follows that the mutual energy of the two circuits is

$$W_m = \frac{\mu i_1 i_2}{4\pi}\oint_2\oint_1 \frac{d\mathbf{s}_1 \cdot d\mathbf{s}_2}{r} \qquad (8\text{-}46)$$

When the currents i_1 and i_2 are each unity, Eq. (8-46) gives the *mutual inductance* of the two circuits,

$$M_{12} = M_{21} = \frac{\mu}{4\pi}\oint_2\oint_1 \frac{d\mathbf{s}_1 \cdot d\mathbf{s}_2}{r} \qquad (8\text{-}47)$$

The self-energy of a single circuit can be obtained from (8-46) by setting $i_2 = i_1$ and $ds_2 = ds_1'$. Then

$$W_m = \frac{\mu i_1{}^2}{4\pi} \oint_1 \oint_1 \frac{ds_1 \cdot ds_1'}{r} = L_1 i_1{}^2 \tag{8-48}$$

where
$$L_1 \equiv \frac{\mu}{4\pi} \oint_1 \oint_1 \frac{ds_1 \cdot ds_1'}{r} \tag{8-49}$$

is known as the *self-inductance* of the circuit 1.

The integral (8-46) can be written

$$W_m = \frac{\mu i_1 i_2}{8\pi} \oint \oint \frac{ds_1 \cdot ds_2}{r} \tag{8-50}$$

where the factor ½ has been introduced because the contour integrals now cover *each* of the circuits twice.

8-8. ENERGY IN THE MAGNETIC FIELD

It is of interest to express the mutual energy of the two circuits in terms of the field vectors.   Let us suppose that the current i_1 in the circuit 1 flows in a wire of cross section S_1.   Then

$$i_1 = \iint \mathbf{j}_1 \cdot d\mathbf{S}_1 = \iint j_1 \frac{ds_1 \cdot d\mathbf{S}_1}{ds_1} \tag{8-51}$$

where j_1 is the current density and the integration is over the cross section of the wire.   Similarly, if the current i_2 flows in a wire of cross section S_2,

$$i_2 = \iint j_2 \frac{ds_2 \cdot d\mathbf{S}_2}{ds_2} \tag{8-52}$$

Substitution of (8-51) into (8-50) yields

$$W_m = \frac{\mu i_2}{8\pi} \iint j_1 \frac{ds_1 \cdot d\mathbf{S}_1}{ds_1} \oint \oint \frac{ds_1 \cdot ds_2}{r}$$

$$= \frac{\mu i_2}{8\pi} \oint \oint \iint j_1 \frac{ds_1 \cdot d\mathbf{S}_1}{r} \frac{ds_1 \cdot ds_2}{ds_1}$$

$$= \frac{i_2}{2} \oint \left(\int \frac{\mu j_1}{4\pi r} d\tau_1 \right) \cdot ds_2$$

or
$$W_m = \frac{i_2}{2} \oint \mathbf{A}_1 \cdot ds_2 \tag{8-53}$$

where $d\tau_1 = ds_1 \cdot d\mathbf{S}_1$ and $\mathbf{A}_1$ is the vector potential at the current element $i_2 \, ds_2$ due to the current i_1 flowing in circuit 1.

Substitution of (8-52) into (8-53) yields

$$W_m = \frac{1}{2} \iint j_2 \frac{ds_2 \cdot dS_2}{ds_2} \oint \mathbf{A}_1 \cdot d\mathbf{s}_2$$

$$= \tfrac{1}{2} \iint \oint \mathbf{A}_1 \cdot j_2 (d\mathbf{s}_2 \cdot d\mathbf{S}_2)$$

$$= \tfrac{1}{2} \int j_2 \cdot \mathbf{A}_1 \, d\tau_2 \tag{8-54}$$

where $d\tau_2 = d\mathbf{s}_2 \cdot d\mathbf{S}_2$. Since $j_2 = 0$ outside the circuit 2, the integral in (8-54) can be taken over all space. In general,

$$W_m = \tfrac{1}{2}\!\int\! \mathbf{j} \cdot \mathbf{A} \, d\tau \tag{8-55}$$

where $\mathbf{j}$ is the current density in the volume element $d\tau$ and $\mathbf{A}$ is the vector potential at $d\tau$ due to all sources *except* those in $d\tau$.

Since

$$\text{div} \, (\mathbf{H} \times \mathbf{A}) = \mathbf{A} \cdot \text{curl} \, \mathbf{H} - \mathbf{H} \cdot \text{curl} \, \mathbf{A}$$
$$= \mathbf{A} \cdot \mathbf{j} - \mathbf{H} \cdot \mathbf{B}$$

by Eqs. (8-13) and (8-20), (8-55) becomes

$$W_m = \tfrac{1}{2}\!\int \text{div} \, (\mathbf{H} \times \mathbf{A}) \, d\tau + \tfrac{1}{2}\!\int\! \mathbf{H} \cdot \mathbf{B} \, d\tau$$
$$= \tfrac{1}{2}\!\iint (\mathbf{H} \times \mathbf{A}) \cdot d\mathbf{S} + \tfrac{1}{2}\!\int\! \mathbf{H} \cdot \mathbf{B} \, d\tau \tag{8-56}$$

where $d\mathbf{S}$ is an element of the surface S which bounds the volume τ. If the volume τ includes all space, the surface integral vanishes and (8-56) reduces to

$$W_m = \tfrac{1}{2}\!\int\! \mathbf{H} \cdot \mathbf{B} \, d\tau \tag{8-57}$$

This expression for the energy in the magnetic field is analogous to the relation

$$W = \tfrac{1}{2}\!\int\! \mathbf{D} \cdot \mathbf{E} \, d\tau \tag{2-45}$$

for the energy in the electrostatic field.

EXERCISES

8-1. Show that the potential energy of a magnetic dipole of moment $\mathbf{p}_m$ in a constant induction field $\mathbf{B}$ is $W_m = -\mathbf{p}_m \cdot \mathbf{B}$.

8-2. Show that the force $\mathbf{F}_m$ on a magnetic dipole of moment $\mathbf{p}_m$ fixed in an inhomogeneous induction field $\mathbf{B}$ is given by

$$\mathbf{F}_m = (\mathbf{p}_m \cdot \mathbf{\nabla})\mathbf{B}$$

8-3. Derive the expression for the mutual potential energy of two magnetic dipoles $\mathbf{p}_{m_1}$ and $\mathbf{p}_{m_2}$, the former located at the origin of coordinates, the latter at a point $\mathbf{r}$ distant from the origin. Then calculate the force in the $\mathbf{r}$ direction and the couple exerted on $\mathbf{p}_{m_2}$ by $\mathbf{p}_{m_1}$.

8-4. Consider a surface separating two media, one of permeability μ_1, the other of permeability μ_2. Show that the boundary conditions at this interface are (a) the normal component of the magnetic induction **B** is continuous and (b) the tangential component of the magnetic field intensity **H** is continuous.

8-5. Find the magnetic induction due to a small plane circuit of arbitrary shape at a point P whose distance from the circuit is large compared with the linear dimensions of the circuit.

8-6. Find the magnetic induction due to a circular current of radius a at a point P whose distance from the center of the circle is $r > a$. Then obtain the magnetic induction in the special cases when (a) P is in the plane of the circle and (b) P is on the axis of the circle.

8-7. Find the mutual inductance between a circular current i_1 of radius a and an infinite straight-line current i_2 in the same plane. Then calculate the force between the circuits.

8-8. Consider the interface between two media, one of permeability μ_1, the other of permeability μ_2. Show that the boundary conditions on the vector potential A at this interface are

(a) $A_{2t} = A_{1t}$

(b) $\dfrac{1}{\mu_1} (\nabla \times \mathbf{A})_{1t} = \dfrac{1}{\mu_2} (\nabla \times \mathbf{A})_{2t}$

where the subscript t denotes the tangential component.

8-9. The vector potential **A** at a point r distant from a volume element $d\tau$ in which there flows current of density j is given by (8-39). Let the positions at which **A** is to be determined be specified by the vector **R**, and let the position of the volume element be specified by $\mathbf{r'}$. Then $r = |\mathbf{R} - \mathbf{r'}|$ and

$$\mathbf{A} = \frac{\mu}{4\pi} \int \frac{\mathbf{j}}{|\mathbf{R} - \mathbf{r'}|} \, d\tau$$

Show that, if $R \gg r'$, that is, if the point at which **A** is to be determined is far from all the currents, then the multipole expansion for the vector potential is

$$\mathbf{A} = \frac{\mu}{4\pi} \int \mathbf{j} \left[\frac{1}{R} + \frac{\mathbf{r'} \cdot \mathbf{R}}{R^3} + \frac{3(\mathbf{r'} \cdot \mathbf{R})^2 - r'^2 R^2}{2R^5} + \cdots \right] d\tau$$

For stationary currents, $\int \mathbf{j} \, d\tau = 0$.

REFERENCES

Abraham, M., and R. Becker: "The Classical Theory of Electricity and Magnetism," chaps. 7 and 9, Hafner Publishing Company, Inc., New York, 1950.

Panofsky, W. K. H., and M. Phillips: "Classical Electricity and Magnetism," chaps. 7, 8, and 10, Addison-Wesley Publishing Company, Inc., Cambridge, Mass., 1955.

Smythe, W. R.: "Static and Dynamic Electricity," 2d ed., chap. 7, McGraw-Hill Book Company, Inc., New York, 1950.

Sommerfeld, A.: "Electrodynamics," paragraphs 15 and 16, Academic Press, Inc., New York, 1952.

Stratton, J. A.: "Electromagnetic Theory," chaps. 2 and 4, McGraw-Hill Book Company, Inc., New York, 1941.

CHAPTER 9

The Equations of Maxwell and the Wave Equations

9-1. INTRODUCTION

The electrostatic field due to a stationary configuration of charge is completely described by the relations

$$\text{curl } \mathbf{E} = 0 \tag{2-11}$$
$$\text{div } \mathbf{D} = \text{div } (\epsilon\mathbf{E}) = \rho_F \tag{4-32}$$

The magnetic field due to steady currents is described by

$$\text{curl } \mathbf{B} = \mu\mathbf{j} \tag{8-13}$$
$$\text{div } \mathbf{B} = 0 \tag{8-14}$$

The four equations (2-11), (4-32), (8-13), and (8-14) are too restrictive to describe the electromagnetic field. We show in Sec. 9-2 that a non-conservative electric field is required to produce a steady current. Thus (2-11) is violated and must be replaced by a more general relation. Also (8-13) must be replaced by a more general relation which applies to nonsteady as well as steady currents.

The generalization of (2-11) is known as the differential form of Faraday's law and is discussed in Sec. 9-5. The generalization of (8-13) is carried out in Sec. 9-6. These two relations plus (4-32) and (8-14) constitute the four fundamental equations describing the electromagnetic field which are known as Maxwell's equations.

The remainder of the chapter is concerned with the wave equations which are a direct consequence of Maxwell's equations.

9-2. OHM'S LAW AND JOULE'S LAW

The electric current density $\mathbf{j}$ within a conductor depends on the electric field intensity $\mathbf{E}'$ in the conductor. This dependence is usually expressed by the linear relation

$$\mathbf{j} = \sigma\mathbf{E}' \tag{9-1}$$

155

in which σ is known as the *electric conductivity*. In the case of isotropic conductors σ is a scalar quantity; in anisotropic conductors it is a symmetric tensor. In most of what follows we shall confine our attention to homogeneous isotropic conductors in which σ is a constant (that is, $\nabla\sigma = 0$). Equation (9-1) is known as the *differential form of Ohm's law*.

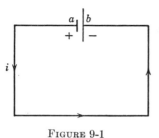

FIGURE 9-1

The work performed in carrying a unit positive charge once around an electric circuit is called the *emf* and denoted by the symbol $\mathcal{E}$. According to (9-1)

$$\mathcal{E} = \oint \mathbf{E'} \cdot d\mathbf{s} = \oint \frac{\mathbf{j}}{\sigma} \cdot d\mathbf{s} \qquad (9\text{-}2)$$

where $d\mathbf{s}$ is an element of the circuit s. If there is a steady flow of current in the circuit, $\mathbf{j} \cdot d\mathbf{s} \neq 0$. Hence $\oint \mathbf{E'} \cdot d\mathbf{s} \neq 0$ and the electric field cannot be a purely conservative field. We therefore rewrite (9-1) as

$$\mathbf{j} = \sigma(\mathbf{E} + \mathbf{E}^{(e)}) \qquad (9\text{-}3)$$

where $\mathbf{E}$ represents the conservative part of the field and $\mathbf{E}^{(e)}$, the so-called *impressed* or *applied* force per unit charge, represents the nonconservative part of the field. Practically, the impressed forces are produced by voltaic cells or other generators. Outside such generators, $\mathbf{E}^{(e)} = 0$.

Consider a circuit composed of a homogeneous isotropic linear conductor of length l, uniform cross section S, and conductivity σ in series with a generator (Fig. 9-1). The current flowing through the conductor is

$$i = \iint \mathbf{j} \cdot d\mathbf{S} = \sigma \iint \mathbf{E'} \cdot d\mathbf{S} = \sigma \iint \mathbf{E} \cdot d\mathbf{S} \qquad (9\text{-}4)$$

where $d\mathbf{S}$ is an element of the cross section. If the current flow is steady, (9-4) reduces to

$$i = \sigma E S \qquad (9\text{-}5)$$

Then
$$\int_a^b i\, ds = il = \sigma S \int_a^b E\, ds = \sigma S(\phi_b - \phi_a) \qquad (9\text{-}6)$$

or
$$\phi_b - \phi_a = \frac{l}{\sigma S} i \equiv Ri \qquad (9\text{-}7)$$

The quantity

$$R = \frac{l}{\sigma S} \qquad (9\text{-}8)$$

is known as the *resistance* of the conductor of length l, cross section S, and conductivity σ. The unit of resistance is called the *ohm*. Since the unit of potential is the volt and the unit of current the ampere, it follows from (9-7) that

$$1 \text{ ohm} = 1 \frac{\text{volt}}{\text{ampere}} \tag{9-9}$$

Then, from (9-8), the unit of conductivity is found to be mho/meter, where 1 mho = $(1 \text{ ohm})^{-1}$.

Equation (9-7) is the mathematical statement of *Ohm's law:* The potential difference between the ends of a linear conductor is equal to the product of the resistance of the conductor with the current which is flowing through it.

Joule's law states that the rate $\mathcal{P}$ at which heat is developed in a conductor of resistance R in which is flowing a current i is given by

$$\mathcal{P} = Ri^2 \tag{9-10}$$

The rate at which heat is developed per unit volume of the conductor is then

$$\frac{\mathcal{P}}{lS} = \frac{R}{lS} i^2 = \sigma \left(\frac{i}{\sigma S} \right)^2 = \sigma E^2 = \sigma E'^2 = \mathbf{j} \cdot (\mathbf{E} + \mathbf{E}^{(e)}) \tag{9-11}$$

The unit of power is called the *watt*. Clearly

$$1 \text{ watt} = (1 \text{ ohm})(1 \text{ ampere})^2 = (1 \text{ volt})(1 \text{ ampere}) \tag{9-12}$$

9-3. THE ELECTRIC CIRCUIT

Consider again the circuit of Fig. 9-1. According to Eq. (9-2) the emf is given by

$$\mathcal{E} = \oint \mathbf{E}' \cdot d\mathbf{s} = \int_a^b \mathbf{E} \cdot d\mathbf{s} + \int_b^a (\mathbf{E} + \mathbf{E}^{(e)}) \cdot d\mathbf{s}$$

$$= \oint \mathbf{E} \cdot d\mathbf{s} + \int_b^a \mathbf{E}^{(e)} \cdot d\mathbf{s} \tag{9-13}$$

$$\mathcal{E} = \int_b^a \mathbf{E}^{(e)} \cdot d\mathbf{s} = \oint \frac{\mathbf{j}}{\sigma} \cdot d\mathbf{s} \tag{9-13a}$$

since $\oint \mathbf{E} \cdot d\mathbf{s} = 0$. Equation (9-13a) states that the electric current is due to the impressed force alone.

If the circuit of Fig. 9-1 is opened, the impressed force $\mathbf{E}^{(e)}$ and the electrostatic field $\mathbf{E}$ counterbalance each other within the generator: $\int_b^a (\mathbf{E} + \mathbf{E}^{(e)}) \cdot d\mathbf{s} = 0$. It follows, then, from (9-13) that

$$\mathcal{E} = \int_a^b \mathbf{E} \cdot d\mathbf{s} \tag{9-14}$$

which states that the emf equals the open-circuit potential difference.

The rate at which heat is developed in the circuit is

$$\mathcal{P} = \int \mathbf{j} \cdot (\mathbf{E} + \mathbf{E}^{(e)}) \, d\tau \tag{9-15}$$

where the integration is over the entire region traversed by the current. Since $\mathbf{E}$ is conservative,

$$\mathbf{j} \cdot \mathbf{E} = -\mathbf{j} \cdot \nabla \phi = \phi \operatorname{div} \mathbf{j} - \operatorname{div} (\phi \mathbf{j})$$

Hence in the steady state where div $\mathbf{j} = 0$, Eq. (9-15) becomes

$$\begin{aligned} \mathcal{P} &= \int \mathbf{j} \cdot \mathbf{E}^{(e)} \, d\tau - \int \operatorname{div} (\phi \mathbf{j}) \, d\tau \\ &= \int \mathbf{j} \cdot \mathbf{E}^{(e)} \, d\tau - \int\!\!\int \phi j_n \, dS \end{aligned} \tag{9-16}$$

where dS is an element of the surface S which bounds the volume τ and j_n is the component of $\mathbf{j}$ normal to the surface. But j_n must be zero at every point of S. Therefore

$$\mathcal{P} = \int \mathbf{j} \cdot \mathbf{E}^{(e)} \, d\tau \tag{9-17}$$

which states that the rate at which heat is dissipated in the circuit is equal to the rate at which the impressed force does work.

9-4. THE RELAXATION TIME

Consider a homogeneous conductor having a charge ρ_0 per unit volume. When it is placed in an electric field $\mathbf{E}$, a current of density

$$\mathbf{j} = \sigma \mathbf{E} \tag{9-18}$$

will be produced and there will be a dispersal of the charge. The time required for the charge to decrease to $1/e$th of its original value is called the *relaxation time* or *modulus of decay*.

Application of the equation of continuity (1-65) to the flow of electricity gives

$$\operatorname{div} \mathbf{j} = -\frac{\partial}{\partial t} \rho_F$$

which, using (9-18), can be written

$$\frac{\partial}{\partial t} \rho_F = -\operatorname{div} (\sigma \mathbf{E}) \tag{9-19}$$

But

$$\operatorname{div} \mathbf{D} = \operatorname{div} \epsilon \mathbf{E} = \rho_F \tag{4-32}$$

Hence, for constant σ and ϵ,

$$\frac{\partial}{\partial t} \rho_F = -\frac{\sigma}{\epsilon} \rho_F \tag{9-20}$$

the solution of which is

$$\rho_F = \rho_0 e^{-t/\tau} \tag{9-21}$$

where $\tau = \epsilon/\sigma$ is the relaxation time. For metals, τ is too small to be measured with any accuracy (i.e., for copper $\tau \simeq 10^{-18}$ sec).

According to (9-21) any original distribution of charge decays exponentially at a rate which is independent of any other electromagnetic disturbances which may be occurring simultaneously.

The result (9-21) justifies putting ρ_F equal to zero in most problems.

It should be noted that (9-21) refers only to the volume distribution of charge in a conductor and not to the surface distribution.

9-5. FARADAY'S LAW OF INDUCTION

In 1831 Faraday made the fundamental discovery that when the flux of magnetic induction through a closed circuit changes, a current is

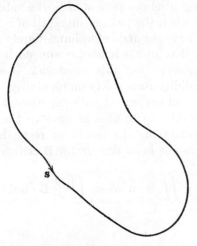

FIGURE 9-2

generated in the circuit. Consider a closed circuit s formed by a wire of resistance R (Fig. 9-2). Let S be an arbitrary surface bounded by the circuit. Then Faraday's law states that the current i generated by the flux of induction through the circuit is given by

$$Ri = -\frac{d}{dt} \iint \mathbf{B} \cdot \mathbf{n} \, dS \tag{9-22}$$

where $\mathbf{n}$ is the unit normal to the element dS of the arbitrary surface S. Its direction is that of the advance of a right-hand screw rotating in the direction in which the contour s is described.

According to (9-7), $Ri = \oint \mathbf{E} \cdot d\mathbf{s}$. Since there are no impressed forces acting in the circuit, it follows from (9-13) that $\mathcal{E} = \oint \mathbf{E} \cdot d\mathbf{s}$. Hence Eq. (9-22) can be rewritten

$$\mathcal{E} = \oint \mathbf{E} \cdot d\mathbf{s} = -\frac{d}{dt} \iint \mathbf{B} \cdot \mathbf{n} \, dS \tag{9-23}$$

which states that an emf equal to the negative time rate of change of the flux of induction through the circuit is induced. The minus sign expresses what is commonly known as *Lenz's law:* "The induced emf is in such a direction as to oppose the motion that generates it."

The law of induction (9-23) has been derived for a physical circuit, a wire of resistance R. Because (9-23) contains no reference to the circuit other than its shape, we make the conjecture that perhaps the law holds for any closed path whatever and is independent of the presence of the wire. This conjecture is strengthened by the fact that, because of the continuity of the tangential component of $\mathbf{E}$, the value of the line integral $\oint \mathbf{E} \cdot d\mathbf{s}$ is the same when the path of integration is along the wire itself and when it is along a curve outside but immediately adjacent to the wire. We therefore assert that (9-23) holds for any path whatever. It must be remembered, however, that this conclusion is an abstraction from experiment whose validity rests solely on its ability to lead to theoretical conclusions which are in agreement with experiment.

This new view permits us to pass at once to the differential form of Faraday's law of induction. In media at rest, the flux of induction changes only as far as the induction vector $\mathbf{B}$ changes. Hence

$$\frac{d}{dt} \iint \mathbf{B} \cdot \mathbf{n} \, dS = \iint \frac{\partial}{\partial t} \mathbf{B} \cdot \mathbf{n} \, dS \tag{9-24}$$

and (9-23) becomes

$$\oint \mathbf{E} \cdot d\mathbf{s} = -\iint \frac{\partial}{\partial t} \mathbf{B} \cdot \mathbf{n} \, dS \tag{9-25}$$

Since this relation holds for any surface element, however located, application of Stokes' theorem yields

$$\oint \mathbf{E} \cdot d\mathbf{s} = \iint \operatorname{curl} \mathbf{E} \cdot \mathbf{n} \, dS = -\iint \frac{\partial}{\partial t} \mathbf{B} \cdot \mathbf{n} \, dS$$

or
$$\operatorname{curl} \mathbf{E} = -\frac{\partial}{\partial t} \mathbf{B} \tag{9-26}$$

the differential form of Faraday's law.

9-6. THE DISPLACEMENT CURRENT

It was demonstrated in Sec. 8-3 that the relation

$$\text{curl } \mathbf{B} = \mu \mathbf{j} \tag{8-13}$$

holds only in the case of steady currents. We now seek a more general relation valid for all currents, nonsteady as well as steady.

Application of the equation of continuity (1-65) to the flow of electricity gives

$$\text{div } \mathbf{j} = -\frac{\partial}{\partial t} \rho_F$$

But according to (4-32), $\rho_F = \text{div } \mathbf{D}$. Consequently,

$$\text{div } \mathbf{j} = -\frac{\partial}{\partial t} (\text{div } \mathbf{D})$$

or

$$\text{div} \left(\mathbf{j} + \frac{\partial}{\partial t} \mathbf{D} \right) = 0 \tag{9-27}$$

Thus, even when div j is not zero, the divergence of the quantity (j + $\partial \mathbf{D}/\partial t$) is zero. Hence this quantity may always represent the curl of a vector. We therefore conjecture that the current density j in the right-hand member of (8-13) should be replaced by (j + $\partial \mathbf{D}/\partial t$), so that

$$\text{curl } \mathbf{B} = \mu \left(\mathbf{j} + \frac{\partial}{\partial t} \mathbf{D} \right) \tag{9-28}$$

The quantity $\partial \mathbf{D}/\partial t$ is called the *displacement current density* to distinguish it from j, the conduction current density.

The correctness of the conjecture that the conduction current density in (8-13) should be augmented by the displacement current density is attested to by the electromagnetic waves (cf. Chaps. 10 *et seq.*) whose existence is explained only because of the presence of the displacement current density in (9-28).

As written, Eq. (9-28) applies only to a homogeneous isotropic medium of permeability μ. However, explicit reference to the medium can be removed by rewriting it in terms of the magnetic field intensity $\mathbf{H}$. Since $\mathbf{H} = \mu^{-1}\mathbf{B}$, Eq. (9-28) becomes

$$\text{curl } \mathbf{H} = \mathbf{j} + \frac{\partial}{\partial t} \mathbf{D} \tag{9-28a}$$

which has general validity.

9-7. MAXWELL'S EQUATIONS IN STATIONARY MEDIA

The entire electromagnetic theory can be summarized in the form of four fundamental equations which are known as Maxwell's equations.

They are

$$\operatorname{curl} \mathbf{H} = \mathbf{j} + \frac{\partial}{\partial t}\mathbf{D} \qquad (9\text{-}28a)$$

$$\operatorname{curl} \mathbf{E} = -\frac{\partial}{\partial t}\mathbf{B} \qquad (9\text{-}26)$$

$$\operatorname{div} \mathbf{B} = 0 \qquad (8\text{-}14)$$

$$\operatorname{div} \mathbf{D} = \rho_F \qquad (4\text{-}32)$$

These equations are not complete in themselves. To obtain a complete system Maxwell's equations must be supplemented by the *constitutive equations*

$$\mathbf{D} = \epsilon\mathbf{E} \qquad (4\text{-}31)$$
$$\mathbf{H} = \mu^{-1}\mathbf{B} \qquad (8\text{-}20)$$
$$\mathbf{j} = \sigma(\mathbf{E} + \mathbf{E}^{(e)}) \qquad (9\text{-}3)$$

These equations apply to a nonferromagnetic isotropic body in which the conductivity is σ, the permittivity ϵ, and the permeability μ. $\mathbf{E}^{(e)}$ is the impressed electric force due to, say, a generator or battery. For our purposes $\mathbf{E}^{(e)}$ will usually be zero, so that, in such cases, (9-3) reduces to

$$\mathbf{j} = \sigma\mathbf{E} \qquad (9\text{-}29)$$

9-8. MAXWELL'S EQUATIONS AND THEIR RELATIVISTIC TRANSFORMATION

Consider two cartesian coordinate systems $OX_1X_2X_3$ and $O'X_1'X_2'X_3'$ with coincident X_1 and X_1' axes, and let the primed system be moving with a uniform velocity v in the X_1 direction with respect to the unprimed system. According to the first postulate of the special theory of relativity (cf. Sec. 7-2) the Maxwell equations must have the same form in each coordinate system. Thus, in the unprimed system the Maxwell equations are

$$\operatorname{curl} \mathbf{H} = \mathbf{j} + \frac{\partial}{\partial t}\mathbf{D} \qquad (9\text{-}28a)$$

$$\operatorname{curl} \mathbf{E} = -\frac{\partial}{\partial t}\mathbf{B} \qquad (9\text{-}26)$$

$$\operatorname{div} \mathbf{B} = 0 \qquad (8\text{-}14)$$

$$\operatorname{div} \mathbf{D} = \rho_F \qquad (4\text{-}32)$$

In the primed coordinate system they are

$$\operatorname{curl}' \mathbf{H}' = \mathbf{j}' + \frac{\partial}{\partial t'}\mathbf{D}' \qquad (9\text{-}30)$$

$$\operatorname{curl}' \mathbf{E}' = -\frac{\partial}{\partial t'}\mathbf{B}' \qquad (9\text{-}31)$$

$$\operatorname{div}' \mathbf{B}' = 0 \qquad (9\text{-}32)$$

$$\operatorname{div}' \mathbf{D}' = \rho_F' \qquad (9\text{-}33)$$

According to Sec. 7-3,

$$x_1' = \kappa(x_1 - vt) \qquad x_1 = \kappa(x_1' + vt')$$
$$x_2' = x_2 \qquad\qquad x_2 = x_2'$$
$$x_3' = x_3 \qquad\qquad x_3 = x_3'$$
$$t' = \kappa\left(t - \frac{v}{c^2}\,x_1\right) \qquad t = \kappa\left(t' + \frac{v}{c^2}\,x_1'\right)$$

Hence

$$\frac{\partial}{\partial x_1'} = \frac{\partial}{\partial x_1'}\frac{\partial x_1}{\partial x_1} + \frac{\partial}{\partial t'}\frac{\partial t'}{\partial x_1} = \kappa\left(\frac{\partial}{\partial x_1'} - \frac{v}{c^2}\frac{\partial}{\partial t'}\right)$$

$$\frac{\partial}{\partial x_2} = \frac{\partial}{\partial x_2'}$$

$$\frac{\partial}{\partial x_3} = \frac{\partial}{\partial x_3'}$$

$$\frac{\partial}{\partial t} = \frac{\partial}{\partial x_1'}\frac{\partial x_1'}{\partial t} + \frac{\partial}{\partial t'}\frac{\partial t'}{\partial t} = \kappa\left(\frac{\partial}{\partial t'} - v\frac{\partial}{\partial x_1'}\right)$$

so that

$$\text{curl } \mathbf{E} = \mathbf{i}_1\left(\frac{\partial}{\partial x_2}E_3 - \frac{\partial}{\partial x_3}E_2\right) + \mathbf{i}_2\left(\frac{\partial}{\partial x_3}E_1 - \frac{\partial}{\partial x_1}E_3\right)$$
$$+ \mathbf{i}_3\left(\frac{\partial}{\partial x_1}E_2 - \frac{\partial}{\partial x_2}E_1\right)$$
$$= \mathbf{i}_1\left(\frac{\partial}{\partial x_2'}E_3 - \frac{\partial}{\partial x_3'}E_2\right) + \mathbf{i}_2\left(\frac{\partial}{\partial x_3'}E_1 - \frac{\partial}{\partial x_1'}\kappa E_3 + \frac{\kappa v}{c^2}\frac{\partial}{\partial t'}E_3\right)$$
$$+ \mathbf{i}_3\left(\frac{\partial}{\partial x_1'}\kappa E_2 - \frac{\kappa v}{c^2}\frac{\partial}{\partial t'}E_2 - \frac{\partial}{\partial x_2'}E_1\right)$$

and

$$-\frac{\partial}{\partial t}\mathbf{B} = -\kappa\left(\frac{\partial}{\partial t'} - v\frac{\partial}{\partial x_1'}\right)\mathbf{B}$$

Therefore

$$\frac{\partial}{\partial x_2'}E_3 - \frac{\partial}{\partial x_3'}E_2 = -\kappa\frac{\partial}{\partial t'}B_1 + \kappa v\frac{\partial}{\partial x_1'}B_1$$

$$\frac{\partial}{\partial x_3'}E_1 - \frac{\partial}{\partial x_1'}\kappa E_3 + \frac{\kappa v}{c^2}\frac{\partial}{\partial t'}E_3 = -\kappa\frac{\partial}{\partial t'}B_2 + \kappa v\frac{\partial}{\partial x_1'}B_2$$

$$\frac{\partial}{\partial x_1'}\kappa E_2 - \frac{\kappa v}{c^2}\frac{\partial}{\partial t'}E_2 - \frac{\partial}{\partial x_2'}E_1 = -\kappa\frac{\partial}{\partial t'}B_3 + \kappa v\frac{\partial}{\partial x_1'}B_3$$

so that (9-31) is satisfied provided that

$$E_1 = E_1' \qquad\qquad B_1 = B_1'$$
$$E_2 = \kappa(E_2' + vB_3') \qquad B_2 = \kappa\left(B_2' - \frac{v}{c^2}E_3'\right) \qquad (9\text{-}34)$$
$$E_3 = \kappa(E_3' - vB_2') \qquad B_3 = \kappa\left(B_3' + \frac{v}{c^2}E_2'\right)$$

or

$$\mathbf{E}_\parallel = \mathbf{E}_\parallel' \qquad\qquad\qquad \mathbf{B}_\parallel = \mathbf{B}_\parallel'$$
$$\mathbf{E}_\perp = \kappa(\mathbf{E}_\perp' - \mathbf{v}\times\mathbf{B}_\perp') \qquad \mathbf{B}_\perp = \kappa\left(\mathbf{B}_\perp' + \frac{\mathbf{v}}{c^2}\times\mathbf{E}_\perp'\right) \qquad (9\text{-}34a)$$

where $E_\parallel$, $B_\parallel$ and $E_\perp$, $B_\perp$ are the components of E and B parallel and normal to v, respectively.

The transformation equations (9-34) and (9-34a) can be solved for the primed quantities in terms of the unprimed quantities, yielding

$$E'_1 = E_1 \qquad\qquad B'_1 = B_1$$

$$E'_2 = \kappa(E_2 - vB_3) \qquad B'_2 = \kappa\left(B_2 + \frac{v}{c^2}E_3\right)$$

$$E'_3 = \kappa(E_3 + vB_2) \qquad B'_3 = \kappa\left(B_3 - \frac{v}{c^2}E_2\right) \tag{9-35}$$

or

$$E'_\parallel = E_\parallel \qquad\qquad B'_\parallel = B_\parallel$$

$$E'_\perp = \kappa(E_\perp + v \times B_\perp) \qquad B'_\perp = \kappa\left(B_\perp - \frac{v}{c^2} \times E_\perp\right) \tag{9-35a}$$

It should be remembered that E' and B' are the fields in the primed coordinate system at time t' when E and B are the fields in the unprimed coordinate system at time t.

The transformation equations for H and D can be obtained from (9-28a) and (9-30). Thus, from (9-28a)

$$\left(\frac{\partial}{\partial x_2}H_3 - \frac{\partial}{\partial x_3}H_2\right) = j_1 + \frac{\partial}{\partial t}D_1$$

$$\left(\frac{\partial}{\partial x_3}H_1 - \frac{\partial}{\partial x_1}H_3\right) = j_2 + \frac{\partial}{\partial t}D_2$$

$$\left(\frac{\partial}{\partial x_1}H_2 - \frac{\partial}{\partial x_2}H_1\right) = j_3 + \frac{\partial}{\partial t}D_3$$

Hence

$$\left(\frac{\partial}{\partial x'_2}H_3 - \frac{\partial}{\partial x'_3}H_2\right) = j_1 + \kappa\frac{\partial}{\partial t'}D_1 - \kappa v\frac{\partial}{\partial x'_1}D_1$$

$$\left(\frac{\partial}{\partial x'_3}H_1 - \kappa\frac{\partial}{\partial x'_1}H_3 + \kappa\frac{v}{c^2}\frac{\partial}{\partial t'}H_3\right) = j_2 + \kappa\frac{\partial}{\partial t'}D_2 - \kappa v\frac{\partial}{\partial x'_1}D_2$$

$$\left(\kappa\frac{\partial}{\partial x'_1}H_2 - \kappa\frac{v}{c^2}\frac{\partial}{\partial t'}H_2 - \frac{\partial}{\partial x'_2}H_1\right) = j_3 + \kappa\frac{\partial}{\partial t'}D_3 - \kappa v\frac{\partial}{\partial x'_1}D_3$$

and Eq. (9-30) is satisfied provided that

$$D_1 = D'_1 \qquad\qquad H_1 = H'_1 \qquad\qquad j_1 = \kappa j'_1 + v\rho'_F$$

$$D_2 = \kappa\left(D'_2 + \frac{v}{c^2}H'_3\right) \qquad H_2 = \kappa(H'_2 - vD'_3) \qquad j_2 = j'_2$$

$$D_3 = \kappa\left(D'_3 - \frac{v}{c^2}H'_2\right) \qquad H_3 = \kappa(H'_3 + vD'_2) \qquad j_3 = j'_3 \tag{9-36}$$

Solving for the primed quantities in terms of the unprimed quantities yields

$$D_1' = D_1 \qquad H_1' = H_1 \qquad j_1' = \kappa j_1 - v\rho_F$$

$$D_2' = \kappa\left(D_2 - \frac{v}{c^2}H_3\right) \qquad H_2' = \kappa(H_2 + vD_3) \qquad j_2' = j_2$$

$$D_3' = \kappa\left(D_3 + \frac{v}{c^2}H_2\right) \qquad H_3' = \kappa(H_3 - vD_2) \qquad j_3' = j_3 \tag{9-37}$$

The transformation equations for ρ_F are obtained from (4-32) and (9-33). Thus

$$\rho_F = \operatorname{div} \mathbf{D} = \frac{\partial}{\partial x_1}D_1 + \frac{\partial}{\partial x_2}D_2 + \frac{\partial}{\partial x_3}D_3$$

$$= \kappa\frac{\partial}{\partial x_1'}D_1 - \kappa\frac{v}{c^2}\frac{\partial}{\partial t'}D_1 + \frac{\partial}{\partial x_2'}D_2 + \frac{\partial}{\partial x_3'}D_3$$

$$= \kappa\frac{\partial}{\partial x_1'}D_1' - \kappa\frac{v}{c^2}\frac{\partial}{\partial t'}D_1' + \kappa\frac{\partial}{\partial x_2'}D_2' + \kappa\frac{v}{c^2}\frac{\partial}{\partial x_2'}H_3'$$

$$+ \kappa\frac{\partial}{\partial x_3'}D_3' - \kappa\frac{v}{c^2}\frac{\partial}{\partial x_3'}H_2'$$

$$= \kappa\operatorname{div}'\mathbf{D}' + \kappa\frac{v}{c^2}j_1' = \kappa\rho_F' + \kappa\frac{v}{c^2}j_1'$$

$$= \kappa\left(\rho_F' + \frac{\mathbf{v}\cdot\mathbf{j}'}{c^2}\right) \tag{9-38}$$

Similarly

$$\rho_F' = \kappa\left(\rho_F - \frac{\mathbf{v}\cdot\mathbf{j}}{c^2}\right) \tag{9-39}$$

9-9. THE WAVE EQUATIONS

In the case of a homogeneous isotropic medium at rest, Maxwell's equations become

$$\operatorname{curl}\mathbf{B} = \mu\mathbf{j} + \mu\epsilon\frac{\partial}{\partial t}\mathbf{E} = \mu\mathbf{j} + \frac{KK_m}{c^2}\frac{\partial}{\partial t}\mathbf{E} \tag{9-40}$$

$$\operatorname{curl}\mathbf{E} = -\frac{\partial}{\partial t}\mathbf{B} \tag{9-41}$$

$$\operatorname{div}\mathbf{B} = 0 \tag{9-42}$$

$$\operatorname{div}\mathbf{E} = \frac{\rho_F}{\epsilon} \tag{9-43}$$

where use has been made of the constitutive equations $\mathbf{D} = \epsilon\mathbf{E}$ and $\mathbf{H} = \mu^{-1}\mathbf{B}$ and the relation

$$\mu\epsilon = \frac{KK_m}{c^2} \tag{7-75}$$

in which K and K_m are, respectively, the relative permittivity and the relative permeability of the medium and c is the velocity of light in vacuum.

Taking the curl of (9-40) we obtain, after making use of the constitutive equation $\mathbf{j} = \sigma\mathbf{E}$,

$$\text{curl curl } \mathbf{B} = \mu\sigma \text{ curl } \mathbf{E} + \frac{KK_m}{c^2}\frac{\partial}{\partial t}\text{ curl } \mathbf{E}$$

$$= -\mu\sigma\frac{\partial}{\partial t}\mathbf{B} - \frac{KK_m}{c^2}\frac{\partial^2}{\partial t^2}\mathbf{B}$$

by (9-41). Hence, using the fact that

$$\text{curl curl } \mathbf{B} = \text{grad div } \mathbf{B} - \nabla^2\mathbf{B}$$
$$= -\nabla^2\mathbf{B}$$

because of (9-42), we obtain

$$\nabla^2\mathbf{B} - \frac{KK_m}{c^2}\frac{\partial^2}{\partial t^2}\mathbf{B} - \mu\sigma\frac{\partial}{\partial t}\mathbf{B} = 0 \qquad (9\text{-}44)$$

Similar consideration of Eq. (9-41) yields

$$\nabla^2\mathbf{E} - \frac{KK_m}{c^2}\frac{\partial^2}{\partial t^2}\mathbf{E} - \mu\sigma\frac{\partial}{\partial t}\mathbf{E} = \text{grad }\frac{\rho_F}{\epsilon} \qquad (9\text{-}45)$$

which reduces to

$$\nabla^2\mathbf{E} - \frac{KK_m}{c^2}\frac{\partial^2}{\partial t^2}\mathbf{E} - \mu\sigma\frac{\partial}{\partial t}\mathbf{E} = 0 \qquad (9\text{-}46)$$

if the density of free charge is zero.

Equations (9-44) and (9-46) are known as the *equations of telegraphy*.

In the case of nonconducting media, $\sigma = 0$ and the equations of telegraphy reduce to

$$\nabla^2\mathbf{B} - \frac{KK_m}{c^2}\frac{\partial^2}{\partial t^2}\mathbf{B} = 0 \qquad (9\text{-}47)$$

and

$$\nabla^2\mathbf{E} - \frac{KK_m}{c^2}\frac{\partial^2}{\partial t^2}\mathbf{E} = 0 \qquad (9\text{-}48)$$

the well-known *wave equations*.

9-10. GAUGE TRANSFORMATIONS

Consider the Maxwell equations in a homogeneous isotropic medium at rest, Eqs. (9-40) through (9-43). According to (9-42), div $\mathbf{B} = 0$. Since the divergence of the curl of any vector is always zero, we can write

$$\mathbf{B} = \text{curl } \mathbf{A} \qquad (9\text{-}49)$$

as was done in Sec. 8-6. Substitution for $\mathbf{B}$ in (9-41) by means of (9-49) then yields

$$\text{curl } \mathbf{E} = - \frac{\partial}{\partial t} \text{ curl } \mathbf{A}$$

or

$$\text{curl} \left(\mathbf{E} + \frac{\partial}{\partial t} \mathbf{A} \right) = 0 \qquad (9\text{-}50)$$

Since any vector whose curl is zero can be expressed as the gradient of a scalar function ϕ, we write

$$\mathbf{E} + \frac{\partial}{\partial t} \mathbf{A} = - \text{ grad } \phi \qquad (9\text{-}51)$$

which reduces to the familiar $\mathbf{E} = - \text{ grad } \phi$ when the vector potential $\mathbf{A}$ is independent of time.

Note that according to the relations (9-49) and (9-51) the field strengths $\mathbf{B}$ and $\mathbf{E}$ are completely determined by the vector and scalar potentials $\mathbf{A}$ and ϕ. However, the fields do not completely determine the potentials. Thus, the vector potential $\mathbf{A}$ in (9-49) can be replaced by the vector potential

$$\mathbf{A}' = \mathbf{A} - \nabla S$$

where S is an arbitrary scalar function, without changing the value of $\mathbf{B}$. When this substitution is made into (9-51) also, it is seen that the value of $\mathbf{E}$ remains unchanged provided that ϕ is replaced by the scalar potential

$$\phi' = \phi + \frac{\partial}{\partial t} S$$

Since the transformation

$$\mathbf{A}' = \mathbf{A} - \nabla S$$
$$\phi' = \phi + \frac{\partial}{\partial t} S \qquad (9\text{-}52)$$

leaves the field strengths $\mathbf{B}$ and $\mathbf{E}$ unchanged, it also leaves unchanged the form of Maxwell's equations (9-40) to (9-43). For this reason it is known as a *gauge transformation*. The function S is called the *gauge function*.

We noted above that the vector and scalar potentials are not completely specified by the relations (9-49) and (9-51). To complete their specification we may require that

$$\text{div } \mathbf{A} + \frac{KK_m}{c^2} \frac{\partial \phi}{\partial t} = 0 \qquad (9\text{-}53)$$

This is known as the *Lorentz condition*. When the vector and scalar potential satisfy (9-53), the gauge is known as a *Lorentz gauge*. The advantage of the Lorentz gauge will become evident in the following section.

Substitution of the gauge transformation equations (9-52) into (9-53) yields

$$\nabla^2 S - \frac{KK_m}{c^2} \frac{\partial^2}{\partial t^2} S = -\left(\text{div } \mathbf{A}' + \frac{KK_m}{c^2} \frac{\partial}{\partial t} \phi'\right) \qquad (9\text{-}54)$$

as the inhomogeneous wave equation which the gauge function S must satisfy. When the potentials $\mathbf{A}'$ and ϕ' satisfy the Lorentz condition, the gauge function S is a solution of the homogeneous wave equation

$$\nabla^2 S - \frac{KK_m}{c^2} \frac{\partial^2}{\partial t^2} S = 0 \qquad (9\text{-}55)$$

Thus, the Lorentz condition is invariant under those gauge transformations for which the gauge functions are solutions of the homogeneous wave equation.

Another interesting gauge is the so-called "solenoidal gauge" in which the divergence of the vector potential is zero. We make the transformation

$$\mathbf{A}_s = \mathbf{A} - \nabla S$$
$$\phi_s = \phi + \frac{\partial}{\partial t} S \qquad (9\text{-}56)$$

where $$\text{div } \mathbf{A}_s = 0 \qquad (9\text{-}57)$$

Then $\text{div } \mathbf{A}_s + \dfrac{KK_m}{c^2} \dfrac{\partial}{\partial t} \phi_s = \text{div } \mathbf{A} + \dfrac{KK_m}{c^2} \dfrac{\partial}{\partial t} \phi - \nabla^2 S + \dfrac{KK_m}{c^2} \dfrac{\partial^2}{\partial t^2} S$

or, using (9-57) and (9-53),

$$\frac{KK_m}{c^2} \frac{\partial}{\partial t} \phi_s = -\nabla^2 S + \frac{KK_m}{c^2} \frac{\partial^2}{\partial t^2} S \qquad (9\text{-}58)$$

Thus, in the solenoidal gauge the gauge function S is a solution of an inhomogeneous wave equation unless the scalar potential is independent of the time.

9-11. THE ELECTRODYNAMIC POTENTIALS

We begin with the relations

$$\mathbf{B} = \text{curl } \mathbf{A} \qquad (9\text{-}49)$$

$$\mathbf{E} = -\frac{\partial}{\partial t} \mathbf{A} - \text{grad } \phi \qquad (9\text{-}51)$$

derived in the preceding section from the Maxwell equations (9-41) and

(9-42). Substitution of these relations into the Maxwell equation (9-40) gives

$$\text{curl curl } \mathbf{A} = \mu\mathbf{j} + \frac{KK_m}{c^2}\frac{\partial}{\partial t}\left(-\frac{\partial}{\partial t}\mathbf{A} - \text{grad }\phi\right)$$

or $\quad \nabla^2\mathbf{A} - \frac{KK_m}{c^2}\frac{\partial^2}{\partial t^2}\mathbf{A} = -\mu\mathbf{j} + \text{grad}\left(\text{div }\mathbf{A} + \frac{KK_m}{c^2}\frac{\partial\phi}{\partial t}\right) \quad$ (9-59)

Taking the divergence of (9-51) yields

$$\text{div }\mathbf{E} + \frac{\partial}{\partial t}\text{div }\mathbf{A} = -\nabla^2\phi$$

or, using (9-43),

$$\nabla^2\phi = -\frac{\rho_F}{\epsilon} - \frac{\partial}{\partial t}\text{div }\mathbf{A} \qquad (9\text{-}60)$$

Note that the partial differential equations (9-59) and (9-60) for the potentials $\mathbf{A}$ and ϕ are coupled. If, however, we require the potentials to satisfy the Lorentz condition

$$\text{div }\mathbf{A} + \frac{KK_m}{c^2}\frac{\partial}{\partial t}\phi = 0 \qquad (9\text{-}53)$$

(9-59) and (9-60) reduce to

$$\nabla^2\mathbf{A} - \frac{KK_m}{c^2}\frac{\partial^2}{\partial t^2}\mathbf{A} = -\mu\mathbf{j} \qquad (9\text{-}61)$$

and $\quad \nabla^2\phi - \frac{KK_m}{c^2}\frac{\partial^2}{\partial t^2}\phi = -\frac{\rho_F}{\epsilon} \qquad$ (9-62)

Thus the advantage of the Lorentz gauge over other gauges is that in the Lorentz gauge the partial differential equations for the potentials are uncoupled.

The solutions of Eqs. (9-61) and (9-62) are (cf. Appendix II)

$$\mathbf{A}(x_1,x_2,x_3,t) = \frac{\mu}{4\pi}\int\!\!\!\int\!\!\!\int_{-\infty}^{\infty}\frac{\mathbf{j}(x_1',x_2',x_3',t \pm |\mathbf{r}-\mathbf{r}'|/v)}{[(x_1-x_1')^2 + (x_2-x_2')^2 + (x_3-x_3')^2]^{1/2}}dx_1'\,dx_2'\,dx_3'$$

(9-63)

and

$$\phi(x_1,x_2,x_3,t) = \frac{1}{4\pi\epsilon}\int\!\!\!\int\!\!\!\int_{-\infty}^{\infty}\frac{\rho_F(x_1',x_2',x_3',t \pm |\mathbf{r}-\mathbf{r}'|/v)}{[(x_1-x_2')^2 + (x_2-x_2')^2 + (x_3-x_3')^2]^{1/2}}dx_1'\,dx_2'\,dx_3'$$

(9-64)

respectively, in which

$$\mathbf{r} = x_1\mathbf{i}_1 + x_2\mathbf{i}_2 + x_3\mathbf{i}_3$$
$$\mathbf{r}' = x_1'\mathbf{i}_1 + x_2'\mathbf{i}_2 + x_3'\mathbf{i}_3$$

and $v = c/\sqrt{KK_m}$. Mathematically, both the plus and minus signs in $t \pm |\mathbf{r} - \mathbf{r}'|/v$ are valid. The solutions with the plus sign are known as the *advanced potentials*. Those with the minus sign are called *retarded potentials*. According to the principle of causality, only the retarded potentials are physically significant: A disturbance at the point (x_1', x_2', x_3') at the time $t - |\mathbf{r} - \mathbf{r}'|/v$ produces an effect at the point (x_1, x_2, x_3) at the later time t.

Substitution of (9-56) into (9-60) yields

$$\nabla^2 \phi_s = - \frac{\rho_F}{\epsilon} \tag{9-65}$$

Thus, in the solenoidal gauge the scalar potential satisfies Poisson's equation.

Similarly, substitution of (9-56) into (9-59) yields

$$\nabla^2 \mathbf{A}_s - \frac{KK_m}{c^2} \frac{\partial^2}{\partial t^2} \mathbf{A}_s = -\mu \mathbf{j} + \nabla \left(\frac{KK_m}{c^2} \frac{\partial}{\partial t} \phi_s \right) \tag{9-66}$$

where we have used (9-57).

When the charge density ρ_F is independent of the time t, the partial differential equations (9-65) and (9-66) for the potentials become uncoupled. Thus, from (9-65), when ρ_F is independent of the time, ϕ_s is the static, instantaneous Coulomb potential. Then the inhomogeneous wave equation (9-58) for the gauge function S reduces to the homogeneous wave equation (9-55), and (9-66) reduces to

$$\nabla^2 \mathbf{A}_s - \frac{KK_m}{c^2} \frac{\partial^2}{\partial t^2} \mathbf{A}_s = -\mu \mathbf{j}$$

where, from the equation of continuity, div $\mathbf{j} = 0$.

9-12. THE HERTZ POTENTIAL

We have seen in the preceding sections that the electromagnetic field can be described either by the field vectors $\mathbf{B}$ and $\mathbf{E}$ or by the electrodynamic potentials $\mathbf{A}$ and ϕ. Hertz showed that it is possible to describe the electromagnetic field in terms of a single vector function $\boldsymbol{\pi}$, which has since become known as the Hertz potential.

Suppose that

$$\mathbf{A} = \frac{KK_m}{c^2} \frac{\partial}{\partial t} \boldsymbol{\pi} \tag{9-67}$$

According to the Lorentz condition,

$$\text{div } \mathbf{A} + \frac{KK_m}{c^2} \frac{\partial}{\partial t} \phi = 0 \tag{9-53}$$

ϕ can be expressed in terms of π by the relation

$$\phi = -\operatorname{div} \pi \tag{9-68}$$

Then
$$\mathbf{B} = \operatorname{curl} \mathbf{A} = \frac{KK_m}{c^2} \frac{\partial}{\partial t} \operatorname{curl} \pi \tag{9-69}$$

and
$$\mathbf{E} = -\operatorname{grad} \phi - \frac{\partial}{\partial t} \mathbf{A} = \operatorname{grad} \operatorname{div} \pi - \frac{KK_m}{c^2} \frac{\partial^2}{\partial t^2} \pi \tag{9-70}$$

Substitution of (9-67) into (9-61) and (9-68) into (9-62) yields

$$\frac{KK_m}{c^2} \frac{\partial}{\partial t} \left(\nabla^2 \pi - \frac{KK_m}{c^2} \frac{\partial^2}{\partial t^2} \pi \right) = -\mu \mathbf{j} \tag{9-71}$$

and
$$-\operatorname{div} \left(\nabla^2 \pi - \frac{KK_m}{c^2} \frac{\partial^2}{\partial t^2} \pi \right) = -\frac{\rho_F}{\epsilon} \tag{9-72}$$

respectively. Since the current density $\mathbf{j}$ and charge density ρ_F satisfy the equation of continuity

$$\operatorname{div} \mathbf{j} + \frac{\partial}{\partial t} \rho_F = 0$$

we can introduce the vector $\boldsymbol{\wp}$ defined by the relations

$$\mathbf{j} = \epsilon \frac{\partial}{\partial t} \boldsymbol{\wp} \tag{9-73}$$

$$\rho_F = -\epsilon \operatorname{div} \boldsymbol{\wp} \tag{9-74}$$

Equations (9-71) and (9-72) then reduce to the identical equation

$$\nabla^2 \pi - \frac{KK_m}{c^2} \frac{\partial^2}{\partial t^2} \pi = -\boldsymbol{\wp} \tag{9-75}$$

The solution of (9-75) is

$$\pi(x_1, x_2, x_3, t) = \frac{1}{4\pi} \int\int\int_{-\infty}^{+\infty} \frac{\boldsymbol{\wp}(x_1', x_2', x_3', t - |\mathbf{r} - \mathbf{r}'|/v)}{[(x_1 - x_1')^2 + (x_2 - x_2')^2 + (x_3 - x_3')^2]^{1/2}} \, dx_1' \, dx_2' \, dx_3' \tag{9-76}$$

where $v = c/\sqrt{KK_m}$.

9-13. THE POYNTING VECTOR

Let us take the scalar product of (9-28a) with $-\mathbf{E}$ and of (9-26) with $\mathbf{H}$ and add. We obtain

$$\mathbf{H} \cdot \operatorname{curl} \mathbf{E} - \mathbf{E} \cdot \operatorname{curl} \mathbf{H} = \operatorname{div} (\mathbf{E} \times \mathbf{H})$$

$$= -\mathbf{H} \cdot \frac{\partial}{\partial t} \mathbf{B} - \mathbf{j} \cdot \mathbf{E} - \mathbf{E} \cdot \frac{\partial}{\partial t} \mathbf{D} \tag{9-77}$$

In the case where the constitutive equations (4-31), (8-20), and (9-3) are satisfied, (9-77) reduces to

$$\text{div } (\mathbf{E} \times \mathbf{H}) = - \left(\frac{j^2}{\sigma} - \mathbf{j} \cdot \mathbf{E}^{(e)} + \frac{\partial}{\partial t} \frac{\mathbf{D} \cdot \mathbf{E} + \mathbf{H} \cdot \mathbf{B}}{2} \right) \qquad (9\text{-}78)$$

Integration of (9-78) over any volume τ yields

$$\int \text{div } (\mathbf{E} \times \mathbf{H}) \, d\tau = \int (\mathbf{E} \times \mathbf{H}) \cdot d\mathbf{S}$$

$$= - \int \frac{j^2}{\sigma} \, d\tau + \int \mathbf{j} \cdot \mathbf{E}^{(e)} \, d\tau$$

$$- \frac{\partial}{\partial t} \int \frac{1}{2} (\mathbf{D} \cdot \mathbf{E} + \mathbf{H} \cdot \mathbf{B}) \, d\tau$$

or

$$- \frac{\partial}{\partial t} \int \frac{1}{2} (\mathbf{D} \cdot \mathbf{E} + \mathbf{H} \cdot \mathbf{B}) \, d\tau = \int \frac{j^2}{\sigma} \, d\tau - \int \mathbf{j} \cdot \mathbf{E}^{(e)} \, d\tau$$

$$+ \int (\mathbf{E} \times \mathbf{H}) \cdot d\mathbf{S} \quad (9\text{-}79)$$

where $d\mathbf{S}$ is an element of the surface bounding the volume τ.

Equation (9-79) is a statement of the conservation of energy. According to (2-45) and (8-57), the electromagnetic field possesses an energy density

$$w = \tfrac{1}{2}(\mathbf{D} \cdot \mathbf{E} + \mathbf{H} \cdot \mathbf{B}) \qquad (9\text{-}80)$$

Hence the left-hand member of (9-79) represents the time rate of decrease of the field energy in the volume τ. This decrease in the field energy is due to the transformation of electrical energy into heat, work done against impressed electric forces, and streaming of energy out of the volume τ, which are represented, respectively, by the terms in the right-hand member of (9-79).

The surface integral

$$\int \mathbf{N} \cdot d\mathbf{S} \equiv \int (\mathbf{E} \times \mathbf{H}) \cdot d\mathbf{S} \qquad (9\text{-}81)$$

represents the energy streaming out of the volume τ through its bounding surface S each second. The vector

$$\mathbf{N} \equiv \mathbf{E} \times \mathbf{H} \qquad (9\text{-}82)$$

is known as the *Poynting vector*, and the surface integral (9-81) as the *Poynting flux*.

It should be noted that the above remarks concerning the energy density and the Poynting flux are merely interpretations of (9-79). The entire interpretation is based on the fact that certain combinations of

Maxwell's equations can be split up into surface and volume integrals, as was done in Eq. (9-79). However, this equation is not unique in this respect. Consider, for example, div $(\mathbf{A} \times \mathbf{H})$, where $\mathbf{A}$ is the vector potential. Then

$$\text{div } (\mathbf{A} \times \mathbf{H}) = \mathbf{H} \cdot \text{curl } \mathbf{A} - \mathbf{A} \cdot \text{curl } \mathbf{H}$$
$$= \mathbf{H} \cdot \mathbf{B} - \mathbf{A} \cdot \text{curl } \mathbf{H}$$

so that

$$\frac{1}{2} \frac{\partial}{\partial t} \int \text{div } (\mathbf{A} \times \mathbf{H}) \, d\tau = \frac{1}{2} \frac{\partial}{\partial t} \int (\mathbf{A} \times \mathbf{H}) \cdot d\mathbf{S}$$

$$= \frac{1}{2} \frac{\partial}{\partial t} \int (\mathbf{H} \cdot \mathbf{B} - \mathbf{A} \cdot \text{curl } \mathbf{H}) \, d\tau$$

where dS is an element of the surface S bounding an arbitrary volume τ. Addition of this equation to (9-79) gives

$$-\frac{\partial}{\partial t} \int \frac{1}{2} (\mathbf{D} \cdot \mathbf{E} + \mathbf{A} \cdot \text{curl } \mathbf{H}) \, d\tau = \int \frac{j^2}{\sigma} \, d\tau - \int \mathbf{j} \cdot \mathbf{E}^{(e)} \, d\tau$$

$$+ \int \left[\mathbf{E} \times \mathbf{H} + \frac{1}{2} \frac{\partial}{\partial t} (\mathbf{A} \times \mathbf{H}) \right] \cdot d\mathbf{S}$$

This equation can also be considered as a statement of the conservation of energy. One can then interpret

$$\tfrac{1}{2}(\mathbf{D} \cdot \mathbf{E} + \mathbf{A} \cdot \text{curl } \mathbf{H}) \equiv \tfrac{1}{2}[\mathbf{D} \cdot \mathbf{E} + \mathbf{H} \cdot \mathbf{B} - \text{div } (\mathbf{A} \times \mathbf{H})] \quad (9\text{-}83)$$

as the energy density and the vector

$$\mathbf{E} \times \mathbf{H} + \frac{1}{2} \frac{\partial}{\partial t} (\mathbf{A} \times \mathbf{H}) \qquad\qquad (9\text{-}84)$$

as the rate of flow of energy per unit area.

In a like manner, one can obtain other expressions which can be interpreted as the energy density and the rate of flow of energy per unit area. We shall use the expressions (9-80) and (9-82) throughout the text. Their validity rests solely on their ability to lead to theoretical conclusions which are in agreement with experiment.

EXERCISES

9-1. A large sphere of radius b is made of material of conductivity σ and permittivity ϵ except for a concentric spherical cavity of radius $a < b$. At time $t = 0$, a charge Q_0 is uniformly distributed over the surface of the cavity. Show that, at any time $t > 0$, the charge Q on the surface of the cavity is given by

$$Q = Q_0 e^{-t/\tau} \qquad \tau = \frac{\epsilon}{\sigma}$$

In addition, show that the total Joule heat loss during the discharge is just equal to the decrease in the electrostatic energy and is given by

$$\frac{Q_0{}^2}{8\pi\epsilon}\left(\frac{1}{a}-\frac{1}{b}\right)$$

9-2. Consider the charging of a condenser, and show that the displacement current in the condenser is equal to the conduction current in the circuit.

9-3. Consider two cartesian coordinate systems $OX_1X_2X_3$ and $O'X_1'X_2'X_3'$ with coincident X_1 and X_1' axes, and let the primed system be moving with a uniform velocity in the X_1 direction with respect to the unprimed system. Continue the discussion of Sec. 9-8, and, using the constitutive equations

$$\mathbf{B} = \mu\mathbf{H} \qquad \mathbf{B'} = \mu\mathbf{H'}$$
$$\mathbf{j} = \sigma\mathbf{E} \qquad \mathbf{j'} = \sigma'\mathbf{E'}$$

obtain (a) the transformation equations for $\mathbf{P}$ and $\mathbf{M}$ and (b) the transformation equations for σ.

Also, show that the general forms of the constitutive equations, applicable to both reference systems, are

$$\mathbf{D} + \frac{\mathbf{v} \times \mathbf{H}}{c^2} = \epsilon(\mathbf{E} + \mathbf{v} \times \mathbf{B})$$

$$\mathbf{B} - \frac{\mathbf{v} \times \mathbf{E}}{c^2} = \mu(\mathbf{H} - \mathbf{v} \times \mathbf{D})$$

where $\mathbf{v}$ is zero in the unprimed coordinate system.

9-4. Verify that Faraday's law of induction (9-24) can be written

$$\oint \mathbf{E} \cdot d\mathbf{s} = -\frac{d}{dt}\oint \mathbf{A} \cdot d\mathbf{s}$$

where $\mathbf{A}$ is the vector potential. Then show that

$$\mathbf{E} = -\operatorname{grad} \phi = \frac{\partial}{\partial t}\mathbf{A}$$

where ϕ is the scalar potential.

9-5. A point charge q moves in empty space with a velocity $\mathbf{u}$. Show that for this case the retarded potentials (9-63) and (9-64) reduce to the *Lienard-Wiechert potentials*

$$\mathbf{A}(x_1,x_2,x_3,t) = \frac{\mu_0}{4\pi}\frac{q\mathbf{u}}{R - \dfrac{\mathbf{R}\cdot\mathbf{u}}{c}}\bigg|_{t-R/c}$$

$$\phi(x_1,x_2,x_3,t) = \frac{1}{4\pi\epsilon_0}\frac{q}{R - \dfrac{\mathbf{R}\cdot\mathbf{u}}{c}}\bigg|_{t-R/c}$$

where $\mathbf{R} = \mathbf{r} - \mathbf{r'} = (x_1 - x_1')\mathbf{i}_1 + (x_2 - x_2')\mathbf{i}_2 + (x_3 - x_3')\mathbf{i}_3$.

9-6. From the results of Exercise 9-5 determine the fields $\mathbf{E}$ and $\mathbf{B}$ due to a point charge q moving in empty space with velocity $\mathbf{u}$.

9-7. Show that the quantities $\mathbf{E}\cdot\mathbf{B}$ and $\mathbf{H}\cdot\mathbf{B} - \mathbf{E}\cdot\mathbf{D}$ are relativistically invariant; that is, their form does not change when a Lorentz transformation is made.

REFERENCES

Abraham, M., and R. Becker: "The Classical Theory of Electricity and Magnetism," chaps. 7, 8, and 10, Hafner Publishing Company, Inc., New York, 1950.

Cullwick, E. G.: "Electromagnetism and Relativity," Longmans, Green & Co., Ltd., London, 1957.

Morse, P. M., and H. Feshbach: "Methods of Theoretical Physics," chap. 2, McGraw-Hill Book Company, Inc., New York, 1953.

Panofsky, W. K. H., and M. Phillips: "Classical Electricity and Magnetism," chaps. 7 and 9, Addison-Wesley Publishing Company, Inc., Cambridge, Mass., 1955.

Smythe, W. R.: "Static and Dynamic Electricity," 2d ed., chaps. 6, 8, and 13, McGraw-Hill Book Company, Inc., New York, 1950.

Sommerfeld, A.: "Electrodynamics," paragraphs 4, 19, 31, and 34, Academic Press, Inc., New York, 1952.

Stratton, J. A.: "Electromagnetic Theory," chaps. 1 and 2, McGraw-Hill Book Company, Inc., New York, 1941.

CHAPTER 10

Plane Electromagnetic Waves in Unbounded Media

10-1. INTRODUCTION

The purpose of the present chapter is to find and to study the properties of the plane-wave solutions of the wave equations

$$\nabla^2 \mathbf{B} - \frac{1}{v^2} \frac{\partial^2}{\partial t^2} \mathbf{B} = 0 \qquad (9\text{-}47)$$

$$\nabla^2 \mathbf{E} - \frac{1}{v^2} \frac{\partial^2}{\partial t^2} \mathbf{E} = 0 \qquad (9\text{-}48)$$

and the equations of telegraphy

$$\nabla^2 \mathbf{B} - \frac{1}{v^2} \frac{\partial^2}{\partial t^2} \mathbf{B} - \mu\sigma \frac{\partial}{\partial t} \mathbf{B} = 0 \qquad (9\text{-}44)$$

$$\nabla^2 \mathbf{E} - \frac{1}{v^2} \frac{\partial^2}{\partial t^2} \mathbf{E} - \mu\sigma \frac{\partial}{\partial t} \mathbf{E} = 0 \qquad (9\text{-}46)$$

where $v = c/\sqrt{KK_m}$. The treatment is limited to plane waves in unbounded, isotropic media.

10-2. PLANE WAVES IN HOMOGENEOUS ISOTROPIC DIELECTRICS

The general solution of either of the wave equations (9-47) and (9-48), say (9-48), is of the form

$$\mathbf{E} = \mathbf{f}_1(vt - \mathbf{r} \cdot \mathbf{n}) + \mathbf{f}_2(vt + \mathbf{r} \cdot \mathbf{n}) \qquad (10\text{-}1)$$

where $\mathbf{n}$, the *wave normal*, is a unit vector in the direction of propagation of the wave, $\mathbf{r} = x_1\mathbf{i}_1 + x_2\mathbf{i}_2 + x_3\mathbf{i}_3$ is the position vector, $v = c/\sqrt{KK_m}$ is the *phase velocity* of the wave, and $\mathbf{f}_1$ and $\mathbf{f}_2$ are arbitrary vector functions of the single arguments $(vt - \mathbf{r} \cdot \mathbf{n})$ and $(vt + \mathbf{r} \cdot \mathbf{n})$, respectively.

The arbitrary functions $\mathbf{f}_1$ and $\mathbf{f}_2$ represent waves propagated in the positive and negative directions of $\mathbf{n}$, respectively. This can be seen by first considering the case when $\mathbf{f}_2$ is identically zero and then that when

f_1 is identically zero. We then have the identities

$$f_1[v(t + t') - (vt' + \mathbf{r} \cdot \mathbf{n})] \equiv f_1(vt - \mathbf{r} \cdot \mathbf{n})$$
$$f_2[v(t + t') + (-vt' + \mathbf{r} \cdot \mathbf{n})] \equiv f_2(vt + \mathbf{r} \cdot \mathbf{n})$$

so that the first term in the right-hand member of (10-1) has the same value at the point $(vt' + \mathbf{r} \cdot \mathbf{n})$ at the time $(t + t')$ as at the point $\mathbf{r} \cdot \mathbf{n}$ at the time t. Thus it represents a wave moving in the $+\mathbf{n}$ direction with a speed v. Similarly, the second term represents a wave traveling in the $-\mathbf{n}$ direction with the same speed. The forms of the functions f_1 and f_2 are determined by the wave form at the time $t = 0$.

In what follows we shall concern ourselves primarily with waves traveling in the $+\mathbf{n}$ direction only. The solutions of the wave equations (9-47) and (9-48) can be written

$$\mathbf{B} = \mathbf{B}^0 f_B(vt - \mathbf{r} \cdot \mathbf{n}) \tag{10-2}$$

and
$$\mathbf{E} = \mathbf{E}^0 f_E(vt - \mathbf{r} \cdot \mathbf{n}) \tag{10-3}$$

respectively, where $\mathbf{B}^0$ and $\mathbf{E}^0$ are the vector amplitudes of $\mathbf{B}$ and $\mathbf{E}$ and $f_B(vt - \mathbf{r} \cdot \mathbf{n})$ and $f_E(vt - \mathbf{r} \cdot \mathbf{n})$ are scalar functions.

10-3. TRANSVERSENESS OF THE PLANE ELECTROMAGNETIC WAVES

Certain interesting properties of the solutions (10-2) and (10-3) can be found by substitution into the Maxwell equations (9-41) and (9-43). Thus, substitution of (10-2) and (10-3) into

$$\operatorname{curl} \mathbf{E} = -\frac{\partial}{\partial t} \mathbf{B}$$

yields
$$-(\mathbf{n} \times \mathbf{E}^0)f_E'(vt - \mathbf{r} \cdot \mathbf{n}) = -v\mathbf{B}^0 f_B'(vt - \mathbf{r} \cdot \mathbf{n}) \tag{10-4}$$

where the prime on f_E and f_B indicates differentiation with respect to $(vt - \mathbf{r} \cdot \mathbf{n})$. Since (10-4) must hold for all values of t, f_E and f_B must be proportional to each other. We take them equal so that

$$\mathbf{n} \times \mathbf{E}^0 = v\mathbf{B}^0 \qquad \text{or} \qquad \mathbf{n} \times \mathbf{E} = v\mathbf{B} \tag{10-5}$$

It follows from (10-5) that $\mathbf{B}$ is perpendicular to both $\mathbf{n}$ and $\mathbf{E}$.

Substitution of (10-3) into

$$\operatorname{div} \mathbf{E} = 0$$

which is the Maxwell equation (9-43) with $\rho_F = 0$, yields

$$-(\mathbf{n} \cdot \mathbf{E}^0)f'(vt - \mathbf{r} \cdot \mathbf{n}) = 0$$

Hence
$$\mathbf{n} \cdot \mathbf{E}^0 = 0 \qquad \text{or} \qquad \mathbf{n} \cdot \mathbf{E} = 0 \tag{10-6}$$

and $\mathbf{E}$ and $\mathbf{n}$ are mutually perpendicular. Consequently, from (10-5),

$$|\mathbf{E}| = v|\mathbf{B}| \tag{10-7}$$

Since both $\mathbf{B}$ and $\mathbf{E}$ have been demonstrated to be perpendicular to the direction of propagation $\mathbf{n}$ of the wave, it follows that the plane electromagnetic wave is a transverse wave. Note that $\mathbf{B}$ and $\mathbf{E}$ are perpendicular to each other as well as to $\mathbf{n}$. The vectors $\mathbf{E}$, $\mathbf{B}$, and $\mathbf{n}$ form a right-handed coordinate system in the given order.

10-4. ENERGY TRANSMITTED BY A PLANE WAVE

Since the vectors $\mathbf{E}$ and $\mathbf{B}$ are both perpendicular to the direction of propagation $\mathbf{n}$ of a plane wave in an isotropic dielectric, the Poynting vector

$$\mathbf{N} = \mathbf{E} \times \mathbf{H} = \frac{1}{\mu}(\mathbf{E} \times \mathbf{B}) \tag{9-82}$$

represents the energy which passes per second across unit area perpendicular to the direction of propagation of the wave. By (10-7)

$$\mathbf{N} = \frac{v}{\mu} B^2 \mathbf{n} = \frac{1}{\mu} B^2 \mathbf{v} = \mathbf{H} \cdot \mathbf{B} v \tag{10-8}$$

$$= \frac{1}{\mu v} E^2 \mathbf{n} = \frac{1}{\mu \epsilon v^2} \mathbf{D} \cdot \mathbf{E} \mathbf{v} = \mathbf{D} \cdot \mathbf{E} \mathbf{v} \tag{10-9}$$

Hence $$\mathbf{N} = \tfrac{1}{2}(\mathbf{D} \cdot \mathbf{E} + \mathbf{H} \cdot \mathbf{B})\mathbf{v} \equiv w\mathbf{v} \tag{10-10}$$

which states that the energy which crosses unit area perpendicular to the direction of propagation of the plane wave each second is exactly the amount contained in a cylinder of unit cross section and length $|\mathbf{v}|$.

From (10-9) the magnitude of the Poynting vector is given by

$$N = \epsilon v E^2 = \frac{\epsilon c}{\sqrt{KK_m}} E^2 \tag{10-11}$$

The quantity $\epsilon v = \epsilon c / \sqrt{KK_m}$ is known as the *admittance of the medium*. Its reciprocal is called the *impedance* of the medium. In the case of vacuum, (10-11) reduces to

$$N_0 = \epsilon_0 c E_0{}^2 = \frac{1}{120\pi} E_0{}^2 \tag{10-12}$$

The quantity $(\epsilon_0 c)^{-1} = 120\pi$ is known as the *impedance of free space*.

10-5. RADIATION PRESSURE AND ELECTROMAGNETIC MOMENTUM

Consider a homogeneous isotropic material of permittivity ϵ and permeability μ containing a charge ρ_F and current $\mathbf{j}$ per unit volume. If this material is in an electromagnetic field of electric intensity $\mathbf{E}$ and magnetic induction $\mathbf{B}$, it will experience a force

$$\mathbf{F} = \iiint \mathbf{f} \, d\tau \tag{10-13}$$

where the integration is over the entire volume τ of the material and [cf. Eq. (7-68)]

$$\mathbf{f} = \rho_F \mathbf{E} + \mathbf{j} \times \mathbf{B} \tag{10-14}$$

is the force per unit volume.

Since

$$\rho_F = \operatorname{div} \mathbf{D} \tag{4-32}$$

and

$$\mathbf{j} = \mu^{-1} \operatorname{curl} \mathbf{B} - \frac{\partial}{\partial t} \mathbf{D} \tag{9-28}$$

(10-14) becomes

$$\mathbf{f} = (\operatorname{div} \mathbf{D})\mathbf{E} + \mu^{-1} \operatorname{curl} \mathbf{B} \times \mathbf{B} - \frac{\partial}{\partial t} \mathbf{D} \times \mathbf{B} \tag{10-15}$$

But since

$$\operatorname{curl} \mathbf{E} + \frac{\partial}{\partial t} \mathbf{B} = 0 \tag{9-26}$$

and

$$\operatorname{div} \mathbf{B} = 0 \tag{8-14}$$

it follows that

$$\mathbf{f} = (\operatorname{div} \mathbf{D})\mathbf{E} + \mu^{-1}(\operatorname{curl} \mathbf{B}) \times \mathbf{B} - \frac{\partial}{\partial t} \mathbf{D} \times \mathbf{B} + (\operatorname{div} \mathbf{B})\mathbf{H}$$

$$+ (\operatorname{curl} \mathbf{E}) \times \mathbf{D} + \frac{\partial}{\partial t} \mathbf{B} \times \mathbf{D}$$

$$= -\frac{\partial}{\partial t}(\mathbf{D} \times \mathbf{B}) + [(\operatorname{div} \mathbf{D})\mathbf{E} + (\operatorname{curl} \mathbf{E}) \times \mathbf{D}]$$

$$+ [(\operatorname{div} \mathbf{B})\mathbf{H} + \mu^{-1}(\operatorname{curl} \mathbf{B}) \times \mathbf{B}] \tag{10-16}$$

Hence

$$\mathbf{F} = -\iiint \frac{\partial}{\partial t}(\mathbf{D} \times \mathbf{B}) \, d\tau + \iiint [(\operatorname{div} \mathbf{D})\mathbf{E} + (\operatorname{curl} \mathbf{E}) \times \mathbf{D}] \, d\tau$$

$$+ \iiint [(\operatorname{div} \mathbf{B})\mathbf{H} + \mu^{-1}(\operatorname{curl} \mathbf{B}) \times \mathbf{B}] \, d\tau \tag{10-17}$$

or for a homogeneous isotropic medium,

$$\mathbf{F} = -\mu\epsilon \iiint \frac{\partial}{\partial t} \mathbf{N} \, d\tau + \iiint \epsilon[(\operatorname{div} \mathbf{E})\mathbf{E} + (\operatorname{curl} \mathbf{E}) \times \mathbf{E}] \, d\tau$$

$$+ \iiint \mu^{-1}[(\operatorname{div} \mathbf{B})\mathbf{B} + (\operatorname{curl} \mathbf{B}) \times \mathbf{B}] \, d\tau \tag{10-18}$$

where $\mathbf{N} = \mathbf{E} \times \mathbf{H}$ is the Poynting vector.

It was shown in Sec. 5-7 that

$$\iiint \epsilon[(\text{div } \mathbf{E})\mathbf{E} + (\text{curl } \mathbf{E}) \times \mathbf{E}] \, d\tau = \iint \mathbf{T}^{(e)} \, dS \qquad (5\text{-}38)$$

in which dS is an element of the surface S which bounds the volume τ and

$$\mathbf{T}^{(e)} = \underline{T}^{(e)}\mathbf{n} \qquad (5\text{-}41)$$

in which the matrix

$$\underline{T}^{(e)} = \begin{pmatrix} \epsilon(E_1{}^2 - \tfrac{1}{2}E^2) & \epsilon E_1 E_2 & \epsilon E_1 E_3 \\ \epsilon E_1 E_2 & \epsilon(E_2{}^2 - \tfrac{1}{2}E^2) & \epsilon E_2 E_3 \\ \epsilon E_1 E_3 & \epsilon E_2 E_3 & \epsilon(E_3{}^2 - \tfrac{1}{2}E^2) \end{pmatrix} \qquad (5\text{-}42)$$

is the representative of the electric stress tensor in the given coordinate system.

In a like manner it can be shown that

$$\iiint \mu^{-1}[(\text{div } \mathbf{B})\mathbf{B} + (\text{curl } \mathbf{B}) \times \mathbf{B}] \, d\tau = \iint \mathbf{T}^{(m)} \, dS \qquad (10\text{-}19)$$

where
$$\mathbf{T}^{(m)} = \underline{T}^{(m)}\mathbf{n} \qquad (10\text{-}20)$$

in which

$$\underline{T}^{(m)} = \begin{pmatrix} \mu^{-1}(B_1{}^2 - \tfrac{1}{2}B^2) & \mu^{-1}B_1 B_2 & \mu^{-1}B_1 B_3 \\ \mu^{-1}B_1 B_2 & \mu^{-1}(B_2{}^2 - \tfrac{1}{2}B^2) & \mu^{-1}B_2 B_3 \\ \mu^{-1}B_1 B_3 & \mu^{-1}B_2 B_3 & \mu^{-1}(B_3{}^2 - \tfrac{1}{2}B^2) \end{pmatrix} \qquad (10\text{-}21)$$

is the representative of the *magnetic stress tensor* in the given coordinate system.

Thus (10-18) can be written

$$\mathbf{F} = -\mu\epsilon \iiint \frac{\partial}{\partial t} \mathbf{N} \, d\tau + \iint \mathbf{T}^{(em)} \, dS \qquad (10\text{-}22)$$

where $\quad \mathbf{T}^{(em)} = \mathbf{T}^{(e)} + \mathbf{T}^{(m)} = (\underline{T}^{(e)} + \underline{T}^{(m)})\mathbf{n} = \underline{T}^{(em)}\mathbf{n} \qquad (10\text{-}23)$

$$\mathbf{T}^{(em)} = \epsilon(\mathbf{E} \cdot \mathbf{n})\mathbf{E} - \frac{\epsilon}{2}E^2\mathbf{n} + \mu^{-1}(\mathbf{B} \cdot \mathbf{n})\mathbf{B} - \frac{\mu^{-1}}{2}B^2\mathbf{n} \qquad (10\text{-}24)$$

The matrix $\underline{T}^{(em)}$ is the representative of the *electromagnetic stress tensor* in the given coordinate system. The vector $\mathbf{T}^{(em)}$ represents the stress transmitted across the element of area whose positive normal is $\mathbf{n}$. The pressure on the surface element is given by the component of $\mathbf{T}^{(em)}$ which is normal to the element.

In the case of static fields the term

$$\mathbf{F}_\tau = -\mu\epsilon \iiint \frac{\partial}{\partial t} \mathbf{N} \, d\tau \qquad (10\text{-}25)$$

in (10-22) vanishes, and Eq. (10-22) now states that the force on the volume τ containing the charge ρ_F and current j per unit volume can be expressed as the integral of a vector over the surface S bounding the volume τ. However, as long as the fields are time-dependent, $\mathbf{F}_\tau$ does not vanish, even in the case of vacuum, for which (10-22) reduces to

$$\iint \mathbf{T}_0^{(em)} \, dS = \mu_0\epsilon_0 \iiint \frac{\partial}{\partial t} \mathbf{N} \, d\tau \tag{10-26}$$

Since in this case of vacuum the volume τ contains radiation only, the force due to the stresses on its surface must be thought of as acting on the radiation in its interior. Since force is equal to the time rate of change of momentum, the radiation has associated with it a *momentum*

$$\mathbf{G} = \iiint \mu_0\epsilon_0 \mathbf{N} \, d\tau \tag{10-27}$$

or a *momentum density*

$$\mathbf{g} = \mu_0\epsilon_0 \mathbf{N} = \frac{1}{c^2} \mathbf{N} \tag{10-28}$$

One can then define an *angular momentum density* for the radiation:

$$\mathbf{l} = \mathbf{r} \times \mathbf{g} = \frac{1}{c^2} \mathbf{r} \times \mathbf{N} \tag{10-29}$$

where $\mathbf{r}$ is the position vector.

According to (10-10), in the case of a plane wave propagated in vacuum, $\mathbf{N} = w\mathbf{c}$. Then

$$\mathbf{g} = \frac{w}{c^2} \mathbf{c} = \frac{w}{c} \mathbf{n} \tag{10-30}$$

and

$$\mathbf{l} = \frac{w}{c} \mathbf{r} \times \mathbf{n} \tag{10-31}$$

where $\mathbf{n}$ is the wave normal. Equation (10-30) states that the electromagnetic momentum density is equal to the energy density of the electromagnetic field divided by the velocity of propagation.

10-6. DETAILED SOLUTIONS OF THE WAVE EQUATIONS

The general solutions of the wave equations (9-47) and (9-48) were derived and discussed in Sec. 10-2. Here we shall obtain more detailed solutions of the wave equations using the *method of separation of variables*.

Let us take as our coordinate system the $OX_1X_2X_3$ cartesian coordinate system. Then each of the wave equations (9-47) and (9-48) can be considered as a set of three scalar equations, one in each of the rectangular components of the vectors $\mathbf{E}$ and $\mathbf{B}$. The problem of solving the wave equations then reduces to that of solving a scalar wave equation of the form

$$\nabla^2 \Psi(x_1, x_2, x_2, t) - \frac{1}{v^2} \frac{\partial^2}{\partial t^2} \Psi(x_1, x_2, x_3, t) = 0 \qquad (10\text{-}32)$$

To solve (10-32), we assume that

$$\Psi(x_1, x_2, x_3, t) = \psi(x_1, x_2, x_3) T(t) \qquad (10\text{-}33)$$

Substitution of (10-33) into (10-32) followed by division by (10-33) yields

$$\frac{v^2}{\psi} \nabla^2 \psi = \frac{1}{T} \frac{d^2}{dt^2} T \qquad (10\text{-}34)$$

Since the left-hand member of (10-34) is a function of the space coordinates only while the right-hand member is a function of the time alone, both members must be equal to a constant which, for convenience, we write as $-\omega^2$. Then the functions T and ψ satisfy the equations

$$\frac{d^2}{dt^2} T + \omega^2 T = 0 \qquad (10\text{-}35)$$

and

$$\nabla^2 \psi + \frac{\omega^2}{v^2} \psi = 0 \qquad (10\text{-}36)$$

respectively. Equation (10-36) is known as the *time-independent form of the wave equation.*

Equation (10-35) has a solution of the form

$$T(t) = a(\omega) e^{i\omega t} \qquad \omega \neq 0 \qquad -\infty < \omega < +\infty \qquad (10\text{-}37)$$

where $a(\omega)$ is an arbitrary function of ω. Equation (10-37) represents a disturbance which varies sinusoidally with time with angular frequency ω. It is therefore convenient to take ω as positive and to write (10-37) as

$$T(t) = a(\omega) e^{i\omega t} + a'(\omega) e^{-i\omega t} \qquad 0 < \omega < +\infty \qquad (10\text{-}38)$$

where the *angular frequency* ω is related to the frequency ν of the wave by $\omega = 2\pi\nu$.

It is customary to introduce the *wave number* k defined by the relation

$$k = \frac{\omega}{v} = 2\pi \frac{\nu}{v} = \frac{2\pi}{\lambda} \qquad (10\text{-}39)$$

where $\lambda = v/\nu$ is the wavelength of the wave of frequency ν and phase velocity v. The time-independent wave equation (10-36) then becomes

$$\nabla^2 \psi + k^2 \psi = 0 \qquad (10\text{-}36a)$$

To solve (10-36a) we assume that

$$\psi(x_1, x_2, x_3) = \xi(x_1) \eta(x_2) \zeta(x_3) \qquad (10\text{-}40)$$

Equation (10-36a) then splits into the set of three equations

$$\frac{d^2}{dx_1^2}\xi + k_1^2\xi = 0$$

$$\frac{d^2}{dx_2^2}\eta + k_2^2\eta = 0 \tag{10-41}$$

$$\frac{d^2}{dx_3^2}\zeta + k_3^2\zeta = 0$$

where the constants k_1, k_2, and k_3 are arbitrary except that they satisfy the relation

$$k^2 = \frac{\omega^2}{v^2} = k_1^2 + k_2^2 + k_3^2 \tag{10-42}$$

Since each of the equations in the set (10-41) is in the same form as (10-35), it is clear that

$$\psi(x_1,x_2,x_3) = b_1(k_1)b_2(k_2)b_3(k_3)e^{i(k_1x_1+k_2x_2+k_3x_3)}$$
$$= b(k_1,k_2,k_3)e^{i(k_1x_1+k_2x_2+k_3x_3)} \tag{10-43}$$

where $-\infty < k_i < +\infty$ and b is an arbitrary function of k_i, $i = 1, 2, 3$. $b(k_1,k_2,k_3) = b_1(k_1)b_2(k_2)b_3(k_3)$ is an arbitrary function of k_1, k_2, and k_3.

It is convenient to think of k_1, k_2, and k_3 as the components of a vector $\mathbf{k}$ in the direction of propagation of the wave $\mathbf{n}$. Then (10-43) can be written

$$\psi(\mathbf{r}) = b(\mathbf{k})e^{i\mathbf{k}\cdot\mathbf{r}} \tag{10-43a}$$

where $\mathbf{k} = \omega\mathbf{n}/v$ and $\mathbf{r} = x_1\mathbf{i}_1 + x_2\mathbf{i}_2 + x_3\mathbf{i}_3$.

According to (10-33), (10-38), and (10-43a) the solution of the wave equation (10-32) is

$$\Psi(\mathbf{r},t) = a(\omega)b(\mathbf{k})e^{i(\omega t+\mathbf{k}\cdot\mathbf{r})} + a'(\omega)b(\mathbf{k})e^{-i(\omega t-\mathbf{k}\cdot\mathbf{r})}$$
or
$$\Psi(\mathbf{r},t) = g(\mathbf{k},\omega)e^{i(\omega t+\mathbf{k}\cdot\mathbf{r})} + h(\mathbf{k},\omega)e^{-i(\omega t-\mathbf{k}\cdot\mathbf{r})} \tag{10-44}$$

in which $g(\mathbf{k},\omega) = a(\omega)b(\mathbf{k})$ and $h(\mathbf{k},\omega) = a'(\omega)b(\mathbf{k})$ are arbitrary functions of $\mathbf{k}$ and ω.

The general solution of (10-32) is obtained by integrating (10-44) over all permissible values of ω, k_1, k_2, and k_3. Thus

$$\Psi(\mathbf{r},t) = \int_{-\infty}^{\infty} d\mathbf{k} \int_0^{\infty} d\omega\, g(\mathbf{k},\omega)e^{i(\omega t+\mathbf{k}\cdot\mathbf{r})} + \int_{-\infty}^{\infty} d\mathbf{k} \int_0^{\infty} d\omega\, h(\mathbf{k},\omega)e^{-i(\omega t-\mathbf{k}\cdot\mathbf{r})} \tag{10-45}$$

where $d\mathbf{k} = dk_1\, dk_2\, dk_3$.

Since Ψ represents the rectangular components of the vectors $\mathbf{E}$ and $\mathbf{B}$, it must be real. Consequently, the allowable solutions to the wave equation (10-32) are the real parts of (10-44) and (10-45). As a matter of convention we write

$$\Psi(r,t) = (\text{real part})g^*(\mathbf{k},\omega)e^{-(i\omega t + \mathbf{k}\cdot\mathbf{r})} + (\text{real part})h(\mathbf{k},\omega)e^{-i(\omega t - \mathbf{k}\cdot\mathbf{r})}$$

where the asterisk denotes the complex conjugate, or since $g(\mathbf{k},\omega)$ is an arbitrary function of $\mathbf{k}$ and ω,

$$\Psi(r,t) = (\text{real part})g(\mathbf{k},\omega)e^{-i(\omega t + \mathbf{k}\cdot\mathbf{r})} + (\text{real part})h(\mathbf{k},\omega)e^{-i(\omega t - \mathbf{k}\cdot\mathbf{r})} \quad (10\text{-}46)$$

The general solution is given by the integral of this expression over all ω, k_1, k_2, and k_3.

It follows that the solution of the wave equation (9-47) can be written

$$\mathbf{B}(r,t) = (\text{real part})\mathbf{B}_1(\mathbf{k},\omega)e^{-i(\omega t + \mathbf{k}\cdot\mathbf{r})} + (\text{real part})\mathbf{B}_2(\mathbf{k},\omega)e^{-i(\omega t - \mathbf{k}\cdot\mathbf{r})}$$

$$(10\text{-}47)$$

the general solution being obtained by integration over all ω, k_1, k_2, and k_3. Similar solutions hold for the wave equation (9-48).

It is easily verified that the first term in the right-hand member of (10-47) represents a plane wave of angular frequency ω which is traveling in the $-\mathbf{k}$ direction (cf. Sec. 10-2). The second term represents a plane wave of angular frequency ω traveling in the $+\mathbf{k}$ direction.

In most of what follows we shall not consider the general solutions but rather the solutions for plane waves of particular frequency ω. Thus, with $\mathbf{k} = \omega\mathbf{n}/v$, a plane electromagnetic wave of angular frequency ω traveling in the $+\mathbf{n}$ direction with phase velocity v will be represented by

$$\begin{aligned}\mathbf{E}(r,t) &= (\text{real part})\mathbf{E}^0 e^{-i\omega(t - \mathbf{r}\cdot\mathbf{n}/v)} \\ \mathbf{B}(r,t) &= (\text{real part})\mathbf{B}^0 e^{-i\omega(t - \mathbf{r}\cdot\mathbf{n}/v)}\end{aligned} \quad (10\text{-}48)$$

and a wave traveling in the $-\mathbf{n}$ direction by

$$\begin{aligned}\mathbf{E}(r,t) &= (\text{real part})\mathbf{E}^0 e^{-i\omega(t + \mathbf{r}\cdot\mathbf{n}/v)} \\ \mathbf{B}(r,t) &= (\text{real part})\mathbf{B}^0 e^{-i\omega(t + \mathbf{r}\cdot\mathbf{n}/v)}\end{aligned} \quad (10\text{-}49)$$

We frequently shall not include the reminder (real part) but, as in the theory of alternating currents, leave it to the reader to remember that the physical quantity is represented by the real part of the complex expression.

10-7. PLANE WAVES IN HOMOGENEOUS ISOTROPIC CONDUCTORS

The problem at hand is to obtain the plane-wave solutions of the equations of telegraphy

$$\nabla^2\mathbf{B} - \frac{1}{v^2}\frac{\partial^2}{\partial t^2}\mathbf{B} - \mu\sigma\frac{\partial}{\partial t}\mathbf{B} = 0 \quad (9\text{-}44)$$

$$\nabla^2\mathbf{E} - \frac{1}{v^2}\frac{\partial^2}{\partial t^2}\mathbf{E} - \mu\sigma\frac{\partial}{\partial t}\mathbf{E} = 0 \quad (9\text{-}46)$$

where $v = c/\sqrt{KK_m}$. We restrict ourselves to the problem of obtaining the solutions of these equations which correspond to plane waves traveling in the $+\mathbf{n}$ direction. Therefore, based on the experience gained in the preceding section, we assume that the solution of (9-46) can be written

$$\mathbf{E}(\mathbf{r},t) = \mathbf{G}(\mathbf{r})e^{-i\omega t} \tag{10-50}$$

Substitution of (10-50) into (9-46) yields

$$\nabla^2\mathbf{G} + \left(\frac{\omega^2}{v^2} + i\mu\sigma\omega\right)\mathbf{G} = 0 \tag{10-51}$$

as the differential equation which $\mathbf{G}$ must satisfy. The solution of (10-51) is

$$\mathbf{G}(\mathbf{r}) = \mathbf{E}^0 e^{+i(\omega/\alpha)\mathbf{r}\cdot\mathbf{n}} \tag{10-52}$$

where

$$\alpha^2 = \left(\frac{1}{v^2} + i\frac{\mu\sigma}{\omega}\right)^{-1} = \left(\mu\epsilon + i\frac{\mu\sigma}{\omega}\right)^{-1} \tag{10-53}$$

and $\mathbf{E}^0$ is a constant vector. Substitution of (10-52) into (10-50) yields

$$\mathbf{E}(\mathbf{r},t) = \mathbf{E}^0 e^{-i\omega(t-\mathbf{r}\cdot\mathbf{n}/\alpha)} \tag{10-54}$$

as the solution of (9-46) representing a plane wave progressing in the $+\mathbf{n}$ direction. The corresponding solution of (9-44) is

$$\mathbf{B}(\mathbf{r},t) = \mathbf{B}^0 e^{-i\omega(t-\mathbf{r}\cdot\mathbf{n}/\alpha)} \tag{10-55}$$

where $\mathbf{B}^0$ is a constant vector.

Comparison of (10-54) and (10-55) with the corresponding expressions (10-48) for a plane wave in a homogeneous isotropic dielectric shows that the complex quantity α represents the phase velocity of the plane wave in the homogeneous isotropic conductor. The physical significance of a complex phase velocity will become evident from our further considerations.

Let

$$\frac{1}{\alpha} = \frac{1}{v_c} + i\kappa \tag{10-56}$$

where both v_c and κ are real. Then

$$\frac{1}{\alpha^2} = \frac{1}{v_c^2} + 2i\frac{\kappa}{v_c} - \kappa^2 = \mu\epsilon + i\frac{\mu\sigma}{\omega}$$

so that

$$\frac{1}{v_c^2} - \kappa^2 = \mu\epsilon \quad \text{and} \quad 2\frac{\kappa}{v_c} = \frac{\mu\sigma}{\omega}$$

The solutions of these equations are

$$v_c = \frac{\omega}{\sigma} \sqrt{\frac{2\epsilon}{\mu}} \left(\sqrt{1 + \frac{\sigma^2}{\omega^2 \epsilon^2}} - 1 \right)^{\frac{1}{2}} \tag{10-57}$$

$$\kappa = \sqrt{\frac{\mu \epsilon}{2}} \left(\sqrt{1 + \frac{\sigma^2}{\omega^2 \epsilon^2}} - 1 \right)^{\frac{1}{2}} \tag{10-58}$$

Substitution for $1/\alpha$ in (10-54) and (10-55) by means of (10-56) yields

$$\mathbf{E}(\mathbf{r},t) = \mathbf{E}^0 e^{-\omega \kappa (\mathbf{r} \cdot \mathbf{n})} e^{-i\omega(t - \mathbf{r} \cdot \mathbf{n}/v_c)} \tag{10-59}$$

and
$$\mathbf{B}(\mathbf{r},t) = \mathbf{B}^0 e^{-\omega \kappa (\mathbf{r} \cdot \mathbf{n})} e^{-i\omega(t - \mathbf{r} \cdot \mathbf{n}/v_c)} \tag{10-60}$$

These equations show that, as $(\mathbf{r} \cdot \mathbf{n})$ increases, i.e., as the wave progresses, there is a decrease in amplitude. Thus, there is absorption within the conductor. For this reason κ is known as the *coefficient of absorption* or *extinction*. The equations also show that there is dispersion of the electromagnetic wave in the conductor, for, although the quantity $e^{-i\omega(t - \mathbf{r} \cdot \mathbf{n}/v_c)}$ is in appearance just like the quantity $e^{-i\omega(t - \mathbf{r} \cdot \mathbf{n}/v)}$ occurring in the case of a plane wave in a homogeneous dielectric, the velocity v_c is not constant but depends upon the frequency of the wave [cf. Eq. (10-57)].

Substitution of (10-54) and (10-55) into

$$\text{curl } \mathbf{E} = - \frac{\partial}{\partial t} \mathbf{B} \tag{9-41}$$

gives
$$\mathbf{n} \times \mathbf{E} = \alpha B$$

so that
$$|\mathbf{E}| = \alpha |B| \tag{10-61}$$

Hence (10-60) can be written

$$\mathbf{B}(\mathbf{r},t) = \frac{1}{\alpha} E^0 \mathbf{i}_B e^{-\omega \kappa (\mathbf{r} \cdot \mathbf{n})} e^{-i\omega(t - \mathbf{r} \cdot \mathbf{n}/v_c)}$$

where $\mathbf{i}_B$ is a unit vector in the direction of $\mathbf{B}$, or

$$\frac{1}{\alpha} = \frac{1}{v_c} + i\kappa = \sqrt{\frac{1}{v_c^2} + \kappa^2} \, e^{i\omega \delta}$$

where
$$\tan \omega \delta = \kappa v_c$$

$$\mathbf{B}(\mathbf{r},t) = \sqrt{\frac{1}{v_c^2} + \kappa^2} \, E^0 \mathbf{i}_B e^{-\omega \kappa (\mathbf{r} \cdot \mathbf{n})} e^{-i\omega(t - \delta - \mathbf{r} \cdot \mathbf{n}/v_c)} \tag{10-62}$$

This expression shows that in a conductor there is a phase difference between $\mathbf{E}$ and $\mathbf{B}$ whereas they are in phase in a dielectric.

From the above results it is clear that a complex phase velocity indicates (1) absorption in the medium and (2) a phase difference between the electric and magnetic vectors.

The distance d that an electromagnetic wave must travel in a conductor in order for $\mathbf{E}$ and $\mathbf{B}$ to fall to $1/e$th of their initial values is called the *skin depth*. From (10-59) and (10-60) it is seen that

$$d = \frac{1}{\omega \kappa} = \frac{1}{\omega} \sqrt{\frac{2}{\mu \epsilon}} \left(\sqrt{1 + \frac{\sigma^2}{\omega^2 \epsilon^2}} - 1 \right)^{-\frac{1}{2}} \qquad (10\text{-}63)$$

The permittivity in conductors is not accurately known but seems to be of the same order of magnitude as in dielectrics. For metals, therefore, one usually finds that

$$\frac{\sigma}{\omega \epsilon} \gg 1$$

so that

$$d \simeq \sqrt{\frac{2}{\mu \sigma \omega}} \qquad (10\text{-}64)$$

10-8. THE COMPLEX POYNTING VECTOR

A plane electromagnetic wave of angular frequency ω traveling in the $+\mathbf{n}$ direction with phase velocity v is represented by

$$\begin{aligned} \mathbf{E}(\mathbf{r},t) &= (\text{real part})\mathbf{E}^0 e^{-i\omega(t-\mathbf{r}\cdot\mathbf{n}/v)} \\ \mathbf{B}(\mathbf{r},t) &= (\text{real part})\mathbf{B}^0 e^{-i\omega(t-\mathbf{r}\cdot\mathbf{n}/v)} \end{aligned} \qquad (10\text{-}65)$$

Let

$$\begin{aligned} \mathbf{E}^0 &= \mathbf{E}_r{}^0 + i\mathbf{E}_i{}^0 \\ \mathbf{B}^0 &= \mathbf{B}_r{}^0 + i\mathbf{B}_i{}^0 \end{aligned} \qquad (10\text{-}66)$$

Then, Eqs. (10-65) become

$$\begin{aligned} \mathbf{E}(\mathbf{r},t) &= \mathbf{E}_r{}^0 \cos \omega \left(t - \frac{\mathbf{r}\cdot\mathbf{n}}{v} \right) + \mathbf{E}_i{}^0 \sin \omega \left(t - \frac{\mathbf{r}\cdot\mathbf{n}}{v} \right) \\ \mathbf{B}(\mathbf{r},t) &= \mathbf{B}_r{}^0 \cos \omega \left(t - \frac{\mathbf{r}\cdot\mathbf{n}}{v} \right) + \mathbf{B}_i{}^0 \sin \omega \left(t - \frac{\mathbf{r}\cdot\mathbf{n}}{v} \right) \end{aligned} \qquad (10\text{-}67)$$

and the Poynting vector $\mathbf{N} = \mathbf{E} \times \mathbf{H} = \mu^{-1}(\mathbf{E} \times \mathbf{B})$ can be written

$$\mathbf{N} = \mu^{-1} \left[(\mathbf{E}_r{}^0 \times \mathbf{B}_r{}^0) \cos^2 \omega \left(t - \frac{\mathbf{r}\cdot\mathbf{n}}{v} \right) + (\mathbf{E}_i{}^0 \times \mathbf{B}_i{}^0) \sin^2 \omega \left(t - \frac{\mathbf{r}\cdot\mathbf{n}}{v} \right) \right.$$

$$\left. + (\mathbf{E}_r{}^0 \times \mathbf{B}_i{}^0 + \mathbf{E}_i{}^0 \times \mathbf{B}_r{}^0) \cos \omega \left(t - \frac{\mathbf{r}\cdot\mathbf{n}}{v} \right) \sin \omega \left(t - \frac{\mathbf{r}\cdot\mathbf{n}}{v} \right) \right] \qquad (10\text{-}68)$$

The time average of the Poynting vector is then given by

$$\bar{\mathbf{N}} = \frac{\mu^{-1}}{2} (\mathbf{E}_r{}^0 \times \mathbf{B}_r{}^0 + \mathbf{E}_i{}^0 \times \mathbf{B}_i{}^0) \qquad (10\text{-}69)$$

since the average value of both $\cos^2 \omega t$ and $\sin^2 \omega t$ is $\frac{1}{2}$ and the average value of $\sin \omega t \cos \omega t$ is zero.

Consider now the complex vectors

$$\begin{aligned}
\hat{\mathbf{E}}(\mathbf{r},t) &= \mathbf{E}^0 e^{-i\omega(t-\mathbf{r}\cdot\mathbf{n}/v)} \\
\hat{\mathbf{B}}(\mathbf{r},t) &= \mathbf{B}^0 e^{-i\omega(t-\mathbf{r}\cdot\mathbf{n}/v)}
\end{aligned} \tag{10-70}$$

The *complex Poynting vector* is

$$\begin{aligned}
\hat{\mathbf{E}} \times \hat{\mathbf{H}}^* &= \mu^{-1}(\hat{\mathbf{E}} \times \hat{\mathbf{B}}^*) = \mu^{-1}(\mathbf{E}^0 \times \mathbf{B}^{0*}) \\
&= \mu^{-1}(\mathbf{E}_r^0 + i\mathbf{E}_i^0) \times (\mathbf{B}_r^0 - i\mathbf{B}_i^0) \\
&= \mu^{-1}[(\mathbf{E}_r^0 \times \mathbf{B}_r^0) + (\mathbf{E}_i^0 \times \mathbf{B}_i^0) + i(\mathbf{E}_i^0 \times \mathbf{B}_r^0 - \mathbf{E}_r^0 \times \mathbf{B}_i^0)]
\end{aligned} \tag{10-71}$$

where $\hat{\mathbf{H}}^*$ and $\hat{\mathbf{B}}^*$ are, respectively, the complex conjugates of $\hat{\mathbf{H}}$ and $\hat{\mathbf{B}}$. Hence

$$\bar{\mathbf{N}} = \tfrac{1}{2}(\text{real part})\hat{\mathbf{E}} \times \hat{\mathbf{H}}^* \tag{10-72}$$

i.e., the time average of the Poynting vector is equal to one-half the real part of the complex Poynting vector.

It is sometimes also convenient to express the time averages of the energy density, the momentum density, and the angular momentum density of the radiation field in terms of the complex vectors $\hat{\mathbf{E}}$ and $\hat{\mathbf{H}}$. Thus

$$\bar{w} = \tfrac{1}{4}(\epsilon \hat{\mathbf{E}} \cdot \hat{\mathbf{E}}^* + \mu \hat{\mathbf{H}} \cdot \hat{\mathbf{H}}^*) \tag{10-73}$$

$$\bar{\mathbf{g}} = \frac{1}{c^2}\bar{\mathbf{N}} = \frac{1}{2c^2}(\text{real part})\hat{\mathbf{E}} \times \hat{\mathbf{H}}^* \tag{10-74}$$

$$\bar{\mathbf{l}} = \mathbf{r} \times \bar{\mathbf{g}} = \frac{1}{2c^2}(\text{real part})\mathbf{r} \times (\hat{\mathbf{E}} \times \hat{\mathbf{H}}^*) \tag{10-75}$$

EXERCISES

10-1. Extend the theory of plane waves presented in this chapter to that of plane waves in unbounded homogeneous *anisotropic* dielectrics. Begin with the Maxwell equations

$$\text{curl } \mathbf{B} = \mu_0 \frac{\partial}{\partial t} \mathbf{D} \qquad \text{curl } \mathbf{E} = -\frac{\partial}{\partial t} \mathbf{B}$$

$$\text{div } \mathbf{B} = 0 \qquad \text{div } \mathbf{D} = 0$$

Take the electrical axes of the crystalline dielectric as the coordinate axes so that

$$D_i = \epsilon_i E_i \qquad i = 1, 2, 3$$

Assume that

$$\begin{aligned}
\mathbf{D} &= \mathbf{D}^0 e^{-i\omega(t-\mathbf{r}\cdot\mathbf{n}/v)} \\
\mathbf{E} &= \mathbf{E}^0 e^{-i\omega(t-\mathbf{r}\cdot\mathbf{n}/v)} \\
\mathbf{B} &= \mathbf{B}^0 e^{-i\omega(t-\mathbf{r}\cdot\mathbf{n}/v)}
\end{aligned}$$

in which $\mathbf{n}$ is a unit vector in the direction of propagation of the wavefront.

(a) Show that the vectors $\mathbf{n}$, $\mathbf{E}$, and $\mathbf{D}$ lie in a plane, called the *plane of vibration*, and satisfy the relation

$$\mu_0 v^2 \mathbf{D} = \mathbf{E} - (\mathbf{n} \cdot \mathbf{E})\mathbf{n} \tag{10-76}$$

(b) Show that the vectors $\mathbf{D}$ and $\mathbf{n}$ are perpendicular to each other.

(c) Show that the vector $\mathbf{B}$ is perpendicular to the plane of vibration.

(d) Show that the Poynting vector $\mathbf{N}$ is given by

$$\mathbf{N} = \frac{1}{\mu_0 v} [E^2 \mathbf{n} - (\mathbf{n} \cdot \mathbf{E})\mathbf{E}] \tag{10-77}$$

and that the angle between the vectors $\mathbf{D}$ and $\mathbf{E}$ is equal to the angle between the vectors $\mathbf{N}$ and $\mathbf{n}$.

(e) Let $\mathbf{u}$ denote the *velocity of energy flow* in the direction of $\mathbf{N}$. $\mathbf{u}$ is also known as the *ray velocity*. It is related to the phase velocity v by

$$v = \mathbf{u} \cdot \mathbf{n} \tag{10-78}$$

Show that

$$\mathbf{N} = w\mathbf{u}$$

where

$$w = \tfrac{1}{2}(\mathbf{D} \cdot \mathbf{E} + \mathbf{H} \cdot \mathbf{B}) \tag{10-79}$$

is the energy density of the electromagnetic field, and that

$$\mathbf{u} = \frac{E^2 \mathbf{n} - (\mathbf{n} \cdot \mathbf{E})\mathbf{E}}{E^2 - (\mathbf{n} \cdot \mathbf{E})^2} v \tag{10-80}$$

(f) The phase velocities in the direction of the electrical axes are called the *principal velocities of propagation* and are defined by

$$v_i = \frac{1}{\sqrt{\mu_0 \epsilon_i}} \tag{10-81}$$

Show that the components of $\mathbf{E}$ satisfy

$$\left(1 - \frac{v^2}{v_i^2}\right) E_i = (\mathbf{n} \cdot \mathbf{E})n_i \qquad i = 1, 2, 3 \tag{10-82}$$

Also show that

$$\sum_{i=1}^{3} \frac{n_i^2}{v_i^2 - v^2} = 0 \tag{10-83}$$

This equation is known as *Fresnel's equation*. It gives the phase velocity v in terms of the direction of $\mathbf{n}$. It has two real positive roots in v^2 and hence also in v. These roots, v' and v'', lie in two intervals that are bounded by the values of the principal velocities of propagation. Thus if $v_1 \geq v_2 \geq v_3$, the roots v' and v'' lie in the intervals

$$v_1 \geq v' \geq v_2 \geq v'' \geq v_3$$

(g) With each of the phase velocities v' and v'' there correspond field vectors $\mathbf{E}'$, $\mathbf{D}'$ and $\mathbf{E}''$, $\mathbf{D}''$. Show that

$$\mathbf{D}' \cdot \mathbf{D}'' = \mathbf{D}' \cdot \mathbf{E}'' = \mathbf{D}'' \cdot \mathbf{E}' = 0 \tag{10-84}$$
$$\mathbf{E}' \cdot \mathbf{E}'' \neq 0 \tag{10-85}$$

(h) Show that

$$v^2 = \sum_{i=1}^{3} \frac{D_i^2}{D^2} v_i^2 \tag{10-86}$$

(i) Suppose that $v_1 > v_2 > v_3$. Use Fresnel's equation to show that there are two directions in which v has only a single value. Show that this value is v_2. The two directions thus defined are known as the *optical axes* of the crystal, and the crystal is said to be *biaxial*. If $v_2 = v_3$, there is but one direction in which v has only a single value. This is the case for a so-called optically *uniaxial crystal*.

(j) Show that the components of the ray velocity $\mathbf{u}$ satisfy

$$\sum_{i=1}^{3} \frac{u_i{}^2}{u^2 - v_i{}^2} = 1 \tag{10-87}$$

Then show that there are, in general, two real positive values of u, u', and u'', corresponding to each direction. Determine the directions in which $u' = u''$. These directions are called the *secondary optical axes* of the crystal.

10-2. Extend the theory of plane waves presented in this chapter to that of plane waves in unbounded *inhomogeneous* isotropic dielectrics. Begin with the Maxwell equations

$$\text{curl } \mathbf{B} = \mu_0 \frac{\partial}{\partial t} \mathbf{D} \qquad \text{curl } \mathbf{E} = -\frac{\partial}{\partial t} \mathbf{B}$$
$$\text{div } \mathbf{B} = 0 \qquad \text{div } \mathbf{D} = 0$$

and the constitutive equation

$$\mathbf{D} = \epsilon \mathbf{E}$$

where ϵ is a scalar function of position. Assume that

$$\mathbf{E} = \mathbf{E}^0 e^{-i\omega(t - \mathbf{r} \cdot \mathbf{n}/v)}$$
$$\mathbf{B} = \mathbf{B}^0 e^{-i\omega(t - \mathbf{r} \cdot \mathbf{n}/v)}$$

where $\mathbf{n}$ is the wave normal.

(a) Verify that the vectors $\mathbf{E}$, $\mathbf{B}$, and $\mathbf{n}$ form a right-handed coordinate system in the given order.

(b) Show that $\mathbf{B}$ and $\mathbf{E}$ satisfy the wave equations

$$\nabla^2 \mathbf{E} - \mu_0 \epsilon \frac{\partial^2}{\partial t^2} \mathbf{E} = -\nabla \frac{\mathbf{E} \cdot \nabla \epsilon}{\epsilon}$$
$$\nabla^2 \mathbf{B} - \mu_0 \epsilon \frac{\partial^2}{\partial t^2} \mathbf{B} = -\frac{\nabla \epsilon}{\epsilon} \times (\nabla \times \mathbf{B}) \tag{10-88}$$

(c) Assume that $\nabla \epsilon$ is negligibly small, so that, to a good approximation,

$$\nabla^2 \mathbf{E} - \mu_0 \epsilon \frac{\partial^2}{\partial t^2} \mathbf{E} = 0 \qquad \nabla^2 \mathbf{B} - \mu_0 \epsilon \frac{\partial^2}{\partial t^2} \mathbf{B} = 0$$

If ϵ were constant, the solutions would be

$$\mathbf{E} = \mathbf{E}^0 e^{-i\omega(t - \mathbf{r} \cdot \mathbf{n}/v)} \qquad \mathbf{B} = \mathbf{B}^0 e^{-i\omega(t - \mathbf{r} \cdot \mathbf{n}/v)}$$

Since ϵ is assumed to change only gradually, seek solutions resembling the plane wave as closely as possible:

$$\mathbf{E} = \mathbf{E}^0 e^{A(\mathbf{r}) - i\omega[t - S(\mathbf{r})/c]} \qquad \mathbf{B} = \mathbf{B}^0 e^{A(\mathbf{r}) - i\omega[t - S(\mathbf{r})/c]}$$

A is a measure of the amplitude of the wave. The phase function S is called the *eikonal* or *optical path length*, since, if ϵ were constant, S would reduce to $\eta(\mathbf{r} \cdot \mathbf{n})$.

Show that A and S satisfy the equations

$$\nabla^2 A + (\nabla A)^2 + \omega^2 \left(\mu_0 \epsilon - \frac{1}{c^2} (\nabla S)^2 \right) = 0$$

$$\nabla^2 S + 2(\nabla A) \cdot (\nabla S) = 0$$

(10-89)

(d) Show that, when ω becomes very large,

$$(\nabla S)^2 = \mu_0 \epsilon c^2$$

(10-90)

the *eikonal equation of geometrical optics*.

10-3. An ionized gaseous system which has no average space charge is called a *plasma*. Extend the theory of plane waves presented in this chapter to that of plane waves propagated through a plasma. Begin with the Maxwell equations

$$\text{curl } \mathbf{B} = \mu_0 \left(\mathbf{j} + \epsilon_0 \frac{\partial}{\partial t} \mathbf{E} \right) \qquad \text{curl } \mathbf{E} = -\frac{\partial}{\partial t} \mathbf{B}$$

$$\text{div } \mathbf{B} = 0 \qquad\qquad \text{div } \mathbf{E} = \frac{\rho_F}{\epsilon_0}$$

(a) For a plasma containing only electrons and one type of positive ion

$$\mathbf{j} = e(n_i Z \mathbf{v}_i - n_e \mathbf{v}_e)$$

where n_i and n_e represent, respectively, the number of ions and electrons per unit volume. The charge of the electron is $-e$ and its velocity $\mathbf{v}_e$. The charge of the ion is eZ, and its velocity $\mathbf{v}_i$. If there is no steady magnetic field present and we can neglect electron-ion collisions, the equations of motion are

$$m_e \frac{d}{dt} \mathbf{v}_e = -e\mathbf{E}$$

$$m_i \frac{d}{dt} \mathbf{v}_i = eZ\mathbf{E}$$

(10-91)

where m_e and m_i denote, respectively, the electronic and ionic masses. Show that the constitutive equation relating the current density to the electric field intensity is

$$\frac{\partial}{\partial t} \mathbf{j} \simeq \frac{n_e e^2}{m_e} \mathbf{E}$$

(10-92)

Also verify that the charge density is

$$\rho_F = e(n_i Z - n_e)$$

(b) Show that, if $\mathbf{E}$ and $\mathbf{j}$ are perpendicular to the direction of the wave, $\rho_F = 0$ and the wave equations for $\mathbf{E}$ and $\mathbf{B}$ are

$$\nabla^2 \mathbf{E} - \frac{1}{c^2} \frac{\partial^2}{\partial t^2} \mathbf{E} - \frac{\mu_0 n_e e^2}{m_e} \mathbf{E} = 0$$

$$\nabla^2 \mathbf{B} - \frac{1}{c^2} \frac{\partial^2}{\partial t^2} \mathbf{B} - \frac{\mu_0 n_e e^2}{m_e} \mathbf{B} = 0$$

(10-93)

(c) Show that the solutions to the wave equations (10-93) are

$$\mathbf{E}(\mathbf{r},t) = \mathbf{E}_0 e^{-i(\omega t - \mathbf{\kappa} \cdot \mathbf{r})}$$

$$\mathbf{B}(\mathbf{r},t) = \mathbf{B}_0 e^{-i(\omega t - \mathbf{\kappa} \cdot \mathbf{r})}$$

where ω is the frequency of the wave and κ is a vector in the direction of propagation with magnitude

$$\kappa = \left(\frac{\omega^2}{c^2} - \frac{\mu_0 n_e e^2}{m_e}\right)^{\frac{1}{2}} \tag{10-94}$$

The frequency $\omega_p = (\mu_0 n_e e^2 c^2/m_e)^{\frac{1}{2}}$ is called the *plasma frequency*. If $\omega > \omega_p$, κ is real and the wave propagates through the plasma. However, if $\omega < \omega_p$, κ is a pure imaginary and the wave is attenuated.

(d) Show that the phase velocity v of the wave propagated through the plasma is

$$v = c\left[1 - \left(\frac{\omega_p}{\omega}\right)^2\right]^{-\frac{1}{2}} \tag{10-95}$$

so that there is dispersion in a plasma.

(e) If the plasma contains a steady magnetic field, the equations of motion (10-91) must be replaced by

$$m_e \frac{d}{dt} \mathbf{v}_e = -e(\mathbf{E} + \mathbf{v}_e \times \mathbf{B})$$

$$m_i \frac{d}{dt} \mathbf{v}_i = eZ(\mathbf{E} + \mathbf{v}_i \times \mathbf{B})$$

Show that the constitutive equation (10-92) must be replaced by

$$\frac{\partial}{\partial t} \mathbf{j} \simeq \frac{n_e e^2}{m_e} \mathbf{E} - \frac{e}{m_e} \mathbf{j} \times \mathbf{B}$$

$$= \frac{\omega_p^2}{\mu_0 c^2} \mathbf{E} - \mathbf{j} \times \boldsymbol{\omega}_{ge} \tag{10-96}$$

where $\omega_{ge} = eB/m_e$ and $\omega_{ge} = eB/m_e$ is known as the gyromagnetic (or cyclotron) frequency of the electrons.

(f) Suppose that the direction of propagation of the electromagnetic waves is parallel to the steady magnetic field. Then, according to (10-96), the effect of the field is to rotate the vector $\mathbf{j}$ and, consequently, the electric field $\mathbf{E}$. We therefore write

$$\frac{\partial}{\partial t} \mathbf{j} = \boldsymbol{\omega} \times \mathbf{j}$$

where the vector $\boldsymbol{\omega}$ is parallel or antiparallel to the field. Verify that Eq. (10-96) can then be written

$$\frac{\partial}{\partial t} \mathbf{j} = \frac{\omega_p^2}{\mu_0 c^2} \frac{\mathbf{E}}{(1 \pm \omega_{ge}/\omega)} \tag{10-97}$$

(g) Show that the wave equation satisfied by $\mathbf{E}$ is

$$\nabla^2 \mathbf{E} - \frac{1}{c^2} \frac{\partial^2}{\partial t^2} \mathbf{E} - \frac{\omega_p^2}{c^2} \frac{1}{(1 \pm \omega_{ge}/\omega)} \mathbf{E} = 0 \tag{10-98}$$

and has for solution

$$\mathbf{E}(\mathbf{r},t) = \mathbf{E}_0 e^{-i(\omega t - \boldsymbol{\kappa} \cdot \mathbf{r})}$$

where

$$\kappa^2 = \frac{1}{c^2}\left(\omega^2 - \frac{\omega_p^2}{1 \pm \omega_{ge}/\omega}\right) \tag{10-99}$$

The plus and minus signs correspond to the two directions of rotation of the electric vector. If the electric vector rotates in the same direction as the electrons gyrate, the minus sign applies and the wave is known as the ordinary wave. The plus sign applies to the extraordinary wave in which the electric vector rotates in the direction opposite to the gyration of the electrons.

REFERENCES

Abraham, M., and R. Becker: "The Classical Theory of Electricity and Magnetism," chap. 10, Hafner Publishing Company, Inc., New York, 1950.

Joos, G.: "Theoretical Physics," 2d rev. ed., chap. 19, Hafner Publishing Company, Inc., New York, 1951.

Panofsky, W. K. H., and M. Phillips: "Classical Electricity and Magnetism," chap. 11, Addison-Wesley Publishing Company, Inc., Cambridge, Mass., 1955.

Smythe, W. R.: "Static and Dynamic Electricity," 2d ed., chap. 13, McGraw-Hill Book Company, Inc., New York, 1950.

Stratton, J. A.: "Electromagnetic Theory," chap. 5, McGraw-Hill Book Company, Inc., New York, 1941.

CHAPTER 11

Reflection and Refraction of Plane Waves

11-1. INTRODUCTION

The purpose of the present chapter is to serve as an introduction to the electromagnetic theory of light. As we have seen, electromagnetic waves in a homogeneous isotropic medium travel with a phase velocity

$$v = \frac{c}{\sqrt{KK_m}} \tag{11-1}$$

where c is the velocity of light in vacuum and K and K_m are, respectively, the relative permittivity and permeability of the medium. It then follows that, in empty space where $K = K_m = 1$, the electromagnetic waves travel with the velocity of light in vacuum. We therefore infer that light waves are electromagnetic waves. This inference is confirmed by the following facts:

1. The index of refraction of a given medium for an electromagnetic wave is the same as the experimentally determined index of refraction of the medium for a light wave (cf. Sec. 11-2).

2. The laws of reflection and refraction of electromagnetic waves are the same as those established experimentally for light waves (cf. Secs. 11-4 to 11-6).

3. Electromagnetic waves exhibit the phenomenon of polarization characteristic of light waves (cf. Secs. 11-5 and 11-7).

4. The electromagnetic theory of metallic reflection yields an expression for the reflection coefficient whose values are in agreement with those obtained for light waves in the far infrared (cf. Sec. 11.8).

11-2. THE INDEX OF REFRACTION

The ratio of the phase velocity of light in vacuum to that in any other medium is known as the *index of refraction* of the medium and denoted by η. If light is electromagnetic in character, it follows from (11-1) that for dielectrics

$$\eta = \frac{c}{v} = \sqrt{KK_m} = \sqrt{K} \qquad (11\text{-}2)$$

since $K_m = 1$ in dielectrics.

In order to make a fair comparison of values of the square root of the dielectric constant K with values of the index of refraction, K should be measured for electrical vibrations of the same frequency as those of the light for which η is measured. Unfortunately, K cannot be measured at frequencies as high as those for light. Table 11-1 gives a comparison

TABLE 11-1. COMPARISON OF THE SQUARE ROOT OF THE DIELECTRIC CONSTANT WITH THE INDEX OF REFRACTION FOR SOME SUBSTANCES

Substance	Temp, °C	$\sqrt{K}$	Frequency, cps	η	Frequency, cps
Air	20	1.000295	$<3 \times 10^6$	1.0002919	4.5×10^{14}
Paraffin	20	1.45–1.58	10^6		
	38.3	....	....	1.43295	4.5×10^{14}
Petroleum	20	1.46	2×10^7		
	0	....	....	1.4573	5.1×10^{14}
Water	20	8.94	10^8	1.33335	5.1×10^{14}
Sulfur	25	1.94	10^2–10^3		
	110	....	....	1.929	4.5×10^{14}
	400	1.85	10^4		
Benzine	20	1.51	10^4	1.5012	4.5×10^{14}
		1.76	5×10^{10}		

between values of $\sqrt{K}$ and η for a few substances. Since the dielectric constants were measured at frequencies much lower than those for light, the good agreement in most of the substances indicates that the dielectric constants for these substances are not strongly frequency dependent. The disagreement in the case of water demonstrates the strong frequency dependence of its dielectric constant.

The frequency dependence of K is important in optics, since it explains the variation of η with frequency and, hence, the dispersion of light waves. Since K is a measured quantity in Maxwell's theory, one must look elsewhere for an explanation of its variation with frequency, e.g., to electron theory (cf. Sec. 17-7).

The ratio of the phase velocity in a medium, say v_1, to that in another medium, say v_2, is known as the index of refraction of medium 2 relative to medium 1 or, briefly, the *relative index of refraction*. Thus

$$\eta_{21} = \frac{v_1}{v_2} = \frac{\eta_2}{\eta_1} \qquad (11\text{-}3)$$

where η_1 and η_2 are the indices of refraction for medium 1 and medium 2, respectively.

11-3. BOUNDARY CONDITIONS

Consider the boundary surface between two media 1 and 2. Describe a pillbox-shaped surface $ABCD$ (Fig. 11-1) about an area S of the surface of separation. Then, because div $\mathbf{B} = 0$, we obtain from Gauss' theorem

$$\iint \mathbf{B} \cdot \mathbf{n}\, dS = 0 \tag{11-4}$$

where $\mathbf{n}$ is the unit outward drawn normal to the element dS of the surface of the pillbox and the integration is over the entire surface. In the limit as the height of the pillbox goes to zero, (11-4) becomes

$$\mathbf{n} \cdot (\mathbf{B}_2 - \mathbf{B}_1)S = 0$$

so that
$$B_{2n} = B_{1n} \tag{11-5}$$

i.e., the normal component of the magnetic induction is continuous across the interface.

The derivation of the boundary condition

$$D_{2n} = D_{1n} \tag{4-35}$$

i.e., the normal component of the electric displacement is continuous across an uncharged interface, proceeds as in Sec. 4-7.

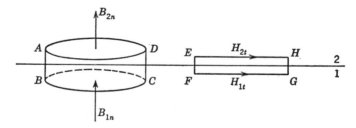

FIGURE 11-1

Consider now the rectangle $EFGH$ (Fig. 11-1) which lies with its longest sides parallel to the surface of separation, one in each medium. Then, from Stokes' theorem and (9-28a),

$$\oint \mathbf{H} \cdot ds = \iint \operatorname{curl} \mathbf{H} \cdot \mathbf{n}\, dS = \iint \left(\mathbf{j} + \frac{\partial \mathbf{D}}{\partial t} \right) \cdot \mathbf{n}\, dS \tag{11-6}$$

where dS is an element of the rectangle and $\mathbf{n}$ is the unit outward drawn normal to the element dS of an arbitrary surface S bounded by the rectangle.   In the limit as the sides EH and FG approach each other, the surface S goes to zero.   If the current density parallel to the interface does not become infinite, (11-6) reduces to

$$(\mathbf{H}_2 - \mathbf{H}_1) \cdot \mathbf{s} = (H_{2t} - H_{1t})s = 0$$

since $\mathbf{D}$ and its derivatives are finite.   Here s denotes the length of the sides EH and FG.   Hence

$$H_{2t} = H_{1t} \tag{11-7}$$

i.e., the tangential component of the magnetic intensity is continuous across the interface.

Consider again the rectangle $EFGH$.   Then

$$\oint \mathbf{E} \cdot d\mathbf{s} = - \iint \frac{\partial \mathbf{B}}{\partial t} \cdot d\mathbf{S} \tag{9-25}$$

where ds is an element of the rectangle and dS is an element of an arbitrary surface S bounded by the rectangle.   In the limit as the sides EH and FG approach each other, S goes to zero and (9-25) reduces to

$$(\mathbf{E}_2 - \mathbf{E}_1) \cdot \mathbf{s} = (E_{2t} - E_{1t})s = 0$$

since $\partial \mathbf{B}/\partial t$ is finite.   Hence

$$E_{2t} = E_{1t} \tag{11-8}$$

i.e., the tangential component of the electric intensity is continuous across the surface of separation, in agreement with (4-36) derived for the static field.

11-4. THE LAWS OF REFLECTION AND REFRACTION

Consider a plane wave traveling in a homogeneous isotropic medium of relative permittivity K_1 and relative permeability K_{m1} striking a plane surface of separation at an angle of incidence i (Fig. 11-2).   Let the relative permittivity and permeability of the second medium be K_2 and K_{m2}, respectively.   For convenience, take the surface of separation to be the $x_1 x_2$ plane and let the wave normal $\mathbf{n}$ be in the $x_1 x_3$ plane.   Then the incident wave is described by (cf. Sec. 10-6)

$$\begin{aligned} \mathbf{E}(\mathbf{r},t) &= \mathbf{E}^0 e^{-i\omega(t - \mathbf{r} \cdot \mathbf{n}/v_1)} \\ \mathbf{B}(\mathbf{r},t) &= \mathbf{B}^0 e^{-i\omega(t - \mathbf{r} \cdot \mathbf{n}/v_1)} \end{aligned} \tag{11-9}$$

where $v_1 = c/\sqrt{K_1 K_{m1}}$.

We assume that the reflected wave is described by

$$\begin{aligned} \mathbf{E}_m &= \mathbf{E}_m{}^0 e^{-i\omega'(t - \mathbf{r} \cdot \mathbf{n}'/v_1)} \\ \mathbf{B}_m &= \mathbf{B}_m{}^0 e^{-i\omega'(t - \mathbf{r} \cdot \mathbf{n}'/v_1)} \end{aligned} \tag{11-10}$$

where ω' and $\mathbf{n}'$ are to be determined. Similarly, we assume that the refracted wave is given by

$$\begin{aligned}
\mathbf{E}_b &= \mathbf{E}_b{}^0 e^{-i\omega''(t-\mathbf{r}\cdot\mathbf{n}''/v_2)} \\
\mathbf{B}_b &= \mathbf{B}_b{}^0 e^{-i\omega''(t-\mathbf{r}\cdot\mathbf{n}''/v_2)}
\end{aligned} \tag{11-11}$$

where $v_2 = c/\sqrt{K_2 K_{m2}}$ and ω'' and $\mathbf{n}''$ are to be determined.

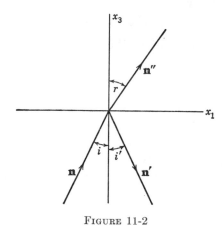

FIGURE 11-2

The boundary conditions on the tangential components of $\mathbf{E}$ and $\mathbf{H}$ require that

$$\begin{aligned}
E_1 + E_{m1} &= E_{b1} \\
E_2 + E_{m2} &= E_{b2} \\
H_1 + H_{m1} &= H_{b1} \\
H_2 + H_{m2} &= H_{b2}
\end{aligned}$$

and

for all x_1, x_2, and t when $x_3 = 0$. These relations can be satisfied only if

$$\omega = \omega' = \omega'' \tag{11-12}$$

and

$$\frac{\mathbf{r}\cdot\mathbf{n}}{v_1} = \frac{\mathbf{r}\cdot\mathbf{n}'}{v_1} = \frac{\mathbf{r}\cdot\mathbf{n}''}{v_2} \qquad \text{when } x_3 = 0 \tag{11-13}$$

Equation (11-12) states that there is no change in frequency in either reflection or refraction. From the equality of the first and second terms in (11-13) we obtain

$$n_1 x_1 = n_1' x_1 + n_2' x_2$$

since $n_2 = 0$. Hence

$$n_2' x_2 = 0 \tag{11-14}$$

and

$$n_1 x_1 = n_1' x_1 \tag{11-15}$$

If i and i' denote, respectively, the angles of incidence and reflection,

$n_1 = \sin i$ and $n_1' = \sin i'$, so that (11-15) can be written

$$\sin i = \sin i'$$

which implies that

$$i = i' \tag{11-15a}$$

The relations (11-14) and (11-15) or (11-15a) express the *law of reflection:* The angle of reflection is equal to the angle of incidence and lies in the same plane.

From the equality of the first and third terms in (11-13) we obtain

$$\frac{n_1 x_1}{v_1} = \frac{n_1'' x_1}{v_2} + \frac{n_2'' x_2}{v_2}$$

so that

$$\frac{n_2''}{v_2} x_2 = 0 \tag{11-16}$$

and

$$\frac{n_1 x_1}{v_1} = \frac{n_1'' x_1}{v_2} \tag{11-17}$$

Hence

$$\frac{n_1}{n_1''} \equiv \frac{\sin i}{\sin r} = \frac{v_1}{v_2} = \eta_{21} \tag{11-17a}$$

where r is the angle of refraction and η_{21} the relative index of refraction. Equations (11-16) and (11-17) or (11-17a) express *Snell's law of refraction:* The angles of incidence and refraction lie in the same plane, and the sine of the angle of incidence is equal to the product of the sine of the angle of refraction and the relative index of refraction.

11-5. FRESNEL'S EQUATIONS

Let **n** denote the direction of propagation of a plane wave described by the vectors **E** and **B**. The vectors **E**, **B**, and **n** form a right-handed coordinate system in the given order; i.e.

$$\mathbf{n} \times \mathbf{E} = v\mathbf{B} \tag{10-5}$$

and

$$\mathbf{n} \cdot \mathbf{E} = 0 \tag{10-6}$$

where v is the speed with which the wave is propagated. By definition, the *polarization of the wave* is the direction in which the electric vector **E** points. For example, if **E** lies along the x_2 axis, the wave is said to be polarized in the x_2 direction. Note, however, that the fact that **E** is at right angles to the direction of propagation of the wave [Eq. (10-6)] does not fix its direction and, hence, the polarization of the wave uniquely.

Let us consider again the problem of the preceding section in which a plane wave traveling in a homogeneous isotropic medium strikes a surface of separation at an arbitrary angle of incidence i. Since the polarization of the wave has not been specified, we shall consider the two extreme cases, one in which **E** is along the x_2 axis, the other in which it is in the x_1x_3 plane (Figs. 11-3 and 11-4, respectively). The general case of arbitrary polarization can then be obtained by combining the two extreme cases.

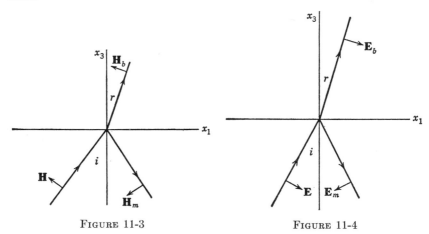

FIGURE 11-3   FIGURE 11-4

Case 1. The electric field vector **E** lies perpendicular to the plane of incidence (i.e., parallel to the surface of separation) and is taken along the x_2 axis. The incident, reflected, and refracted waves can then be described by

$$\mathbf{E(r,}t) = E^0\mathbf{i}_2 e^{-i\omega[t-(n_1x_1+n_3x_3)/v_1]}$$
$$\mathbf{B(r,}t) = \mathbf{B}^0 e^{-i\omega[t-(n_1x_1+n_3x_3)/v_1]} \tag{11-18}$$

$$\mathbf{E}_m = E_m{}^0\mathbf{i}_2 e^{-i\omega[t-(n_1x_1-n_3x_3)/v_1]}$$
$$\mathbf{B}_m = \mathbf{B}_m{}^0 e^{-i\omega[t-(n_1x_1-n_3x_3)/v_1]} \tag{11-19}$$

$$\mathbf{E}_b = E_b{}^0\mathbf{i}_2 e^{-i\omega[t-(n_1''x_1+n_3''x_3)/v_2]}$$
$$\mathbf{B}_b = \mathbf{B}_b{}^0 e^{-i\omega[t-(n_1''x_1+n_3''x_3)/v_2]} \tag{11-20}$$

respectively.

Application of (10-5) to the incident, reflected, and refracted waves yields, respectively,

$$-n_3E^0 = v_1B_1{}^0$$
$$n_1E^0 = v_1B_3{}^0 \tag{11-21}$$

$$n_3E_m{}^0 = v_1B_{m1}{}^0$$
$$n_1E_m{}^0 = v_1B_{m3}{}^0 \tag{11-22}$$

$$-n_3''E_b{}^0 = v_2B_{b1}{}^0$$
$$n_1''E_b{}^0 = v_2B_{b3}{}^0 \tag{11-23}$$

The boundary conditions at the surface of separation yield
   1. Normal component of $\mathbf{D}$: nothing.
   2. Normal component of $\mathbf{B}$:

$$B_3{}^0 + B_{m3}{}^0 = B_{b3}{}^0$$

or, using (11-21), (11-22) and (11-23),

$$E^0 + E_m{}^0 = \frac{v_1 \, n_1''}{v_2 \, n_1} E_b{}^0 = E_b{}^0 \tag{11-24}$$

by (11-13).
   3. Tangential component of $\mathbf{E}$:

$$E^0 + E_m{}^0 = E_b{}^0$$

which is the same relation as (11-24).
   4. Tangential component of $\mathbf{H}$:

$$H_1{}^0 + H_{m1}{}^0 = H_{b1}{}^0$$

or $$B_1{}^0 + B_{m1}{}^0 = \frac{\mu_1}{\mu_2} B_{b1}{}^0$$

where μ_1 and μ_2 are the permeabilities of the media. Using (11-21), (11-22), and (11-23) this relation becomes

$$E^0 - E_m{}^0 = \frac{v_1 \, n_3'' \, \mu_1}{v_2 \, n_3 \, \mu_2} E_b{}^0 = \eta_{21} \frac{\mu_1 \, n_3''}{\mu_2 \, n_3} E_b{}^0 \tag{11-25}$$

where η_{21} is the relative index of refraction. Since

$$\frac{n_3''}{n_3} = \frac{\cos r}{\cos i}$$

where i and r are, respectively, the angles of incidence and refraction, (11-25) can be written

$$E^0 - E_m{}^0 = \eta_{21} \frac{\mu_1 \cos r}{\mu_2 \cos i} E_b{}^0 \tag{11-25a}$$

Multiplication of (11-24) by $\eta_{21}(\mu_1/\mu_2)(\cos r/\cos i)$ followed by subtraction of the result from (11-25a) yields

$$\frac{E_m{}^0}{E^0} = \frac{\mu_2 \cos i - \eta_{21}\mu_1 \cos r}{\mu_2 \cos i + \eta_{21}\mu_1 \cos r} \tag{11-26}$$

as the equation for the amplitude of the reflected wave.

Addition of (11-24) and (11-25a) yields

$$\frac{E_b{}^0}{E^0} = \frac{2\mu_2 \cos i}{\mu_2 \cos i + \eta_{21}\mu_1 \cos r} \tag{11-27}$$

as the equation for the amplitude of the refracted wave.

Case 2. The electric field vector lies in the plane of incidence, the x_1x_3 plane, and the magnetic induction vector **B** is taken to lie along the x_2 axis. The incident, reflected, and refracted waves are described by

$$\mathbf{E}(\mathbf{r},t) = \mathbf{E}^0 e^{-i\omega[t-(n_1x_1+n_3x_3)/v_1]}$$
$$\mathbf{B}(\mathbf{r},t) = B^0\mathbf{i}_2 e^{-i\omega[t-(n_1x_1+n_3x_3)/v_1]} \tag{11-28}$$

$$\mathbf{E}_m = \mathbf{E}_m{}^0 e^{-i\omega[t-(n_1x_1-n_3x_3)/v_1]}$$
$$\mathbf{B}_m = B_m{}^0\mathbf{i}_2 e^{-i\omega[t-(n_1x_1-n_3x_3)/v_1]} \tag{11-29}$$

$$\mathbf{E}_b = \mathbf{E}_b{}^0 e^{-i\omega[t-(n_1{}''x_1+n_3{}''x_3)/v_2]}$$
$$\mathbf{B}_b = B_b{}^0\mathbf{i}_2 e^{-i\omega[t-(n_1{}''x_1+n_3{}''x_3)/v_2]} \tag{11-30}$$

respectively.

Application of (10-5) and (10-6) to the incident wave gives

$$n_3E_1{}^0 - n_1E_3{}^0 = v_1B^0 = E^0$$
and
$$n_1E_1{}^0 + n_3E_3{}^0 = 0$$

so that

$$E_1{}^0 = \frac{n_3}{n_1{}^2 + n_3{}^2} E^0 = n_3E^0 \qquad E_3{}^0 = \frac{-n_1}{n_1{}^2 + n_3{}^2} E^0 = -n_1E^0 \tag{11-31}$$

Similarly, for the reflected wave,

$$E_{m1}{}^0 = -n_3E_m{}^0 \qquad E_{m3}{}^0 = -n_1E_m{}^0 \tag{11-32}$$

and for the refracted wave,

$$E_{b1}{}^0 = n_3{}''E_b{}^0 \qquad E_{b3}{}^0 = -n_1{}''E_b{}^0 \tag{11-33}$$

The boundary conditions at the surface of separation yield
1. Normal component of **D**:

$$D_3{}^0 + D_{m3}{}^0 = D_{b3}{}^0$$
or
$$\epsilon_1(E_3{}^0 + E_{m3}{}^0) = \epsilon_2E_{b3}{}^0$$

so that, using (11-31), (11-32), and (11-33),

$$n_1\epsilon_1(E^0 + E_m{}^0) = n_1{}''\epsilon_2E_b{}^0 \tag{11-34}$$

2. Normal component of **B**: nothing.
3. Tangential component of **E**:

$$E_1{}^0 + E_{m1}{}^0 = E_{b1}{}^0$$

or, from (11-31), (11-32), and (11-33),

$$n_3(E^0 - E_m{}^0) = n_3'' E_b{}^0 \tag{11-35}$$

4. Tangential component of H:

$$H_2{}^0 + H_{m2}{}^0 = H_{b2}{}^0$$

or

$$\frac{1}{\mu_1}(B^0 + B_m{}^0) = \frac{1}{\mu_2} B_b{}^0$$

so that

$$\frac{1}{\mu_1 v_1}(E^0 + E_m{}^0) = \frac{1}{\mu_2 v_2} E_b{}^0 \tag{11-36}$$

From either (11-34) or (11-36) we obtain

$$E^0 + E_m{}^0 = \frac{\mu_1}{\mu_2} \eta_{21} E_b{}^0 \tag{11-36a}$$

Equation (11-35) can be written

$$E^0 - E_m{}^0 = \frac{\cos r}{\cos i} E_b{}^0 \tag{11-35a}$$

Addition of (11-35a) and (11-36a) yields

$$\frac{E_b{}^0}{E^0} = \frac{2\mu_2 \cos i}{\eta_{21}\mu_1 \cos i + \mu_2 \cos r} \tag{11-37}$$

for the amplitude of the refracted wave.

Substitution of (11-37) into (11-35a) yields

$$\frac{E_m{}^0}{E^0} = \frac{\eta_{21}\mu_1 \cos i - \mu_2 \cos r}{\eta_{21}\mu_1 \cos i + \mu_2 \cos r} \tag{11-38}$$

for the amplitude of the reflected wave.

Thus far we have thought of the electric vector of the incident wave as lying either in the plane of incidence (the $x_1 x_3$ plane) or perpendicular to the plane of incidence (i.e., along the x_2 axis). In the general case of arbitrary polarization the electric vector has components along the x_2 axis and in the $x_1 x_3$ plane. In such a case we represent the respective amplitudes of the components of the electric vector for the incident, reflected, and refracted waves by $E_\parallel{}^0$, $E_\perp{}^0$, $E_{m\parallel}{}^0$, $E_{m\perp}{}^0$ and $E_{b\parallel}{}^0$, $E_{b\perp}{}^0$. The subscript $\parallel$ denotes the component of the electric vector lying in the plane of incidence, while the subscript $\perp$ denotes the component perpendicular to the plane of incidence. The equations (11-26), (11-27),

(11-37), and (11-38) can then be rewritten as

$$\frac{E_{m\perp}{}^0}{E_\perp{}^0} = \frac{\mu_2 \cos i - \eta_{21}\mu_1 \cos r}{\mu_2 \cos i + \eta_{21}\mu_1 \cos r} \tag{11-26a}$$

$$\frac{E_{b\perp}{}^0}{E_\perp{}^0} = \frac{2\mu_2 \cos i}{\mu_2 \cos i + \eta_{21}\mu_1 \cos r} \tag{11-27a}$$

$$\frac{E_{m\parallel}{}^0}{E_\parallel{}^0} = \frac{\eta_{21}\mu_1 \cos i - \mu_2 \cos r}{\eta_{21}\mu_1 \cos i + \mu_2 \cos r} \tag{11-38a}$$

$$\frac{E_{b\parallel}{}^0}{E_\parallel{}^0} = \frac{2\mu_2 \cos i}{\eta_{21}\mu_1 \cos i + \mu_2 \cos r} \tag{11-37a}$$

If we make use of the fact that

$$\eta_{21} = \frac{\sin i}{\sin r} \tag{11-17a}$$

and limit the discussion to dielectric media ($\mu_1 = \mu_2 = 1$), then Eqs. (11-26a), (11-27a), (11-38a), and (11-37a) reduce to the well-known *Fresnel equations*

$$\frac{E_{m\perp}{}^0}{E_\perp{}^0} = -\frac{\sin (i - r)}{\sin (i + r)} \tag{11-39}$$

$$\frac{E_{b\perp}{}^0}{E_\perp{}^0} = \frac{2 \sin r \cos i}{\sin (i + r)} \tag{11-40}$$

$$\frac{E_{m\parallel}{}^0}{E_\parallel{}^0} = \frac{\tan (i - r)}{\tan (i + r)} \tag{11-41}$$

$$\frac{E_{b\parallel}{}^0}{E_\parallel{}^0} = \frac{2 \sin r \cos i}{\sin (i + r) \cos (i - r)} \tag{11-42}$$

The minus sign in Eq. (11-39) indicates a change of phase of π radians on reflection of the component of the electric vector which lies perpendicular to the plane of incidence. The positive sign in Eq. (11-41) indicates that there is no phase change on reflection of the component lying in the plane of incidence until $i + r = \pi/2$ radians, at which point $\tan (i + r)$ becomes negative and hence the phase angle changes by π radians. There is no phase change on refraction.

A very interesting phenomenon occurs when $i + r = \pi/2$ radians. For this value of $i + r$, Eqs. (11-39) through (11-42) reduce to

$$\left.\begin{array}{l} E_{m\perp}{}^0 = -\sin (i - r)E_\perp{}^0 \\ E_{b\perp}{}^0 = 2 \sin r \cos i \, E_\perp{}^0 \\ E_{m\parallel}{}^0 = 0 \\ E_{m\parallel}{}^0 = \dfrac{2 \sin r \cos i}{\cos (i - r)} E_\parallel{}^0 \end{array}\right\} \quad i + r = \frac{\pi}{2} \tag{11-43}$$

These equations show that the wave reflected at this angle of incidence,

$i = \pi/2 - r \equiv \tilde{\imath}$, is polarized entirely with the electric vector lying perpendicular to the plane of incidence. The angle $\tilde{\imath}$ is known as the *polarizing* or *Brewster angle*. At this angle

$$\eta_{21} = \frac{\sin \tilde{\imath}}{\sin r} = \frac{\sin \tilde{\imath}}{\cos \tilde{\imath}} = \tan \tilde{\imath} \tag{11-44}$$

that is, the relative index of refraction is equal to the tangent of Brewster's angle. Equation (11-44) is a statement of *Brewster's law*. It shows that the angle of maximum polarization depends on the refractive index and, therefore, varies with the frequency of the light.

At grazing incidence, when $i = \pi/2$ radians, Fresnel's equations reduce to

$$E_{m\perp}{}^0 = -E_{\perp}{}^0$$
$$E_{b\perp}{}^0 = 0$$
$$E_{m\parallel}{}^0 = -E_{\parallel}{}^0$$
$$E_{b\parallel}{}^0 = 0$$

These show that both components of the electric vector are reflected at grazing incidence.

11-6. REFLECTION AND TRANSMISSION COEFFICIENTS

By definition, the intensity of a wave is the energy falling in unit time on unit area perpendicular to the direction of propagation of the wave. As has already been demonstrated (Sec. 9-13), this quantity is given by the magnitude of the Poynting vector.

Consider a plane wave traveling in a homogeneous isotropic medium and normally incident on a plane surface of separation. Then the reflection coefficient is defined as that fraction of the intensity of the incident wave which is reflected from the surface of separation. The transmission coefficient is that fraction of the intensity of the incident wave which is transmitted through the surface of separation.

In the case of normal incidence $(i = 0)$, Eqs. (11-26a), (11-27a), (11-38a), and (11-37a) reduce to

$$\frac{E_{m\perp}{}^0}{E_{\perp}{}^0} \equiv \frac{E_m{}^0}{E^0} = \frac{\mu_2 - \eta_{21}\mu_1}{\mu_2 + \eta_{21}\mu_1} \tag{11-45}$$

$$\frac{E_{b\perp}{}^0}{E_{\perp}{}^0} \equiv \frac{E_b{}^0}{E^0} = \frac{2\mu_2}{\mu_2 + \eta_{21}\mu_1} \tag{11-46}$$

$$E_{m\parallel}{}^0 = E_{b\parallel}{}^0 = 0 \tag{11-47}$$

since $\cos i = \cos r = 1$ and $E_{\parallel}{}^0 = 0$.

For dielectrics, $\mu_1 = \mu_2 = 1$ and Eqs. (11-45) through (11-47) become

$$\frac{E_{m\perp}{}^0}{E_\perp{}^0} \equiv \frac{E_m{}^0}{E^0} = \frac{1 - \eta_{21}}{1 + \eta_{21}} \tag{11-45a}$$

$$\frac{E_{b\perp}{}^0}{E_\perp{}^0} \equiv \frac{E_b{}^0}{E^0} = \frac{2}{1 + \eta_{21}} \tag{11-46a}$$

$$E_{m\parallel}{}^0 = E_{b\parallel}{}^0 = 0 \tag{11-47a}$$

Hence the reflection coefficient R is

$$R = \frac{|\mathbf{E}_m{}^0 \times \mathbf{H}_m{}^0|}{|\mathbf{E}^0 \times \mathbf{H}^0|} = \frac{E_m{}^0 H_m{}^0}{E^0 K^0} = \left(\frac{E_m{}^0}{E^0}\right)^2$$

$$= \left(\frac{1 - \eta_{21}}{1 + \eta_{21}}\right)^2 \tag{11-48}$$

where we have used (10-7). Similarly, the transmission coefficient T is

$$T = \frac{|\mathbf{E}_b{}^0 \times \mathbf{H}_b{}^0|}{|\mathbf{E}^0 \times \mathbf{H}^0|} = \frac{E_b{}^0 H_b{}^0}{E^0 H^0} = \frac{v_1}{v_2}\left(\frac{E_b{}^0}{E^0}\right)^2$$

$$= \eta_{21}\left(\frac{2}{1 + \eta_{21}}\right)^2 = \frac{4\eta_{21}}{(1 + \eta_{21})^2} \tag{11-49}$$

11-7. TOTAL REFLECTION

Consider an electromagnetic wave passing from a dense dielectric medium of permittivity ϵ to a rarer medium, say a vacuum. The index of refraction of the dense medium is given by

$$\eta = \frac{\sin r}{\sin i}$$

where i is the angle of incidence and r the angle of refraction. When the angle of refraction reaches its maximum, namely 90°, this relation gives

$$i = \arcsin \frac{1}{\eta} \tag{11-50}$$

for the angle of incidence. This particular angle of incidence which makes the angle of refraction 90° is called the *critical angle* for the two media. For larger angles of incidence, $\sin r$ is greater unity, there is no real angle r, and there is total reflection with no transmitted wave.

If the incident wave is given by

$$\mathbf{E}(\mathbf{r},t) = \mathbf{E}^0 e^{-i\omega[t - (n_1 x_1 + n_3 x_3)/v]}$$

the transmitted wave is described by

$$\mathbf{E}_b(\mathbf{r},t) = \mathbf{E}_b{}^0 e^{-i\omega[t - (n_1'' x_1 + n_3'' x_3)/c]}$$

or

$$\mathbf{E}_b(\mathbf{r},t) = \mathbf{E}_b{}^0 e^{-i\omega[t - (x_1 \sin r + x_3 \cos r)/c]} \tag{11-51}$$

which states that, although no transmitted wave is observed, there is still a disturbance.

For angles greater than the critical angle

$$\cos r = -\sqrt{1 - \sin^2 r} = -\sqrt{1 - \eta^2 \sin^2 i} = -i\sqrt{\eta^2 \sin^2 i - 1}\dagger$$

a pure imaginary.   Expression (11-51) can now be written

$$\mathbf{E}_b(\mathbf{r},t) = \mathbf{E}_b{}^0 e^{-i\omega(t - x_1 \sin r/c)} e^{-\omega(x_3/c)\sqrt{\eta^2 \sin^2 i - 1}} \qquad (11\text{-}52)$$

The first factor of the right-hand member represents a wave traveling along the x_3 axis, i.e., parallel to the surface of separation, with a speed $c/\sin r$, which is less than c.   The second factor shows that the amplitude of this wave is damped out as x_3 increases or as the wave moves from the surface of separation into the vacuum.   When $\eta^2 \sin^2 i$ is much greater than unity, the exponent in this factor becomes a very large negative number and the disturbance is too small to be observed.   It is easily demonstrated that the Poynting vector for this wave has no component normal to the surface and so does not carry any energy away.

For our present case of an angle of incidence greater than the critical angle, Fresnel's equations become complex but can still be used.   Thus (11-39) becomes

$$\frac{E_{m\perp}{}^0}{E_\perp{}^0} = \frac{a - ib}{a + ib} \qquad i = \sqrt{-1} \qquad (11\text{-}53)$$

where

$$a = \cos i \sin r$$
$$b = -\sin r \sqrt{\eta^2 \sin^2 i - 1}$$

or in exponential form

$$\frac{E_{m\perp}{}^0}{E_\perp{}^0} = e^{-2i \arctan (b/a)} \qquad (11\text{-}53a)$$

These expressions show that $E_{m\perp}{}^0$ and $E_\perp{}^0$ are of the same magnitude, i.e., all the $\perp$ component of the wave is reflected, but differ in phase. Hence if we define a phase angle $\delta_\perp$ by means of the relation

$$\tan \frac{\delta_\perp}{2} = -\frac{b}{a} = \frac{\sqrt{\eta^2 \sin^2 i - 1}}{\eta \cos i} \qquad (11\text{-}54)$$

expression (11-53a) can be written

$$\frac{E_{m\perp}{}^0}{E_\perp{}^0} = e^{i\delta_\perp} \qquad (11\text{-}53b)$$

† Note that i outside the square root represents $\sqrt{-1}$ while under the square root it represents the angle of incidence.

In a like manner

$$\frac{E_{m\parallel}^{0}}{E_{\parallel}^{0}} = \frac{c - id}{c + id} \tag{11-55}$$

where
$$c = \sin i \cos i$$
$$d = -\sin r \sqrt{\eta^2 \sin^2 i - 1}$$

or
$$\frac{E_{m\parallel}^{0}}{E_{\parallel}^{0}} = e^{i\delta}{}_{\parallel} \tag{11-55a}$$

where
$$\tan \frac{\delta_{\parallel}}{2} = -\frac{d}{c} = \frac{\eta \sqrt{\eta^2 \sin^2 i - 1}}{\cos i} \tag{11-56}$$

The above results show that, in the general case where **E** has both ⊥ and ∥ components, there is a difference in phase between these components upon total reflection. Consequently, linearly polarized light will, in general, become elliptically polarized upon total reflection. To see this, note that two vibrations at right angles, with the same frequency and phase, produce a resultant vector whose extremity moves in a line (plane polarization). However, if the two components differ in phase, the extremity of the vector traces out an ellipse. If the phases differ by 90° and the amplitudes of the two components are equal, the polarization is circular.

From Eqs. (11-54) and (11-56) the difference between the phases is

$$\delta = \delta_{\parallel} - \delta_{\perp}$$

where
$$\tan \frac{\delta}{2} = \frac{\cos i \sqrt{\eta^2 \sin^2 i - 1}}{\eta \sin^2 i}$$

Only in the case of grazing incidence, $i = 90°$, does δ become zero. Hence our remarks on the elliptical polarization of the reflected wave are valid except for this case.

11-8. METALLIC REFLECTION

The development of Fresnel's equations in Sec. 11-5 was completely general up to and including Eq. (11-37a), at which point the discussion was limited to dielectric media. We shall use these general results in the present study of the reflection of electromagnetic waves from metals. An important fact to recall is that in metals the phase velocity of an electromagnetic wave is complex (cf. Sec. 10-7) and, consequently, the index of refraction of a metal is complex. Thus

$$\eta = \frac{c}{\alpha} \tag{11-57}$$

where the phase velocity α is given by

$$\frac{1}{\alpha} = \frac{1}{v_c} + i\kappa \tag{10-56}$$

in which

$$v_c = \frac{\omega}{\sigma} \sqrt{\frac{2\epsilon}{\mu}} \left(\sqrt{1 + \frac{\sigma^2}{\omega^2\epsilon^2}} - 1 \right)^{\frac{1}{2}} \tag{10-57}$$

$$\kappa = \sqrt{\frac{\mu\epsilon}{2}} \left(\sqrt{1 + \frac{\sigma^2}{\omega^2\epsilon^2}} - 1 \right)^{\frac{1}{2}} \tag{10-58}$$

Since $\sigma/\omega\epsilon$ is usually much greater than unity in metals,

$$v_c \simeq \sqrt{\frac{2\omega}{\mu\sigma}}$$

$$\kappa \simeq \sqrt{\frac{\mu\sigma}{2\omega}}$$

Hence

$$\frac{1}{\alpha} \simeq \sqrt{\frac{\mu\sigma}{2\omega}} (1 + i)$$

and

$$\eta \simeq c \sqrt{\frac{\mu\sigma}{2\omega}} (1 + i) \tag{11-58}$$

For an electromagnetic wave in vacuum normally incident upon the surface of a metal [cf. Eq. (11-45)],

$$\frac{E_m{}^0}{E^0} = \frac{\mu - \eta\mu_0}{\mu + \eta\mu_0}$$

Hence the reflection coefficient R is given by

$$R = \left| \frac{E_m{}^0}{E^0} \right|^2 = 1 - \frac{2\mu\mu_0(\eta + \eta^*)}{\eta\eta^*\mu_0{}^2 + \mu\mu_0(\eta + \eta^*) + \mu^2}$$

$$= 1 - \frac{4\mu\mu_0 c \sqrt{\mu\sigma/2\omega}}{c^2\mu_0{}^2(\mu\sigma/\omega) + 2\mu\mu_0 c \sqrt{\mu\sigma/2\omega} + \mu^2}$$

$$\simeq 1 - \frac{2}{c\mu_0} \sqrt{\frac{2\omega\mu}{\sigma}}$$

$$\simeq 1 - 2 \sqrt{\frac{2\omega\epsilon_0\mu}{\sigma\mu_0}} \tag{11-59}$$

For nonferromagnetic materials where $\mu/\mu_0 = 1$, this relation reduces to

$$R \simeq 1 - 2 \sqrt{\frac{2\omega\epsilon_0}{\sigma}}$$

This theoretical formula for the reflection coefficient has been verified in the far infrared ($\lambda = 2\pi c/\omega \simeq 5$ microns) by Hagen and Rubens.[†]

[†] E. Hagen and H. Rubens, *Ann. Physik*, **11**: 873 (1903).

EXERCISES

11-1. A plane wave traveling in a homogeneous isotropic dielectric strikes the plane surface of another dielectric at an angle of incidence i. Show that the reflection and transmission coefficients are

$$R_\perp = \frac{\sin^2 (i - r)}{\sin^2 (i + r)} \qquad T_\perp = \frac{\sin 2i \sin 2r}{\sin^2 (i + r)}$$

in the case where the electric vector of the incident wave is perpendicular to the plane of incidence and

$$R_\| = \frac{\tan^2 (i - r)}{\tan^2 (i + r)} \qquad T_\| = \frac{\sin 2i \sin 2r}{\sin^2 (i + r) \sin^2 (i - r)}$$

in the case where the electric vector of the incident wave lies in the plane of incidence.

11-2. A plane wave is normally incident upon a perfect reflector. Show that in the resultant standing wave **E** and **B** are in time and space quadrature.

11-3. A plane wave traveling in a homogeneous isotropic dielectric strikes the plane surface of a conductor at the angle of incidence i. Assume that the incident wave is described by

$$\mathbf{E}(\mathbf{r},t) = \mathbf{E}^0 e^{-i\omega[t-(n_1 x_1 + n_3 x_3)/v]}$$
$$\mathbf{B}(\mathbf{r},t) = \mathbf{B}^0 e^{-i\omega[t-(n_1 x_1 + n_3 x_3)/v]}$$

the reflected wave by

$$\mathbf{E}_m = \mathbf{E}_m{}^0 e^{-i\omega[t-(n_1 x_1 - n_3 x_3)/v]}$$
$$\mathbf{B}_m = \mathbf{B}_m{}^0 e^{-i\omega[t-(n_1 x_1 - n_3 x_3)/v]}$$

and the refracted wave by

$$\mathbf{E}_b = \mathbf{E}_b{}^0 e^{-i\omega[t-(n_1'' x_1 + n_3'' x_3)/\alpha]}$$
$$\mathbf{B}_b = \mathbf{B}_b{}^0 e^{-i\omega[t-(n_1'' x_1 + n_3'' x_3)/\alpha]}$$

where the phase velocity α is complex (cf. Sec. 10-7).

(a) Show that

$$\frac{n_1''}{n_1} \equiv \frac{\sin r}{\sin i} = \frac{\alpha}{v}$$

i.e., the angle of refraction r is complex.

(b) Show that

$$i \frac{\omega}{\alpha} (n_1'' x_1 + n_3'' x_3) = i \frac{\omega}{v} \left(\sin i x_1 + \sqrt{\frac{v^2}{\alpha^2} - \sin^2 i}\, x_3 \right)$$

and, since

$$\frac{1}{\alpha^2} = \frac{1}{v_c{}^2} + 2i \frac{\kappa}{v_c} - \kappa^2$$

where v_c and κ are given by (10-57) and (10-58), respectively, write

$$a + ib = \sqrt{\frac{v^2}{\alpha^2} - \sin^2 i}$$

and solve for a and b.

(c) Show that the surfaces of constant amplitude of the refracted wave lie parallel to the interface $x_3 = 0$ and are given by $(\omega b/v)x_3 = $ constant.

(d) Show that the surfaces of constant phase of the refracted waves are the planes

$$\frac{1}{v}\left(\sin i x_1 + a x_3\right) = \text{constant}$$

and that the true angle of refraction R, defined as the angle between the normal to the planes of constant phase and the normal to the interface, is given by

$$\cos R = \frac{a}{\sqrt{a^2 + \sin^2 i}} \qquad \sin R = \frac{\sin i}{\sqrt{a^2 + \sin^2 i}}$$

(e) Show that a real index of refraction, defined by

$$\eta = \frac{\sin i}{\sin R}$$

is a function of the angle of incidence. Also show that the phase velocity v'', defined as the velocity of propagation of planes of constant phase, is

$$v'' = \frac{v}{\eta} = \frac{v}{\sqrt{a^2 + \sin^2 i}}$$

(f) Verify that

$$\frac{ab}{v^2} = \frac{\kappa}{v_c} \equiv \frac{\mu\sigma}{2\omega}$$

$$\frac{1}{v^2}\left(\eta^2 - b^2\right) = \frac{1}{v_c^2} - \kappa^2 \equiv \mu\epsilon$$

$$\frac{\eta b}{v^2} = \frac{\kappa/v_c}{\cos R} = \frac{\mu\sigma/2\omega}{\cos R}$$

where μ, ϵ, and σ are constants of the conducting medium. These relations are known as *Ketteler's equations*.

11-4. In Sec. 11-8 the reflection of an electromagnetic wave traveling in vacuum and normally incident upon a conductor was considered. Obtain the reflection coefficients for a wave incident at the arbitrary angle i.

REFERENCES

Joos, G.: "Theoretical Physics," 2d rev. ed., chap. 18, Hafner Publishing Company, Inc., New York, 1951.

Panofsky, W. K. H., and M. Phillips: "Classical Electricity and Magnetism," chap. 11, Addison-Wesley Publishing Company, Inc., Cambridge, Mass., 1955.

Slater, J. C., and N. H. Frank: "Introduction to Theoretical Physics," chap. 23, McGraw-Hill Book Company, Inc., New York, 1933.

Smythe, W. R.: "Static and Dynamic Electricity," 2d ed., chap. 13, McGraw-Hill Book Company, Inc., New York, 1950.

Stratton, J. A.: "Electromagnetic Theory," chap. 9, McGraw-Hill Book Company, Inc., New York, 1941.

CHAPTER 12

Spherical Electromagnetic Waves

12-1. INTRODUCTION

The discussion in this chapter is limited to spherical electromagnetic waves in homogeneous isotropic dielectrics. In Sec. 12-2 it is shown how the electromagnetic field can be resolved into two partial fields, each of which is derivable from a scalar function satisfying the wave equation. This scalar function is expressed in terms of a multipole expansion. Transverse magnetic (TM) waves, i.e., waves in which the radial component of the magnetic induction is zero, are treated in Sec. 12-3. The radiation from an oscillating electric dipole, the simplest TM radiation, is discussed in Sec. 12-4. Transverse electric (TE) waves and the simplest of these, the oscillating magnetic dipole, are treated in Secs. 12-5 and 12-6, respectively.

12-2. SPHERICAL WAVES IN HOMOGENEOUS ISOTROPIC DIELECTRICS

In Sec. 10-6 the wave equations

$$\nabla^2 \mathbf{B} - \frac{1}{v^2} \frac{\partial^2}{\partial t^2} B = 0 \qquad (9\text{-}47)$$

and

$$\nabla^2 \mathbf{E} - \frac{1}{v^2} \frac{\partial^2}{\partial t^2} \mathbf{E} = 0 \qquad (9\text{-}48)$$

were solved in cartesian coordinates by considering each as a set of three scalar equations, one in each of the rectangular components of the vectors $\mathbf{E}$ and $\mathbf{B}$. This procedure was possible because in a cartesian coordinate system the unit vectors $\mathbf{i}_1$, $\mathbf{i}_2$, $\mathbf{i}_3$ are in the same direction at all points in space. In space polar coordinates, however, the unit vectors $\mathbf{i}_r$, $\mathbf{i}_\theta$, $\mathbf{i}_\varphi$ are not in the same direction at all points of space. Consequently a different procedure is required for the solution of the wave equations in this coordinate system.

We assume that

$$\mathbf{B}(r,\theta,\varphi,t) = \mathbf{B}^0(r,\theta,\varphi)e^{-i\omega t} \qquad (12\text{-}1)$$
$$\mathbf{E}(r,\theta,\varphi,t) = \mathbf{E}^0(r,\theta,\varphi)e^{-i\omega t} \qquad (12\text{-}2)$$

Then Eqs. (9-47) and (9-48) reduce to the time-independent wave equations

$$\nabla^2 \mathbf{B}^0 + k^2 \mathbf{B}^0 = 0 \tag{12-3}$$

and
$$\nabla^2 \mathbf{E}^0 + k^2 \mathbf{E}^2 = 0 \tag{12-4}$$

where $k = \omega/v$.

If the scalar function $\psi(r,\theta,\varphi)$ satisfies the time-independent wave equation

$$\nabla^2 \psi(r,\theta,\varphi) + k^2 \psi(r,\theta,\varphi) = 0 \tag{12-5}$$

where

$$\nabla^2 \equiv \frac{1}{r^2}\frac{\partial}{\partial r}\left(r^2 \frac{\partial}{\partial r}\right) + \frac{1}{r^2 \sin\theta}\frac{\partial}{\partial\theta}\left(\sin\theta \frac{\partial}{\partial\theta}\right) + \frac{1}{r^2 \sin^2\theta}\frac{\partial^2}{\partial\varphi^2} \tag{12-6}$$

it is easily verified that the vectors

$$\mathbf{r} \times \nabla\psi = -\nabla \times (\mathbf{r}\psi) \tag{12-7}$$

which is transverse to the position vector $\mathbf{r}$, and

$$\nabla \times (\mathbf{r} \times \nabla\psi) = \nabla^2(\mathbf{r}\psi) - \nabla[\nabla \cdot (\mathbf{r}\psi)]$$

which is directed along $\mathbf{r}$, are solenoidal vectors which satisfy the time-independent wave equation. Thus the problem of solving the wave equations (12-3) and (12-4) is reduced to that of solving (12-5).

To solve (12-5) we assume that

$$\psi(r,\theta,\varphi) = R(r)\Theta(\theta)\Phi(\varphi) \tag{12-8}$$

substitute into (12-5), and divide by ψ. Then, using (12-6),

$$\frac{\sin^2\theta}{R}\frac{d}{dr}\left(r^2 \frac{dR}{dr}\right) + \frac{\sin\theta}{\Theta}\frac{d}{d\theta}\left(\sin\theta \frac{d\Theta}{d\theta}\right) + k^2 r^2 \sin^2\theta = -\frac{1}{\Phi}\frac{d^2}{d\varphi^2}\Phi$$

For a solution, both sides of this equation must be equal to a constant, say m^2. Consequently,

$$\frac{d^2}{d\varphi^2}\Phi + m^2\Phi = 0$$

which has for solution [cf. solution of Eq. (6-24)]

$$\begin{aligned}\Phi &= a(m)e^{im\varphi} + a'(m)e^{-im\varphi} \quad & m \neq 0 \quad & m = \text{positive integer} \\ &= b & m = 0 & \end{aligned} \tag{12-9}$$

and
$$\frac{1}{\Theta \sin\theta}\frac{d}{d\theta}\left(\sin\theta \frac{d}{d\theta}\Theta\right) - \frac{m^2}{\sin^2\theta} = -\frac{1}{R}\frac{d}{dr}\left(r^2 \frac{dR}{dr}\right) - k^2 r^2$$

This last equation also will have a solution only if both sides equal a constant, say $-\beta$. Then

$$\frac{1}{\Theta \sin \theta} \frac{d}{d\theta} \left(\sin \theta \frac{d}{d\theta} \Theta \right) - \frac{m^2}{\sin^2 \theta} = -\beta \tag{12-10}$$

$$\frac{1}{R} \frac{d}{dr} \left(r^2 \frac{d}{dr} R \right) + k^2 r^2 = \beta \tag{12-11}$$

where β is to be determined. Now Eq. (12-10) is precisely Eq. (6-58), whose solution was shown to be

$$\Theta(\theta) = d_1 P_l^m(\cos \theta) + d_2 Q_l^m(\cos \theta) \tag{12-12}$$

in which d_1 and d_2 are arbitrary constants, $\beta = l(l + 1), l = 0, 1, 2, \ldots$, and $m = 0, 1, 2, \ldots, l$. Then (12-11) becomes

$$\frac{d^2}{dr^2} R + \frac{2}{r} \frac{d}{dr} R + \left(k^2 - \frac{l(l + 1)}{r^2} \right) R = 0 \tag{12-13}$$

This equation is similar to Eq. (6-25), whose solutions were found to be cylindrical functions of kr. For this reason we assume that

$$R(r) = g(k) Z_s(kr) f(r) \tag{12-14}$$

where g is an arbitrary function of k and both the order s of the cylindrical function and the function f are to be determined. Substitution of (12-14) into (12-13) gives

$$\frac{d^2}{dr^2} Z_s + \frac{2}{f} \left(\frac{df}{dr} + \frac{f}{r} \right) \frac{dZ_s}{dr} + \frac{1}{f} \left\{ \frac{d^2 f}{dr^2} + \frac{2}{r} \frac{df}{dr} + \left[k^2 - \frac{l(l + 1)}{r^2} \right] f \right\} Z_s = 0$$

Hence, if Z_s is to satisfy an equation of the form of (6-25), we must have

$$\frac{2}{f} \left(\frac{df}{dr} + \frac{f}{r} \right) = \frac{1}{r}$$

which has for solution $f = r^{-\frac{1}{2}}$. Then

$$\frac{1}{f} \left\{ \frac{d^2 f}{dr^2} + \frac{2}{r} \frac{df}{dr} + \left(k^2 - \frac{l(l + 1)}{r^2} \right) f \right\} = k^2 - \frac{(l + \frac{1}{2})^2}{r^2}$$

so that $s = l + \frac{1}{2}$. Hence the solution (12-14) can be written

$$R(r) = g(k,l) \frac{Z_{l+\frac{1}{2}}(kr)}{\sqrt{r}}$$

$$= G(k,l) \sqrt{\frac{\pi}{2kr}} Z_{l+\frac{1}{2}}(kr) \equiv G(k,l) z_l(kr) \tag{12-15}$$

where the functions

$$z_l(\rho) \equiv \sqrt{\frac{\pi}{2\rho}} \, Z_{l+\frac{1}{2}}(\rho) \qquad (12\text{-}16)$$

are known as the spherical cylindrical functions. The properties of these functions are well-known.† Only the spherical Bessel functions $j_l(kr)$ are regular at $r = 0$.

The solutions of the time-independent wave equation (12-5) can now be written

$$
\begin{aligned}
\psi_l{}^m(r,\theta,\varphi) &= G(k,l)z_l(kr)[P_l{}^m(\cos\theta) + dQ_l{}^m(\cos\theta)][a(m)e^{im\varphi} + a'(m)e^{-im\varphi}] \\
& \hspace{7cm} l \neq 0 \qquad m \neq 0 \\
&= G(k,l)z_l(kr)[P_l(\cos\theta) + dQ_l(\cos\theta)] \qquad l \neq 0 \qquad m = 0 \\
&= G(k,0)z_0(kr)[P_0(\cos\theta) + dQ_0(\cos\theta)] \qquad l = 0 \qquad m = 0
\end{aligned}
$$
$$(12\text{-}17)$$

where the indices l and m on ψ have been used to indicate the dependence of ψ on the values of l and m. In terms of normalized spherical harmonics (cf. Sec. 6-6) these expressions become

$$
\begin{aligned}
\psi_l{}^m(r,\theta,\varphi) &= G(k,l,m)z_l(kr)[Y_l{}^m(\theta,\varphi) + d\mathcal{Y}_l{}^m(\theta,\varphi)] \qquad l \neq 0 \qquad m \neq 0 \\
&= G(k,l)z_l(kr)[Y_l{}^0(\theta,\varphi) + d\mathcal{Y}_l{}^0(\theta,\varphi)] \qquad l \neq 0 \qquad m = 0 \\
&= G(k,0)z_0(kr)[Y_0{}^0(\theta,\varphi) + d\mathcal{Y}_0{}^0(\theta,\varphi)] \qquad l = 0 \qquad m = 0
\end{aligned}
$$
$$(12\text{-}18)$$

The general solution of (12-5) is obtained by summing (12-17) or (12-18) over all permissible values of l and m:

$$\psi(r,\theta,\varphi) = \sum_{l,m} \psi_l{}^m(r,\theta,\varphi) \qquad (12\text{-}19)$$

The general solutions of the time-independent wave equations (12-3) and (12-4) are then

$$\mathbf{Q}^0 = \nabla \times (\mathbf{r} \times \nabla\psi_1) + \mathbf{r} \times \nabla\psi_2 \qquad \mathbf{Q} = \mathbf{B} \text{ or } \mathbf{E} \qquad (12\text{-}20)$$

where the ψ_i are given by (12-19). If all the $\psi_l{}^m$ are zero except those for which $l = L$, (12-20) reduces to

$$\mathbf{Q}^0 \equiv \mathbf{Q}_L{}^{m0} = \sum_m [\nabla \times (\mathbf{r} \times \nabla\psi_{1L}{}^m) + \mathbf{r} \times \nabla\psi_{2L}{}^m] \qquad \mathbf{Q}_L{}^m = \mathbf{B}_L{}^m \text{ or } \mathbf{E}_L{}^m$$
$$(12\text{-}21)$$

† See, for instance, P. M. Morse and H. Feshbach, "Methods of Theoretical Physics," McGraw-Hill Book Company, Inc., New York, 1953, or G. Goertzel and N. Tralli, "Some Mathematical Methods of Physics," McGraw-Hill Book Company, Inc., New York, 1960.

The radiation is then called *multipole radiation of order* 2^L (e.g., dipole radiation corresponds to $L = 1$, quadrupole radiation to $L = 2$, etc.) and the fields *multipole fields of order* 2^L.

12-3. TRANSVERSE MAGNETIC (TM) WAVES

If the radial component of the magnetic induction is zero, the solution (12-20) of the time-independent wave equation (12-3) reduces to

$$\mathbf{B}^0 = (\mathbf{r} \times \nabla \psi) \tag{12-22}$$

where we have dropped the subscript 2 on ψ. The wave is then known as a *transverse magnetic* (TM) spherical wave. Since

$$\operatorname{curl} \mathbf{B} = \mu \epsilon \frac{\partial}{\partial t} \mathbf{E} = \frac{1}{v^2} \frac{\partial}{\partial t} \mathbf{E}$$

in current-free homogeneous isotropic media, it follows by use of (12-1) and (12-2) that

$$\mathbf{E}^0 = i \frac{v}{k} \nabla \times (\mathbf{r} \times \nabla \psi) \tag{12-23}$$

The relations (12-22) and (12-23) for the fields $\mathbf{B}$ and $\mathbf{E}$ can be written explicitly in terms of r, θ, and φ:

$$\mathbf{B}^0 = \left(-\frac{1}{\sin \theta} \frac{\partial \psi}{\partial \varphi} \mathbf{i}_\theta + \frac{\partial \psi}{\partial \theta} \mathbf{i}_\varphi \right)$$

$$\mathbf{E}^0 = i \frac{v}{k} \left[\frac{1}{r \sin \theta} \left(\frac{\partial}{\partial \theta} \sin \theta \frac{\partial \psi}{\partial \theta} + \frac{1}{\sin \theta} \frac{\partial^2 \psi}{\partial \varphi^2} \right) \mathbf{i}_r - \frac{1}{r} \frac{\partial}{\partial \theta} \frac{\partial}{\partial r} (r\psi) \mathbf{i}_\theta \right.$$
$$\left. - \frac{1}{r \sin \theta} \frac{\partial}{\partial \varphi} \frac{\partial}{\partial r} (r\psi) \mathbf{i}_\varphi \right] \tag{12-24}$$

12-4. THE OSCILLATING ELECTRIC DIPOLE

The simplest TM multipole radiation is that due to an oscillating dipole ($L = 1$; $m = 0$). In such a case

$$\psi \equiv \psi_1{}^0 = G(k,1) z_1(kr)[Y_1{}^0(\theta,\varphi) + d y_1{}^0(\theta,\varphi)] \tag{12-25}$$

If we desire solutions which are regular everywhere except at the origin of coordinates, we must set the constant d equal to zero and take

$$z_1(kr) = h_1{}^{(1,2)}(kr)$$

As we shall see $h_1^{(1)}(kr)$ corresponds to a wave traveling outward from the origin of coordinates. For such a case (12-25) reduces to

$$\psi = G(k,1)h_1^{(1)}(kr) Y_1^0(\theta,\varphi)$$

or
$$\psi = g(k,1)h_1^{(1)}(kr) \cos \theta \qquad (12\text{-}26)$$

since
$$Y_1^0(\theta,\varphi) = \sqrt{\frac{3}{4\pi}} \cos \theta$$

and we have written $g(k,1)$ for $\sqrt{3/4\pi}\, G(k,1)$.

Substitution of (12-26) into (12-24) then yields

$$\mathbf{B}^0 = -g(k,1)h_1^{(1)}(kr) \sin \theta \mathbf{i}_\varphi$$

$$\mathbf{E}^0 = -iv\, \frac{g(k,1)}{kr}\, \{2h_1^{(1)}(kr) \cos \theta \mathbf{i}_r + [h_1^{(1)}(kr) - krh_0^{(1)}(kr) \sin \theta]\mathbf{i}_\theta\}$$

$$(12\text{-}27)$$

where we have used the relation

$$\left(\frac{l+1}{x} + \frac{d}{dx}\right) z_l(x) = z_{l-1}(x) \qquad (12\text{-}28)$$

For large values of the argument x,

$$h_0^{(1)}(x) \to -\frac{i}{x} e^{ix}$$

$$h_1^{(1)}(x) \to -\left(\frac{1}{x} + \frac{i}{x^2}\right) e^{ix}$$

Hence, at large distances from the origin,

$$\mathbf{B}^0 \simeq g(k,1)\left[\frac{1}{kr} + \frac{i}{(kr)^2}\right] e^{ikr} \sin \theta \mathbf{i}_\varphi$$

$$\mathbf{E}^0 \simeq v\, \frac{g(k,1)}{kr}\, \left\{\left[\frac{2i}{kr} - \frac{2}{(kr)^2}\right] e^{ikr} \cos \theta \mathbf{i}_r + \left[1 + \frac{i}{kr} - \frac{1}{(kr)^2}\right] e^{ikr} \sin \theta \mathbf{i}_\theta\right\}$$

Therefore, using (12-1) and (12-2),

$$\mathbf{B} \simeq -\frac{p(k)}{4\pi}\, \frac{k}{v}\left(\frac{k}{r} + \frac{i}{r^2}\right) \sin \theta e^{-i\omega(t-r/v)}\mathbf{i}_\varphi$$

$$(12\text{-}29)$$

$$\mathbf{E} \simeq \frac{p(k)}{4\pi\epsilon}\left[\left(\frac{2}{r^3} - \frac{2ik}{r^2}\right) \cos \theta \mathbf{i}_r + \left(\frac{1}{r^3} - \frac{ik}{r^2} - \frac{k^2}{r}\right) \sin \theta \mathbf{i}_\theta\right] e^{-i\omega(t-r/v)}$$

where $p(k)/4\pi\epsilon$ has been written for $-vg(k,1)/k^3$.

If the fields (12-29) are indeed those due to an oscillating electric dipole, they should reduce to the fields due to a static electric dipole in the limit of zero frequency of oscillation. In the limit $k \to 0$ ($\omega \to 0$), the expressions (12-29) become

$$\mathbf{B} = 0$$
$$\mathbf{E} = \frac{2p(0)\cos\theta}{4\pi\epsilon r^3}\,\mathbf{i}_r + \frac{p(0)\sin\theta}{4\pi\epsilon r^3}\,\mathbf{i}_\theta \tag{12-30}$$

precisely the fields due to a static electric dipole of moment $p(0)$ [cf. Eq. (4-9)] located at the origin of coordinates and making an angle θ with the position vector $\mathbf{r}$.

At distances r which are large compared with the wavelength λ ($= 2\pi/k$) of the radiation, the expressions (12-29) become

$$\mathbf{B} \sim -\frac{p(k)}{4\pi\epsilon}\frac{k^2}{vr}\sin\theta e^{-i\omega(t-r/v)}\mathbf{i}_\varphi$$
$$\mathbf{E} \sim -\frac{p(k)}{4\pi\epsilon}\frac{k^2}{r}\sin\theta e^{-i\omega(t-r/v)}\mathbf{i}_\theta \tag{12-31}$$

Thus, at large distances the fields $\mathbf{B}$ and $\mathbf{E}$ become perpendicular to each other, perpendicular to the direction of propagation, and of magnitude $|\mathbf{E}| = v|\mathbf{B}|$, just as in the case of plane waves. Furthermore, the relations (12-31) show that $\mathbf{B}$ and $\mathbf{E}$ are zero along the axis of the dipole (because of the factor $\sin\theta$) and are a maximum in the equatorial plane. The radiation is therefore emitted from the dipole in the greatest intensity in directions at right angles to the line of oscillation.

In the case of radio, the source of the electromagnetic radiation is not an oscillating dipole but rather a current filament in which there is a constant back-and-forth flow of electricity. In this case we can write

$$p(k,t) = ql = p(k)e^{-i\omega t}$$
and
$$i(k,t) = \frac{dq}{dt} = i(k)e^{-i\omega t}$$
where
$$i(k)l = -i\omega p(k)$$

Thus, in terms of the current amplitude $i(k)$ the relations (12-31) become

$$\mathbf{B} \simeq -ilk\frac{i(k)}{4\pi\epsilon}\frac{\sin\theta}{r}e^{-i\omega(t-r/v)}\mathbf{i}_\varphi$$
$$\mathbf{E} \simeq -il\omega\frac{i(k)}{4\pi\epsilon}\frac{\sin\theta}{r}e^{-i\omega(t-r/v)}\mathbf{i}_\theta \tag{12-32}$$

According to the results of Sec. 10-8, the time average of the Poynting vector is

$$\bar{\mathbf{N}} = \frac{1}{2}\,(\text{real part})\mathbf{E} \times \frac{1}{\mu}\mathbf{B}^*$$
$$= \frac{\omega^4}{32\pi^2\epsilon v^3 r^2}\,p^2(k)\sin^2\theta\mathbf{i}_r \tag{12-33}$$
or
$$\bar{\mathbf{N}} = \frac{\omega^2 l^2}{32\pi^2\epsilon v^3 r^2}\,i^2(k)\sin^2\theta\mathbf{i}_r \tag{12-33a}$$

Integration of (12-33) or (12-33a) over the surface of a sphere of radius r then yields

$$P_r = \frac{\omega^4 p^2(k)}{12\pi\epsilon v^3} = \frac{\mu\sqrt{\mu\epsilon}}{12\pi}\omega^4 p^2(k) \tag{12-34}$$

or
$$P_r = \frac{\omega^2 l^2 i^2(k)}{12\pi\epsilon v^3} = \frac{\mu\sqrt{\mu\epsilon}}{12\pi}\omega^2 l^2 i^2(k) \tag{12-34a}$$

as the energy radiated per unit time. Equation (12-34) is the well-known relation for the radiation from a dipole. It states that the radiation is proportional to the square of the amplitude of the dipole and to the fourth power of the frequency.

If we let R_0 represent the ohmic resistance of the current filament l in which an alternating current of amplitude $i(k)$ is flowing, the rate of dissipation in the form of heat is

$$P_0 = R_0\left[\frac{i(k)}{\sqrt{2}}\right]^2 \tag{12-35}$$

Addition of (12-34a) and (12-35) yields the total rate of dissipation of energy; namely,

$$P = \left(R_0 + \frac{\omega^2 l^2}{6\pi\epsilon v^3}\right)\left[\frac{i(k)}{\sqrt{2}}\right]^2$$

The quantity

$$R = \frac{\omega^2 l^2}{6\pi\epsilon v^3} = \frac{2\pi}{3}\sqrt{\frac{\mu}{\epsilon}}\left(\frac{l}{\lambda}\right)^2 \quad \text{ohms} \tag{12-36}$$

represents the increase of the effective resistance of the current filament due to the radiation. Consequently, it is known as the *radiation resistance* of the filament.

12-5. TRANSVERSE ELECTRIC (TE) WAVES

If the radial component of the electric field intensity is zero, the solution (12-20) of the time-independent wave equation (12-4) reduces to

$$\mathbf{E}^0 = (\mathbf{r} \times \nabla\psi) \tag{12-37}$$

The wave is then known as a *transverse electric* (TE) spherical wave. Since

$$\text{curl } \mathbf{E} = -\frac{\partial}{\partial t}\mathbf{B} \tag{9-41}$$

it follows by use of (12-1) and (12-2) that

$$\mathbf{B}^0 = -\frac{i}{\omega}[\nabla \times (\mathbf{r} \times \nabla\psi)] \tag{12-38}$$

Comparison of Eqs. (12-38) and (12-37) with Eqs. (12-22) and (12-23), respectively, shows that the fields for the TE waves can be obtained from those for the TM waves by replacing $\mathbf{B}$ by $\mathbf{E}$ and $\mathbf{E}$ by $-v^2\mathbf{B}$.

12-6. THE OSCILLATING MAGNETIC DIPOLE

The expressions for the fields due to an oscillating magnetic dipole can be obtained from Eqs. (12-29) for the fields due to an oscillating electric dipole by replacing $\mathbf{B}$ by $\mathbf{E}$ and $\mathbf{E}$ by $-v^2\mathbf{B}$. Thus

$$\mathbf{E} \simeq -\frac{p(k)}{4\pi\epsilon}\frac{k}{v}\left(\frac{k}{r} + \frac{i}{r^2}\right)\sin\theta e^{-i\omega(t-r/v)}\mathbf{i}_\varphi$$

$$\mathbf{B} \simeq -\frac{p(k)}{4\pi\epsilon}\frac{1}{v^2}\left[\left(\frac{2}{r^3} - \frac{2ik}{r^2}\right)\cos\theta\mathbf{i}_r + \left(\frac{1}{r^3} - \frac{ik}{r^2} - \frac{k^2}{r}\right)\sin\theta\mathbf{i}_\theta\right]e^{-i\omega(t-r/v)}$$

$$(12\text{-}39)$$

In the limit of zero frequency, $k \to 0$, the expressions (12-39) reduce to

$$\mathbf{E} = 0$$

$$\mathbf{B} = -\frac{2p(0)\cos\theta}{4\pi\epsilon v^2 r^3}\mathbf{i}_r - \frac{p(0)\sin\theta}{4\pi\epsilon v^2 r^3}\mathbf{i}_\theta$$

$$= -\frac{\mu}{2\pi}\frac{p(0)\cos\theta}{r^3}\mathbf{i}_r - \frac{\mu}{4\pi}\frac{p(0)\sin\theta}{r^3}\mathbf{i}_\theta$$

precisely the fields due to a magnetic dipole of moment $p(0)$ located at the origin of coordinates and making an angle θ with the position vector $\mathbf{r}$ (cf. Sec. 8-2).

Since $p(0) = i(0)S$, where $i(0)$ is the steady current flowing in a circuit s bounding the surface S, we write

$$p(k) = i(k)S$$

so that Eqs. (12-39) become

$$\mathbf{E} \simeq -\frac{i(k)S}{4\pi\epsilon}\frac{k}{v}\left(\frac{k}{r} + \frac{i}{r^2}\right)\sin\theta e^{-i\omega(t-r/v)}\mathbf{i}_\varphi$$

$$\mathbf{B} \simeq -\frac{\mu i(k)S}{4\pi}\left[\left(\frac{2}{r^3} - \frac{2ik}{r^2}\right)\cos\theta\mathbf{i}_r + \left(\frac{1}{r^3} - \frac{ik}{r^2} - \frac{k^2}{r}\right)\sin\theta\mathbf{i}_\theta\right]e^{-i\omega(t-r/v)}$$

$$(12\text{-}40)$$

At distances r which are large compared with the wavelength λ of the radiation, the relations (12-40) reduce to

$$\mathbf{E} \to -\frac{i(k)S}{4\pi\epsilon}\frac{k^2}{vr}\sin\theta e^{-i\omega(t-r/v)}\mathbf{i}_\varphi$$

$$\mathbf{B} \to \frac{\mu}{4\pi}i(k)S\frac{k^2}{r}\sin\theta e^{-i\omega(t-r/v)}\mathbf{i}_\theta$$

$$(12\text{-}41)$$

The time average of the Poynting vector is then

$$\bar{\mathbf{N}} = \frac{i^2(k)S^2}{32\pi^2\epsilon} \frac{k^4}{vr^2} \sin^2\theta \mathbf{i}_r \tag{12-42}$$

Integration of (12-42) over the surface of a sphere of radius r gives the energy radiated per unit time:

$$P_r = \frac{i^2(k)S^2}{12\pi\epsilon} \frac{k^4}{v} \tag{12-43}$$

Comparison of (12-43) with (12-34a) then shows that

$$\frac{\text{Radiation from magnetic dipole}}{\text{Radiation from electric dipole}} = \left(\frac{kS}{l}\right)^2 = \left(\frac{2\pi S}{\lambda l}\right)^2 \tag{12-44}$$

Since the linear dimensions of an oscillator must be small compared with the wavelength λ of the radiation, the result (12-44) shows that the magnetic dipole is less efficient than the electric dipole.

12-7. SCATTERING OF A PLANE WAVE BY A SPHERE

Let a plane wave traveling in the $+x_3$ direction be incident upon a conducting sphere of radius a. We assume that the electric vector of this incident wave $\mathbf{E}_i$ lies along the x_1 axis. For convenience, the origin of coordinates is taken at the center of the sphere. The problem is to determine the radiation scattered from the sphere.

The electric vector of the incident wave is given by

$$\mathbf{E}_i(\mathbf{r},t) = E^0\mathbf{i}_1 e^{i\omega(t-r\cos\theta/v)} = E^0\mathbf{i}_1 e^{-i\omega t}e^{ikr\cos\theta} \tag{12-45}$$

where θ is the angle between $\mathbf{r}$ and the wave normal $\mathbf{i}_3$. It is desirable to express this vector as a superposition of spherical waves:

$$\mathbf{E}_i(\mathbf{r},t) = e^{-i\omega t} \sum_{l,m} [\nabla \times (\mathbf{r} \times \nabla \psi_{1l}{}^m) + \mathbf{r} \times \nabla \psi_{2l}{}^m]$$

$$= e^{-i\omega t} \sum_{l,m} \left[\frac{1}{r\sin\theta}\left(\frac{\partial}{\partial\theta}\sin\theta\frac{\partial}{\partial\theta}\psi_{1l}{}^m + \frac{1}{\sin\theta}\frac{\partial^2}{\partial\varphi^2}\psi_{1l}{}^m\right)\mathbf{i}_r \right.$$

$$- \left(\frac{1}{\sin\theta}\frac{\partial}{\partial\varphi}\psi_{2l}{}^m + \frac{1}{r}\frac{\partial^2}{\partial\theta\,\partial r}(r\psi_{1l}{}^m)\right)\mathbf{i}_\theta$$

$$\left. + \left(\frac{\partial}{\partial\theta}\psi_{2l}{}^m - \frac{1}{r\sin\theta}\frac{\partial^2}{\partial\varphi\,\partial r}(r\psi_{1l}{}^m)\right)\mathbf{i}_\varphi \right] \tag{12-46}$$

To do this note that

$$\mathbf{i}_1 = \sin\theta\cos\varphi\mathbf{i}_r + \cos\theta\cos\varphi\mathbf{i}_\theta - \sin\varphi\mathbf{i}_\varphi \tag{12-47}$$

and that

$$\sin \theta e^{ikr \cos \theta} = \frac{i}{kr} \frac{\partial}{\partial \theta} e^{ikr \cos \theta}$$

so that (12-45) can be written

$$\mathbf{E}_i(\mathbf{r},t) = E^0 e^{-i\omega t} \left(\mathbf{i}_r \frac{i \cos \varphi}{kr} \frac{\partial}{\partial \theta} + \mathbf{i}_\theta \cos \theta \cos \varphi - \mathbf{i}_\varphi \sin \varphi \right) e^{ikr \cos \theta}$$

But according to Bauer's formula,†

$$e^{ikr \cos \theta} = \sum_{l=0}^{\infty} i^l \sqrt{4\pi(2l + 1)} \, j_l(kr) Y_l^0(\theta) \tag{12-48}$$

Hence

$$\mathbf{E}_i(\mathbf{r},t) = E^0 e^{-i\omega t} \sum_{l=0}^{\infty} i^l \sqrt{4\pi(2l + 1)} \left[i \frac{j_l(kr)}{kr} \frac{d}{d\theta} Y_l^0(\theta) \cos \varphi \mathbf{i}_r \right.$$

$$\left. + \cos \theta j_l(kr) Y_l^0(\theta) \cos \varphi \mathbf{i}_\theta - j_l(kr) Y_l^0(\theta) \sin \varphi \mathbf{i}_\varphi \right] \tag{12-49}$$

Then, since [cf. Eq. (12-10)]

$$\frac{1}{\sin \theta} \left(\frac{\partial}{\partial \theta} \sin \theta \frac{\partial}{\partial \theta} \psi_{1l}{}^m + \frac{1}{\sin \theta} \frac{\partial^2}{\partial \varphi^2} \psi_{1l}{}^m \right) = -l(l + 1)\psi_{1l}{}^m$$

equating the r components in (12-46) and (12-49) gives

$$\sum_m \psi_{1l}{}^m = - \frac{E^0}{k} i^{l+1} \frac{\sqrt{4\pi(2l + 1)}}{l(l + 1)} j_l(kr) \frac{d}{d\theta} Y_l^0(\theta) \cos \varphi$$

$$= - \frac{E^0}{k} i^{l+1} \sqrt{\frac{2(2l + 1)}{l(l + 1)}} j_l(kr)\Theta_l^1(\theta) \cos \varphi \tag{12-50}$$

where we have used the second of the relations‡

$$\left(\frac{d}{d\theta} + m \cot \theta \right) \Theta_l{}^m(\theta) = - \sqrt{(l + m)(l - m + 1)} \, \Theta_l{}^{m-1}(\theta) \tag{12-51}$$

$$\left(\frac{d}{d\theta} - m \cot \theta \right) \Theta_l{}^m(\theta) = \sqrt{(l - m)(l + m + 1)} \, \Theta_l{}^{m+1}(\theta) \tag{12-52}$$

Hence

$$-\frac{1}{r} \frac{\partial^2}{\partial \theta \partial r} \left(r \sum_m \psi_{1l}{}^m \right) = \frac{E^0}{k} i^{l+1} \sqrt{\frac{2(2l + 1)}{l(l + 1)}} \frac{1}{r} \frac{d}{dr} [rj_l(kr)] \frac{d}{d\theta} \Theta_l^1(\theta) \cos \varphi$$

$$-\frac{1}{r \sin \theta} \frac{\partial^2}{\partial \varphi \partial r} \left(r \sum_m \psi_{1l}{}^m \right)$$

$$= - \frac{E^0}{k} i^{l+1} \sqrt{\frac{2(2l + 1)}{l(l + 1)}} \frac{1}{r} \frac{d}{dr} [rj_l(kr)] \frac{\Theta_l^1(\theta)}{\sin \theta} \sin \varphi$$

† See, for instance, G. Goertzel and N. Tralli, "Some Mathematical Methods of Physics," p. 161, McGraw-Hill Book Company, Inc., New York, 1960.
‡ See, for instance, *ibid.*, p. 158.

so that

$$\mathbf{N}_l^1 \equiv \nabla \times \left(\mathbf{r} \times \nabla \sum_m \psi_{1l}{}^m \right)$$

$$= E^0 i^{l+1} \sqrt{\frac{2(2l+1)}{l(l+1)}} \left[l(l+1) \frac{j_l(kr)}{kr} \Theta_l{}^1(\theta) \cos \varphi \mathbf{i}_r \right.$$

$$+ \frac{1}{kr} \frac{d}{dr} [rj_l(kr)] \frac{d}{d\theta} \Theta_l{}^1(\theta) \cos \varphi \mathbf{i}_\theta - \frac{1}{kr} \frac{d}{dr} [rj_l(kr)] \frac{\Theta_l{}^1(\theta)}{\sin \theta} \sin \varphi \mathbf{i}_\varphi \right] \quad (12\text{-}53)$$

Equating the θ and φ components in (12-46) and (12-49) gives

$$-E^0 i^l \sqrt{4\pi(2l+1)}\, j_l(kr) Y_l{}^0(\theta) \cos \theta \cos \varphi$$

$$= \frac{1}{\sin \theta} \frac{\partial}{\partial \varphi} \left(\sum_m \psi_{2l}{}^m \right) + \frac{1}{r} \frac{\partial^2}{\partial \theta \partial r} \left(r \sum_m \psi_{1l}{}^m \right) \quad (12\text{-}54)$$

$$-E^0 i^l \sqrt{4\pi(2l+1)}\, j_l(kr) Y_l{}^0(\theta) \sin \varphi$$

$$= \frac{\partial}{\partial \theta} \left(\sum_m \psi_{2l}{}^m \right) - \frac{1}{r \sin \theta} \frac{\partial^2}{\partial \varphi \partial r} \left(r \sum_m \psi_{1l}{}^m \right) \quad (12\text{-}55)$$

Operate on (12-54) from the left with $(1/\sin \theta)(\partial/\partial\varphi)$, on (12-55) from the left with $(1/\sin \theta)(\partial/\partial\theta) \sin \theta$, and add the resulting equations to obtain

$$l(l+1) \sum_m \psi_{2l}{}^m = E^0 i^l \sqrt{4\pi(2l+1)}\, j_l(kr) \frac{d}{d\theta} Y_l{}^0(\theta) \sin \varphi$$

or

$$\sum_m \psi_{2l}{}^m = -E^0 i^l \sqrt{\frac{2(2l+1)}{l(l+1)}}\, j_l(kr) \Theta_l{}^1(\theta) \sin \varphi \quad (12\text{-}56)$$

Then

$$-\frac{1}{\sin \theta} \frac{\partial}{\partial \varphi} \sum_m \psi_{2l}{}^m = E^0 i^l \sqrt{\frac{2(2l+1)}{l(l+1)}}\, j_l(kr) \frac{\Theta_l{}^1(\theta)}{\sin \theta} \cos \varphi$$

and

$$\frac{\partial}{\partial \theta} \left(\sum_m \psi_{2l}{}^m \right) = -E^0 i^l \sqrt{\frac{2(2l+1)}{l(l+1)}}\, j_l(kr) \frac{d}{d\theta} \Theta_l{}^1(\theta) \sin \varphi$$

so that

$$\mathbf{M}_l^1 \equiv \mathbf{r} \times \nabla \sum_m \psi_{2l}{}^m$$

$$= E^0 i^l \sqrt{\frac{2(2l+1)}{l(l+1)}}\, j_l(kr) \left[\frac{\Theta_l{}^1(\theta)}{\sin \theta} \cos \varphi \mathbf{i}_\theta - \frac{d}{d\theta} \Theta_l{}^1 \sin \varphi \mathbf{i}_\varphi \right] \quad (12\text{-}57)$$

Hence

$$\mathbf{E}_i(\mathbf{r},t) = e^{-i\omega t} \sum_l (\mathbf{N}_l^1 + \mathbf{M}_l^1) \quad (12\text{-}58)$$

where the vectors $\mathbf{N}^1$ and $\mathbf{M}^1$ are given by (12-53) and (12-57), respectively.

The electric field of the radiation scattered by the sphere is also of the form of (12-58). However, since the scattered wave travels outward from the origin of coordinates (the center of the sphere), we must replace $j_l(kr)$ by $h_l^{(1)}(kr)$. Thus, for the electric vector $\mathbf{E}_s$ of the scattered wave

$$\mathbf{E}_s(\mathbf{r},t) = e^{-i\omega t} \sum_l (a_l\bar{\mathbf{N}}^1 + b_l\bar{\mathbf{M}}^1) \tag{12-59}$$

where a_l and b_l are constants to be determined and $\bar{\mathbf{N}}_l^1$ and $\bar{\mathbf{M}}_l^1$ are obtained from $\mathbf{N}_l^1$ and $\mathbf{M}_l^1$, respectively, by replacing $j_l(kr)$ by $h_l^{(1)}(kr)$.

The total electric field $\mathbf{E}(\mathbf{r},t)$ is the sum of the electric fields of the incident and scattered waves:

$$\mathbf{E}(\mathbf{r},t) = \mathbf{E}_i(\mathbf{r},t) + \mathbf{E}_s(\mathbf{r},t) \tag{12-60}$$

It must satisfy the condition that its component perpendicular to the radius vector vanish at the surface of the sphere. Consequently,

$$a_l = - \left. \frac{d/dr[rj_l(kr)]}{\dfrac{d}{dr}[rh_l^{(1)}(kr)]} \right|_{r=a} \tag{12-61}$$

$$b_l = - \frac{j_l(ka)}{h_l^{(1)}(ka)} \tag{12-62}$$

and the electric vector of the scattered wave is completely determined. The magnetic induction vector of the scattered wave can then be obtained from

$$\frac{\partial}{\partial t}\mathbf{B} = -\operatorname{curl}\mathbf{E} \tag{9-41}$$

EXERCISES

12-1. A plane electromagnetic wave is incident upon a perfectly conducting sphere of radius a (cf. Sec. 12-7).

(a) For large values of the argument x

$$h_l^{(1)}(x) \simeq (-1)^{l+1} \frac{e^{ix}}{x}$$

Use this relation to determine the field vectors of the scattered wave at points far from the sphere.

(b) Determine the time average of the Poynting vector of the scattered wave. Integrate this over the surface of a sphere to obtain the total rate at which the radiation is scattered.

(c) Divide the total rate of energy scattered by the sphere by the time average of the Poynting vector of the incident beam to obtain the *scattering cross section* σ.

Verify that

$$\sigma = \frac{2\pi}{k^2} \sum_l (2l + 1)(\sin^2 \gamma_l + \sin^2 \gamma_l') \tag{12-63}$$

where

$$\tan \gamma_l = j_l(ka)/n_l(ka) \tag{12-64}$$

$$\tan \gamma_l' = \frac{d/dr \; [rj_l(kr)]}{\dfrac{d}{dr} \; [rn_l(kr)]} \Bigg|_{r=a} \tag{12-65}$$

in which n_l is the spherical Neumann function.

(d) Show that, in the limit of long wavelengths where $ka \to 0$, the scattering cross section reduces to

$$\sigma = \frac{10\pi}{3} k^4 a^6 \tag{12-66}$$

12-2. A plane electromagnetic wave traveling in a homogeneous isotropic medium of permittivity ϵ_1 and permeability μ_1 is incident upon a dielectric sphere of radius a, permittivity ϵ_2, and permeability μ_2. Determine the field vectors of the scattered radiation.

12-3. Verify that the solutions of the wave equations

$$\nabla^2 \mathbf{A}(r,\theta,\varphi,t) - \frac{1}{v^2}\frac{\partial^2}{\partial t^2}\mathbf{A}(r,\theta,\varphi,t) = 0$$

$$\nabla^2 \phi(r,\theta,\varphi,t) - \frac{1}{v^2}\frac{\partial^2}{\partial t^2}\phi(r,\theta,\varphi,t) = 0$$

are

$$\phi(r,\theta,\varphi,t) = e^{-i\omega t} \sum_{l,m} \phi_l{}^m(r,\theta,\varphi) \tag{12-67}$$

$$\mathbf{A}(r,\theta,\varphi,t) = e^{-i\omega t} \sum_{l,m} [a_l{}^m \mathbf{A}_l{}^{m(e)}(r,\theta,\varphi) + b_l{}^m \mathbf{A}_l{}^{m(m)}] \tag{12-68}$$

where the $a_l{}^m$ and $b_l{}^m$ are arbitrary constants, the $\phi_l{}^m$ are of the form of the $\psi_l{}^m$ in (12-18), and

$$\mathbf{A}_l{}^{m(e)} \equiv \nabla \times (\mathbf{r} \times \nabla \phi_l{}^m) \qquad \mathbf{A}_l{}^{m(m)} \equiv \mathbf{r} \times \nabla \phi_l{}^m$$

Then make the gauge transformation

$$\mathbf{A}_s = \mathbf{A} - \nabla S$$

$$\phi_s = \phi + \frac{\partial}{\partial t} S$$

where

$$\nabla^2 S - \frac{1}{v^2}\frac{\partial^2 S}{\partial t^2} = 0$$

$$\mathrm{div}\; \mathbf{A}_s = 0$$

and show that the scalar and vector potential become

$$\phi_s = \mathrm{constant}$$

$$\mathbf{A}_s = e^{-i\omega t} \sum_{l,m} [a_l{}^m \mathbf{A}_l{}^{m(e)} + b_l{}^m \mathbf{A}_l{}^{m(m)} + c_l{}^m \mathbf{A}_l{}^{m(l)}]$$

where the $c_l{}^m$ are arbitrary constants and

$$\mathbf{A}_l{}^{m(l)} = \nabla \phi_l{}^m$$

Thus, in this gauge the scalar potential is constant and the vector potential consists of a transverse electric part $A_l{}^{m(e)}$, a transverse magnetic part $A_l{}^{m(m)}$, and a *longitudinal* part $A_l{}^{m(l)}$.

12-4. Show that for charge and current distributions

$$\rho_F(\mathbf{r},t) = \rho_F{}^0(\mathbf{r})e^{-i\omega t} \qquad \mathbf{j}(\mathbf{r},t) = \mathbf{j}^0(\mathbf{r})e^{-i\omega t}$$

where both $\rho_F{}^0$ and $\mathbf{j}^0$ are zero for $r > a$, the solutions of the wave equations (9-61) and (9-62) for the electrodynamic potentials are

$$\phi(\mathbf{r},t) = -\frac{1}{\epsilon} \int G(\mathbf{r};\mathbf{r}')\rho(\mathbf{r}',t) \, d\mathbf{r}'$$

$$\mathbf{A}(\mathbf{r},t) = -\mu \int G(\mathbf{r};\mathbf{r}')\mathbf{j}(\mathbf{r}',t) \, d\mathbf{r}'$$

where the integrations are over a sphere of radius a, and Green's function is

$$G(\mathbf{r};\mathbf{r}') = -\frac{1}{4\pi} \frac{e^{ik|\mathbf{r}-\mathbf{r}'|}}{|\mathbf{r} - \mathbf{r}'|}$$

$$= -ik \sum_{l,m} h_l{}^{(1)}(kr)j_l(kr')\overline{Y_l{}^m(\theta',\varphi')}Y_l{}^m(\theta,\varphi) \qquad r > r'$$

in which $k = \omega/v = \omega K K_m/c$.

12-5. Show that, when $ka \ll 1$, i.e., when the wavelength of the radiation is much larger than the source dimension, successive terms in the expansions of Exercise 12-4 are in the ratio

$$\frac{(L + 1)\text{th term}}{L\text{th term}} \simeq \frac{kr'}{2L + 3}$$

Thus the expansions converge quite rapidly, and only a few terms are important.

REFERENCES

Morse, P. M., and H. Feshbach: "Methods of Theoretical Physics," chap. 13, McGraw-Hill Book Company, Inc., New York, 1953.

Stratton, J. A.: "Electromagnetic Theory," chap. 7, McGraw-Hill Book Company, Inc., New York, 1941.

CHAPTER 13

Cylindrical Electromagnetic Waves

13-1. INTRODUCTION

The discussion of cylindrical electromagnetic waves in this chapter is limited to the propagation of these waves in unbounded homogeneous isotropic dielectrics. Just as in the case of spherical waves, discussed in the preceding chapter, it is found that the electromagnetic field can be resolved into two partial fields, each of which is derivable from a scalar function satisfying the wave equation.

13-2. CYLINDRICAL WAVES IN HOMOGENEOUS ISOTROPIC DIELECTRICS

To solve the wave equations (9-47) and (9-48) in cylindrical coordinates, we first assume that

$$\mathbf{B}(r,\theta,x_3,t) = \mathbf{B}^0(r,\theta,x_3)e^{-i\omega t} \tag{13-1}$$
$$\mathbf{E}(r,\theta,x_3,t) = \mathbf{E}^0(r,\theta,x_3)e^{-i\omega t} \tag{13-2}$$

Then (9-47) and (9-48) reduce to the time-independent wave equations

$$\nabla^2\mathbf{B}^0 + k^2\mathbf{B}^0 = 0 \tag{13-3}$$
$$\nabla^2\mathbf{E}^0 + k^2\mathbf{E}^0 = 0 \tag{13-4}$$

where $k = \omega/v$.

If the scalar function $\psi(r,\theta,x_3)$ satisfies the time-independent wave equation

$$\nabla^2\psi(r,\theta,x_3) + k^2\psi(r,\theta,x_3) = 0 \tag{13-5}$$

where
$$\nabla^2 \equiv \frac{1}{r}\frac{\partial}{\partial r}\left(r\frac{\partial}{\partial r}\right) + \frac{1}{r^2}\frac{\partial^2}{\partial\theta^2} + \frac{\partial^2}{\partial x_3^2} \tag{13-6}$$

it is easily verified that the vectors

$$\mathbf{i}_3 \times \nabla\psi = -\nabla \times (\mathbf{i}_3\psi) \tag{13-7}$$

which is transverse to the x_3 axis, and

$$\nabla \times (\mathbf{i}_3 \times \nabla\psi) \tag{13-8}$$

227

which is directed along the x_3 axis, are solenoidal vectors which satisfy the time-independent wave equation. Thus, the problem of solving the wave equations (13-3) and (13-4) is reduced to that of solving (13-5).

To solve (13-5) we assume that

$$\psi(r,\theta,x_3) = R(r)\Theta(\theta)X_3(x_3) \tag{13-9}$$

substitute into (13-5), and divide by ψ. Then, using (13-6),

$$\frac{1}{rR}\frac{d}{dr}\left(r\frac{dR}{dr}\right) + \frac{1}{r^2\Theta}\frac{d^2\Theta}{d\theta^2} + k^2 = -\frac{1}{X_3}\frac{d^2X_3}{dx_3^2}$$

For a solution, both sides of this equation must be equal to a constant, say k_3^2. Consequently,

$$\frac{d^2X_3}{dx_3^2} + k_3^2X_3 = 0$$

which has for solution

$$
\begin{aligned}
X_3 &= a(k_3)e^{ik_3x_3} + a'(k_3)e^{-ik_3x_3} & k_3 &\neq 0 \\
&= b & k_3 &= 0
\end{aligned}
\tag{13-10}
$$

and
$$\frac{r}{R}\frac{d}{dr}\left(r\frac{dR}{dr}\right) + (k^2 - k_3^2)r^2 = -\frac{1}{\Theta}\frac{d^2\Theta}{d\theta^2}$$

This last equation also will have a solution only if both sides equal a constant, say l^2. Then

$$\frac{d^2}{d\theta^2}\Theta + l^2\Theta = 0$$

which has for solution [cf. solution of Eq. (6-24)]

$$
\begin{aligned}
\Theta(\theta) &= c(l)e^{il\theta} + c'(l)e^{-il\theta} & l &\neq 0 \qquad l = \text{positive integer} \\
&= d & l &= 0
\end{aligned}
\tag{13-11}
$$

and
$$\frac{1}{r}\frac{d}{dr}\left(r\frac{dR}{dr}\right) + \left(\kappa^2 - \frac{l^2}{r^2}\right)R = 0$$

where $\kappa^2 = k^2 - k_3^2$. The solution of this last equation is [cf. solution of Eq. (6-25)]

$$R(r) = Z_l(\kappa r) \qquad \kappa \neq 0 \tag{13-12}$$

The solution of the time-independent wave equation (13-5) is then

$$
\begin{aligned}
\psi_{l,k,k_3}(r,\theta,x_3) &= Z_l(\kappa r)[c(l)e^{il\theta} + c'(l)e^{-il\theta}][a(k_3)e^{ik_3x_3} + a'(k_3)e^{-ik_3x_3}] \\
& \hspace{6cm} l \neq 0 \qquad k_3 \neq 0 \\
&= bZ_l(\kappa r)[c(l)e^{il\theta} + c'(l)e^{-il\theta}] \qquad l \neq 0 \qquad k_3 = 0 \\
&= dZ_0(\kappa r)[a(k_3)e^{ik_3x_3} + a'(k_3)e^{-ik_3x_3}] \qquad l = 0 \qquad k_3 \neq 0 \\
&= bZ_0(\kappa r) \qquad l = 0 \qquad k_3 = 0
\end{aligned}
\tag{13-13}
$$

where $\kappa^2 = k^2 - k_3{}^2$ and the indices l, k, and k_3 on ψ have been used to indicate the dependence of ψ on the values of l, k, and k_3.

The general solution of (13-5) is obtained by summing (13-13) over the appropriate values of l and integrating over k_3:

$$\psi = \sum_l \int dk_3 \, \psi_{l,k,k_3}(r,\theta,x_3) \tag{13-14}$$

The general solutions of the time-independent wave equations (13-3) and (13-4) are then

$$Q^0 = \nabla \times (i_3 \times \nabla \psi_1) + i_3 \times \nabla \psi_2 \qquad Q = B \text{ or } E \tag{13-15}$$

where the ψ_i are given by (13-14).

13-3. TRANSVERSE MAGNETIC (TM) WAVES

If the axial (i_3) component of the magnetic induction is zero, the solution (13-15) of the time-independent wave equation (13-3) reduces to

$$B^0 = i_3 \times \nabla \psi \tag{13-16}$$

Since

$$\text{curl } B = \frac{1}{v^2} \frac{\partial E}{\partial t}$$

it follows by use of (13-1) and (13-2) that

$$E^0 = i \frac{v}{k} \nabla \times (i_3 \times \nabla \psi) \tag{13-17}$$

The relations (13-16) and (13-17) define a *transverse magnetic* (TM) cylindrical wave.

Explicitly, we can write (13-16) and (13-17) as

$$B^0 = \left(-\frac{1}{r} \frac{\partial \psi}{\partial \theta} i_r + \frac{\partial \psi}{\partial r} i_\theta \right) \tag{13-16a}$$

$$E^0 = i \frac{v}{k} \left[-\frac{\partial^2 \psi}{\partial r \, \partial x_3} i_r - \frac{1}{r} \frac{\partial^2 \psi}{\partial \theta \, \partial x_3} i_\theta + \left(\frac{\partial^2 \psi}{\partial r^2} + \frac{1}{r^2} \frac{\partial^2 \psi}{\partial \theta^2} \right) i_3 \right] \tag{13-17a}$$

13-4. TRANSVERSE ELECTRIC (TE) WAVES

If the axial component of the electric field intensity is zero, the solution (13-15) of the time-independent wave equation (13-3) reduces to

$$E^0 = i_3 \times \nabla \psi \tag{13-18}$$

Since

$$\text{curl } E = -\frac{\partial}{\partial t} B \tag{9-41}$$

it follows by use of (13-1) and (13-2) that

$$\mathbf{B}^0 = -\frac{i}{\omega}[\nabla \times (\mathbf{i}_3 \times \nabla\psi)] \tag{13-19}$$

The relations (13-18) and (13-19) define a *transverse electric* (TE) cylindrical wave.

Expressions (13-18) and (13-19) can be written explicitly as

$$\mathbf{E}^0 = \left(-\frac{1}{r}\frac{\partial\psi}{\partial\theta}\,\mathbf{i}_r + \frac{\partial\psi}{\partial r}\,\mathbf{i}_\theta\right) \tag{13-18a}$$

$$\mathbf{B}^0 = -\frac{i}{\omega}\left[-\frac{\partial^2\psi}{\partial r\,\partial x_3}\,\mathbf{i}_r - \frac{1}{r}\frac{\partial^2\psi}{\partial\theta\,\partial x_3}\,\mathbf{i}_\theta + \left(\frac{\partial^2\psi}{\partial r^2} + \frac{1}{r^2}\frac{\partial^2\psi}{\partial\theta^2}\right)\mathbf{i}_3\right] \tag{13-19a}$$

13-5. SCATTERING OF A PLANE WAVE BY AN INFINITELY LONG CYLINDER

Let a plane electromagnetic wave be incident normal to the axis of a perfectly conducting cylinder of radius r_0. Take the axis of the cylinder along the x_3 axis. The problem is to find the electromagnetic field at any point (r,θ), $r > r_0$.

Let $\mathbf{E}(\mathbf{r},t)$ represent the electric field vector at $\mathbf{r}$ at any time t. Then

$$\mathbf{E}(\mathbf{r},t) = \mathbf{E}_i(\mathbf{r},t) + \mathbf{E}_s(\mathbf{r},t) \tag{13-20}$$

where $\mathbf{E}_i$ is the electric vector of the incident plane wave and $\mathbf{E}_s$ that of the wave scattered from the cylinder.

Two cases must be considered: (1) $\mathbf{E}_i$ is in the direction of the axis of the cylinder, and (2) $\mathbf{E}_i$ is perpendicular to the axis of the cylinder. In the first case

$$\mathbf{E}_i(\mathbf{r},t) = \mathbf{E}^0\mathbf{i}_3 e^{-i\omega(t-r\cos\theta/v)} \tag{13-21}$$

where θ is the angle between $\mathbf{r}$ and the wave normal.

According to (13-15) the general expression for the electric field of the radiation scattered from the cylinder is

$$\mathbf{E}_s(\mathbf{r},t) = e^{-i\omega t}[\nabla \times (\mathbf{i}_3 \times \nabla\psi_1) + \mathbf{i}_3 \times \nabla\psi_2] \tag{13-22}$$

where the ψ_i are given by (13-14). Since $\mathbf{E}_i$ is along $\mathbf{i}_3$, ψ_2 must be taken equal to zero. Since the solution must be independent of x_3, (13-14) reduces to

$$\psi = \sum_{l=0}^{\infty} \psi_{l,k}(r,\theta)$$

$$= \sum_{l=0}^{\infty} H_l^{(1)}(kr)[c(l)e^{il\theta} + c'(l)e^{-il\theta}] \tag{13-23}$$

where we have used (13-13) and taken $Z_l(kr) = H_l^{(1)}(kr)$ because the scattered wave travels outward from the x_3 axis. Thus, the electric field of the scattered wave can be written

$$\mathbf{E}_s(\mathbf{r},t) = e^{-i\omega t}\nabla \times (\mathbf{i}_3 \times \nabla\psi)$$
$$= e^{-i\omega t}\left(\frac{\partial^2}{\partial r^2}\psi + \frac{1}{r^2}\frac{\partial^2\psi}{\partial\theta^2}\right)\mathbf{i}_3 \qquad (13\text{-}24)$$

where ψ is given by (13-23).

Since the cylinder is a perfect conductor, the component of the electric field tangent to the cylinder must vanish. Hence

$$E^0 e^{i(\omega/v)r_0 \cos\theta} + \left(\frac{\partial^2\psi}{\partial r^2} + \frac{1}{r^2}\frac{\partial^2\psi}{\partial\theta^2}\right)\bigg|_{r=r_0} = 0 \qquad (13\text{-}25)$$

Since†

$$e^{i(\omega/v)r_0 \cos\theta)} \equiv e^{ikr_0\cos\theta} = \sum_{l=-\infty}^{+\infty} i^l J_l(kr_0)e^{il\theta}$$
$$= \sum_{l=0}^{\infty} \epsilon_l i^l J_l(kr_0)\cos l\theta \qquad (13\text{-}26)$$

where
$$\epsilon_0 = 1$$
$$\epsilon_l = 2 \qquad \text{for } l \neq 0$$

and, using (13-23),

$$\frac{\partial^2\psi}{\partial r^2} + \frac{1}{r^2}\frac{\partial^2\psi}{\partial\theta^2} = \sum_{l=0}^{\infty}\left(\frac{d^2}{dr^2} - \frac{l^2}{r^2}\right)H_l^{(1)}(kr)[c(l)e^{il\theta} + c'(l)e^{-il\theta}]$$

we find on substitution into (13-25) that

$$c(l) = c'(l) = -\frac{1}{2}\frac{E^0\epsilon_l i^l J_l(kr_0)}{\left(\dfrac{d^2}{dr^2} - \dfrac{l^2}{r^2}\right)H_l^{(1)}(kr)\bigg|_{r=r_0}} \qquad (13\text{-}27)$$

Hence the electric vector of the scattered wave is given by

$$\mathbf{E}_s(\mathbf{r},t) = e^{-i\omega t}\mathbf{i}_3\, 2\sum_{l=0}^{\infty} c(l)\left(\frac{d^2}{dr^2} - \frac{l^2}{r^2}\right)H_l^{(1)}(kr)\cos l\theta \qquad (13\text{-}28)$$

where the $c(l)$ are given by (13-27). Substitution of (13-21) and (13-28) into (13-20) gives the electric field vector at $\mathbf{r}$ at time t. The magnetic induction vector can then be obtained from

$$\frac{\partial}{\partial t}\mathbf{B} = -\text{ curl }\mathbf{E} \qquad (9\text{-}41)$$

---

† See, for instance, G. Goertzel and N. Tralli, "Some Mathematical Methods of Physics," p. 139, McGraw-Hill Book Company, Inc., New York, 1960.

Consider now the second case in which $\mathbf{E}_i$, the electric vector of the incident wave, is perpendicular to the axis of the cylinder. In this case

$$\mathbf{E}_i(\mathbf{r},t) = E^0(\sin\theta\mathbf{i}_r + \cos\theta\mathbf{i}_\theta)e^{-i\omega(t-r\cos\theta/v)} \qquad (13\text{-}29)$$

Proceeding as we did in the first case, we find that the electric vector of the scattered wave is given by

$$\begin{aligned}
\mathbf{E}_s(\mathbf{r},t) &= e^{-i\omega t}\mathbf{i}_3 \times \nabla\psi \\
&= e^{-i\omega t}\left(-\frac{1}{r}\frac{\partial\psi}{\partial\theta}\mathbf{i}_r + \frac{\partial\psi}{\partial r}\mathbf{i}_\theta\right) \qquad (13\text{-}30)
\end{aligned}$$

where ψ is given by (13-23).

The boundary condition at $r = r_0$ then yields

$$E^0\cos\theta e^{ikr_0\cos\theta} + \frac{\partial\psi}{\partial r}\bigg|_{r=r_0} = 0$$

or

$$\frac{\partial}{\partial r}\left(-\frac{i}{k}E^0 e^{ikr\cos\theta} + \psi\right)\bigg|_{r=r_0} = 0$$

Substitution by means of (13-23) and (13-26) then yields

$$\sum_{l=0}^{\infty}\{E^0\epsilon_l i^{l-1}J_l'(kr)\cos l\theta + kH_l^{(1)'}(kr)[c(l)e^{il\theta} + c'(l)e^{-il\theta}]\}\bigg|_{r=r_0} = 0$$

where the prime denotes differentiation with respect to the argument. Hence

$$c(l) = c'(l) = -\frac{1}{2}\frac{E^0}{k}\epsilon_l i^{l-1}\frac{J_l'(kr_0)}{H_l^{(1)'}(kr_0)} \qquad (13\text{-}31)$$

and

$$\mathbf{E}_s(\mathbf{r},t) = e^{-i\omega t}2\sum_{l=0}^{\infty}c(l)\left[\frac{l}{r}H_l^{(1)}(kr)\sin l\theta\mathbf{i}_r + kH_l^{(1)'}(kr)\cos l\theta\mathbf{i}_\theta\right] \qquad (13\text{-}32)$$

The magnetic induction vector can then be obtained from (9-41).

EXERCISES

13-1. A plane electromagnetic wave is incident normal to the axis of a perfectly conducting cylinder of radius r_0 (cf. Sec. 13-5).

(a) For large values of the argument x

$$H_l^{(1)}(x) \simeq (-1)^{l+\frac{1}{2}}\sqrt{\frac{2}{\pi x}}e^{ix}$$

Use this relation to determine the field vectors of the scattered wave at points far from the cylinder.

(b) Determine the time average of the Poynting vector of the scattered wave. Integrate this over a cylindrical surface to obtain the total rate of energy scattered per unit length of the cylinder.

(c) Divide the total rate of energy scattered per unit length of the cylinder by the time average of the Poynting vector of the incident beam to obtain the *scattering cross section* of the cylinder σ.

(d) Obtain the expression for the scattering cross section in the limit of long wavelengths where $kr_0 \to 0$, and comment on the result.

(e) Determine the differential scattering cross section $\sigma(\theta)$ defined as the ratio of the rate of energy scattered per unit length of the cylinder into a unit angle at θ to the time average of the Poynting vector of the incident beam.

13-2. A plane electromagnetic wave traveling in a homogeneous isotropic medium of permittivity ϵ_1 and permeability μ_1 is incident normal to the axis of a dielectric cylinder of radius r_0, permittivity ϵ_2, and permeability μ_2. Determine the field vectors of the scattered radiation.

REFERENCES

Morse, P. M., and H. Feshbach: "Methods of Theoretical Physics," chap. 13, McGraw-Hill Book Company, Inc., New York, 1953.

Stratton, J. A.: "Electromagnetic Theory," chap. 6, McGraw-Hill Book Company, Inc., New York, 1941.

CHAPTER 14

Cavity Resonators

14-1. INTRODUCTION

Any region of space totally enclosed by highly conducting walls may serve as a cavity resonator or rhumbatron. Any such resonator has an infinite number of resonant frequencies and associated wave fields.

We shall develop the theory for resonators composed of homogeneous isotropic dielectrics contained by walls of infinite conductivity. For such cases the depth of penetration of the electromagnetic wave into the walls is, from (10-64), zero. The condition that the tangential component of the electric intensity $\mathbf{E}$ be continuous across the boundary then requires that the tangential component be zero. Hence the electric field intensity is normal to the walls of the resonator.

The problem is to solve the wave equations

$$\nabla^2 \mathbf{B} - \frac{1}{v^2} \frac{\partial^2}{\partial t^2} \mathbf{B} = 0 \qquad (9\text{-}47)$$

$$\nabla^2 \mathbf{E} - \frac{1}{v^2} \frac{\partial^2}{\partial t^2} \mathbf{E} = 0 \qquad (9\text{-}48)$$

subject to the boundary conditions that $\mathbf{E}$ be normal and, hence, $\mathbf{B}$ tangential to the perfectly conducting walls.

We assume that

$$\mathbf{B}(\mathbf{r},t) = \mathbf{B}^0(\mathbf{r})e^{i\omega t} \qquad (14\text{-}1)$$
$$\mathbf{E}(\mathbf{r},t) = \mathbf{E}^0(\mathbf{r})e^{i\omega t} \qquad (14\text{-}2)$$

where ω is 2π times the frequency of the wave. Substitution of (14-1) and (14-2) into the wave equations (9-47) and (9-48) then yields the time-independent wave equations

$$\nabla^2 \mathbf{B}^0 + k^2 \mathbf{B}^0 = 0 \qquad (14\text{-}3)$$
$$\nabla^2 \mathbf{E}^0 + k^2 \mathbf{E}^0 = 0 \qquad (14\text{-}4)$$

where $k = \omega/v$, as the equations to be solved. However, since

$$\operatorname{curl} \mathbf{E} = -\frac{\partial}{\partial t} \mathbf{B} \qquad (9\text{-}26)$$

234

it follows that

$$\mathbf{B}^0 = -\frac{i}{\omega} \operatorname{curl} \mathbf{E}^0 \qquad (14\text{-}5)$$

Consequently, it is necessary only to find an appropriate solution of the wave equation (14-4) for $\mathbf{E}^0$ satisfying the boundary condition that $\mathbf{E}$ be normal to the walls. The associated magnetic field automatically satisfying the boundary condition on $\mathbf{B}^0$ is obtained from the electric field by means of (14-5).

14-2. RECTANGULAR CAVITY RESONATORS

Because of its simplicity, involving only trigonometric functions, we consider first the problem of the rectangular resonator. This problem is quite similar to the quantum mechanical problem of a particle in a box, from which we shall borrow much of the terminology. The electromagnetic problem, however, is somewhat more complicated because the wave amplitude is a vector quantity which must satisfy not only (14-4) but also the relation div $\mathbf{E}^0 = 0$.

Let the walls of the rectangular cavity resonator be at the ends of the ranges

$$0 < x_1 < A \qquad 0 < x_2 < B \qquad 0 < x_3 < C$$

We assume that the solution of (14-4) is of the form

$$\mathbf{E}^0(x_1, x_2, x_3) = \mathbf{E}_0 e^{i(k_1 x_1 + k_2 x_2 + k_3 x_3)} \qquad (14\text{-}6)$$

where $\mathbf{E}_0$ is a constant vector. Substitution of (14-6) into (14-5) yields

$$k^2 \equiv \frac{\omega^2}{v^2} = k_1{}^2 + k_2{}^2 + k_3{}^2 \qquad (14\text{-}7)$$

as the condition which the k_i must satisfy. Application of the condition div $\mathbf{E}^0 = 0$ to (14-6) gives

$$k_1 E_{01} + k_2 E_{02} + k_3 E_{03} = 0 \qquad (14\text{-}8)$$

as the condition which the three constant amplitudes E_{01}, E_{02}, and E_{03} (the components of $\mathbf{E}_0$) must satisfy. If we think of the k_i as the components of a vector $\mathbf{k}$, then any vector $\mathbf{E}_0$ perpendicular to $\mathbf{k}$ is permissible. Consequently, for each set of k_i there are two linearly independent modes of oscillation, i.e., two particular solutions for $\mathbf{E}_0$. All other modes of oscillation can be expressed in terms of these two.

The solution (14-6) can be written equally well in terms of sines and cosines; namely,

$$\mathbf{E}^0(x_1, x_2, x_3) = \mathbf{E}_0(\cos k_1 x_1 + i \sin k_1 x_1)(\cos k_2 x_2 + i \sin k_2 x_2)$$
$$(\cos k_3 x_3 + i \sin k_3 x_3) \qquad (14\text{-}6a)$$

Consider the x_1 component only, and apply the condition that $\mathbf{E}^0$ must be normal to all walls. Then at $x_2 = 0$ and $x_3 = 0$, $E_1{}^0$ must be zero. Consequently, the terms $\cos k_2x_2$ and $\cos k_3x_3$ are not permissible. Also, at $x_2 = B$ and $x_3 = C$, $E_1{}^0$ must again be zero. This condition requires that

$$\sin k_2B = 0 \qquad \text{and} \qquad \sin k_3C = 0$$

or

$$k_2 = \frac{m\pi}{B} \qquad \text{and} \qquad k_3 = \frac{n\pi}{c}$$

where m and n are zero or positive integers. Next, since when $x_1 = 0$, it is not necessary that $E_1{}^0$ be zero, the term $\sin k_1x_1$ is not permissible. From a similar consideration of $E_2{}^0$ or $E_3{}^0$ we find that

$$k_1 = \frac{l\pi}{A}$$

where l is zero or a positive integer. Hence

$$E_1{}^0 = E_{01} \cos \frac{l\pi x_1}{A} \sin \frac{m\pi x_2}{B} \sin \frac{n\pi x_3}{C}$$

On similar consideration of the x_2 and x_3 components we obtain

$$E_1{}^0 = E_{01} \cos \frac{l\pi x_1}{A} \sin \frac{m\pi x_2}{B} \sin \frac{n\pi x_3}{C}$$

$$E_2{}^0 = E_{02} \sin \frac{l\pi x_1}{A} \cos \frac{m\pi x_2}{B} \sin \frac{n\pi x_3}{C} \qquad (14\text{-}9)$$

$$E_3{}^0 = E_{03} \sin \frac{l\pi x_1}{A} \sin \frac{m\pi x_2}{B} \cos \frac{n\pi x_3}{C}$$

The conditions (14-7) and (14-8) now become

$$\frac{\omega^2}{v^2} = \frac{l^2\pi^2}{A^2} + \frac{m^2\pi^2}{B^2} + \frac{n^2\pi^2}{C^2}$$

or

$$\left(\frac{v}{v}\right)^2 = \left(\frac{l}{2A}\right)^2 + \left(\frac{m}{2B}\right)^2 + \left(\frac{n}{2C}\right)^2 \qquad (14\text{-}7a)$$

and

$$\frac{l\pi}{A} E_{01} + \frac{m\pi}{B} E_{02} + \frac{n\pi}{C} E_{03} = 0 \qquad (14\text{-}8a)$$

Equation (14-7a) gives the possible resonant frequencies v. From (14-8a) it is seen that at least two of the integers l, m, and n are not zero. For the modes in which one of the integers is zero, (14-9) shows that the electric field is everywhere parallel to the axis whose integer is zero and (14-7a) that the resonant frequency is independent of the dimension along that axis. For each such set of integers there is only one vector satisfying (14-8a) and so only a single solution for such a set.

Each frequency for which there exists a solution of the wave equations satisfying the boundary conditions will be called an *allowed* or *proper frequency*. The smallest allowed frequency is called the *fundamental frequency*. The higher allowed frequencies are called *harmonics* only if they are integral multiples of the fundamental frequency.

Any frequency for which there is more than one mode of oscillation, i.e., more than one solution to the wave equation, is referred to as a *degenerate frequency*. The *order of degeneracy* is the number of linearly independent modes associated with the degenerate frequency. Because of the two linearly independent solutions of (14-8a) that are possible when none of the integers l, m, n is zero, these modes are twofold degenerate. This type of degeneracy is called *polarization degeneracy*. Degeneracy also occurs because of symmetry in the shape of the resonator. If an integral relation exists among A, B, and C, certain frequencies will occur which correspond to two or more distinct sets of the integers l, m, n and so to two or more independent modes of oscillation. Such degeneracy is called *symmetry degeneracy*. For example, if the resonator is a cube with $A = B = C$, most of the frequencies will have symmetry degeneracy as well as polarization degeneracy. The lowest frequency, $\nu = v/\sqrt{2}\,A$, with integers $110, 011$, or 101 (for l, m, n, respectively) has a threefold symmetry degeneracy but no polarization degeneracy. The next frequency, $\nu = \sqrt{3/4}\,v/A$, with integers 111 has no symmetry degeneracy but has polarization degeneracy.

It has just been demonstrated that Eq. (14-4) possesses various satisfactory solutions, corresponding to various values of the frequency ν. Let us indicate these values of ν by attaching the subscripts lmn, and similarly represent the mode of oscillation corresponding to ν_{lmn} as $\mathbf{E}_{lmn}{}^0$. The general solution of (14-4) is the sum of all the particular solutions with arbitrary coefficients

$$\mathbf{E}^0 = \sum_{l,m,n} a_{lmn}\mathbf{E}_{lmn}{}^0 \tag{14-10}$$

The arbitrary constants a_{lmn} must be so chosen as to ensure the convergence of the series. With the help of suitable conventions the triply subscripted symbols $\mathbf{E}_{lmn}{}^0$ can be replaced by singly subscripted $\mathbf{E}^0$'s. Thus we might denote $\mathbf{E}_{110}{}^0$ by $\mathbf{E}_0{}^0$, $\mathbf{E}_{011}{}^0$ by $\mathbf{E}_1{}^0$, $\mathbf{E}_{101}{}^0$ by $\mathbf{E}_2{}^0$, etc. When this is done Eq. (14-10) can be written

$$\mathbf{E}^0 = \sum_i a_i\mathbf{E}_i{}^0 \tag{14-10a}$$

where we regard the index i as labeling all the independent modes. It will then happen that the associated ν_i are equal for several different values of the index i.

14-3. ORTHOGONALITY OF THE MODES. NORMALIZATION

Let E_i^0 be a solution of the time-independent wave equation

$$\nabla^2 E_i^0 + k_i^2 E_i^0 = 0 \qquad (14\text{-}11)$$

in a cavity of volume τ. Then E_i^{0*}, the complex conjugate of E_i^0, satisfies the wave equation

$$\nabla^2 E_i^{0*} + k_i^2 E_i^{0*} = 0 \qquad (14\text{-}12)$$

in the same cavity. We shall show that E_i^0 and E_i^{0*} satisfy the relation

$$\iiint E_i^{0*} \cdot E_j^0 \, d\tau = 0 \qquad i \neq j \qquad (14\text{-}13)$$

where the integration is performed over the cavity in question. For example, in the case of the rectangular resonator, (14-13) takes the form

$$\int^A \int^B \int_0^C E_i^{0*} \cdot E_j^0 \, dx_1 \, dx_2 \, dx_3 = 0 \qquad i \neq j$$

Any two functions E_i^0 and E_j^0 which satisfy the *orthogonality relation* (14-13) are said to be *mutually orthogonal* or simply *orthogonal* in the region τ.

If in addition to satisfying (14-13) the functions E_i^0 and E_j^0 satisfy the *normalization condition*

$$\iiint E_\kappa^{0*} \cdot E_\kappa^0 \, d\tau = 1 \qquad \kappa = i \text{ or } j \qquad (14\text{-}14)$$

they are said to be *orthonormal* in the region τ. If Eq. (14-14) is not satisfied but the integral is finite and not identically zero, then we can multiply the E_κ^0 by a constant N such that

$$\iiint E_\kappa^{0*} \cdot E_\kappa^0 \, d\tau = \frac{1}{N^*N} \qquad (14\text{-}15)$$

so obtaining the normalized function NE_κ^0. The number N satisfying (14-15) is called the *normalizing factor* of E_κ^0. Since a particular solution of the time-independent wave equation is still a solution when multiplied by a constant, we shall always assume our modes E_i^0 to be normalized, i.e., that they have already been multiplied by a normalizing factor.

The two relations (14-13) and (14-14) can be combined to form the *orthonormality relation*

$$\iiint E_i^{0*} \cdot E_j^0 \, d\tau = \delta_{ij} \qquad (14\text{-}16)$$

where the Kronecker delta δ_{ij} is equal to unity when $i = j$ and equal to zero when $i \neq j$.

In the case of scalar functions $\phi_i(x_1,x_2,x_3)$, the orthonormality relation (14-16) reduces to

$$\iiint \phi_i^* \phi_j \, d\tau = \delta_{ij} \qquad (14\text{-}17)$$

To verify the relation (14-13), take the scalar product of (14-12) and $\mathbf{E}_j{}^0$, the scalar product of

$$\nabla^2 \mathbf{E}_j{}^0 + k_j{}^2 \mathbf{E}_j{}^0 = 0$$

and $\mathbf{E}_i{}^{0*}$, and subtract the second from the first. The result is

$$(k_i{}^2 - k_j{}^2)\mathbf{E}_i{}^{0*} \cdot \mathbf{E}_j{}^0 = \mathbf{E}_j{}^{0*} \cdot \nabla^2 \mathbf{E}_j{}^0 - \mathbf{E}_j{}^0 \cdot \nabla^2 \mathbf{E}_i{}^{0*}$$
$$= \operatorname{div}\left[\mathbf{E}_i{}^{0*} \times (\nabla \times \mathbf{E}_j{}^0) + (\nabla \times \mathbf{E}_i{}^{0*}) \times \mathbf{E}_j{}^0\right] \quad (14\text{-}18)$$

where use has been made of the relation $\operatorname{div} \mathbf{E}_i{}^0 = 0$ and of the results of Exercises 1-3e and 1-3g.

Integration of (14-18) over the volume τ of the cavity and transformation of the right-hand member by means of Gauss' theorem yield

$$(k_i{}^2 - k_j{}^2)\iiint \mathbf{E}_i{}^{0*} \cdot \mathbf{E}_j{}^0 \, d\tau = \iint [\mathbf{E}_i{}^{0*} \times (\nabla \times \mathbf{E}_j{}^0) + (\nabla \times \mathbf{E}_i{}^{0*}) \times \mathbf{E}_j{}^0] \cdot d\mathbf{S}$$

where $d\mathbf{S}$ is an element of the surface S which bounds the volume τ. Because of the boundary condition on the $\mathbf{E}_i{}^0$, namely, that they must be normal to the cavity walls, the surface integral vanishes. Hence

$$(k_i{}^2 - k_j{}^2)\iiint \mathbf{E}_i{}^{0*} \cdot \mathbf{E}_j{}^0 \, d\tau = 0$$

from which (14-13) follows, since $k_i{}^2 \neq k_j{}^2$.

14-4. EXPANSION IN SERIES OF ORTHONORMAL FUNCTIONS

If it can be shown that in the region τ the function $\mathbf{E}^0$ admits of an expansion

$$\mathbf{E}^0 = \sum_i a_i \mathbf{E}_i{}^0 \qquad (14\text{-}19)$$

in terms of the set $\mathbf{E}_0{}^0$, $\mathbf{E}_1{}^0$, $\mathbf{E}_2{}^0$, . . . which is orthonormal in the region τ, then the *expansion coefficients* a_i can be evaluated as follows: Write (14-19) with the a_i undetermined and take the scalar product of (14-19) and $\mathbf{E}_j{}^{0*}$. Then

$$\mathbf{E}_j{}^{0*} \cdot \mathbf{E}^0 = \sum_i a_i \mathbf{E}_j{}^{0*} \cdot \mathbf{E}_i{}^0$$

and
$$\iiint \mathbf{E}_j{}^{0*} \cdot \mathbf{E}^0 \, d\tau = \sum_i a_i \iiint \mathbf{E}_j{}^{0*} \cdot \mathbf{E}_i{}^0 \, d\tau \qquad (14\text{-}20)$$

Because of the orthogonality of the $\mathbf{E}_i{}^0$, all terms in the right-hand member of (14-20) except the one for which $i = j$ vanish. Hence

$$a_j \int\int\int \mathbf{E}_j{}^{0*} \cdot \mathbf{E}_j{}^0 \, d\tau = \int\int\int \mathbf{E}_j{}^{0*} \cdot \mathbf{E}^0 \, d\tau$$

or
$$a_j = \int\int\int \mathbf{E}_j{}^{0*} \cdot \mathbf{E}^0 \, d\tau \qquad (14\text{-}21)$$

if the $E_i{}^0$ have already been normalized.

The most useful sets of orthonormal functions for our purposes are the wave functions or modes belonging to a given wave equation. In making expansions in terms of orthonormal functions, it is necessary to be sure that the set of functions is *complete*. The set of functions $E_i{}^0$ is said to be complete if the series $\sum\limits_i a_i \mathbf{E}_i{}^0$ converges to the value $\mathbf{E}^0$.

If the set $\mathbf{E}_i{}^0$ is not complete, it is quite possible for the series to be convergent but to converge to a value other than $\mathbf{E}^0$. This requirement of completeness necessitates that all the solutions of the wave equation be included when these solutions are used for an expansion of an arbitrary function. We shall assume that such a set is a complete one.

14-5. SPHERICAL RESONATORS

Let the resonator be of radius a. In the case of TM waves the solutions of (14-3) and (14-4) are

$$\mathbf{B}^0 = \left(-\frac{1}{\sin\theta} \frac{\partial}{\partial\varphi} \psi \mathbf{i}_\theta + \frac{\partial}{\partial\theta} \psi \mathbf{i}_\varphi \right)$$

$$\mathbf{E}^0 = \frac{iv}{k} \left[\frac{1}{r\sin\theta} \left(\frac{\partial}{\partial\theta} \sin\theta \frac{\partial}{\partial\theta} \psi + \frac{1}{\sin\theta} \frac{\partial^2}{\partial\varphi^2} \psi \right) \mathbf{i}_r \right. \qquad (12\text{-}24)$$

$$\left. -\frac{1}{r} \frac{\partial}{\partial\theta} \frac{\partial}{\partial r}(r\psi)\mathbf{i}_\theta - \frac{1}{r\sin\theta} \frac{\partial}{\partial\varphi} \frac{\partial}{\partial r}(r\psi)\mathbf{i}_\varphi \right]$$

where
$$\psi = \sum_{l,m} \psi_l{}^m(r,\theta,\varphi) \qquad (12\text{-}19)$$

with
$$\psi_l{}^m = G(k,l,m)j_l(kr)Y_l{}^m(\theta,\varphi) \qquad (14\text{-}22)$$

and satisfies the boundary condition

$$\frac{\partial}{\partial r}(r\psi)\bigg|_{r=a} = 0 \qquad (14\text{-}23)$$

Substitution into the boundary condition (14-23) yields

$$\frac{d}{d(kr)}[krj_l(kr)]\bigg|_{r=a} = 0 \qquad (14\text{-}24)$$

or
$$\frac{1}{2ka} J_{l+\frac{1}{2}}(kr) + \frac{d}{d(kr)} J_{l+\frac{1}{2}}(kr)\bigg|_{r=a} = 0 \qquad (14\text{-}24a)$$

This relation can be satisfied only for certain values of k, say k_{l1}, k_{l2}, k_{l3}, ... Because of the properties of the Bessel functions there are an infinite number of such roots. There are therefore an infinite number of allowed frequencies

$$\nu_{li} = \frac{v}{2\pi} k_{li} \qquad i = 1, 2, 3, \ldots \qquad (14\text{-}25)$$

It should be noted that the allowed frequencies are independent of m. They are functions of l only.

In the case of TE waves the solutions of (14-3) and (14-4) are

$$\mathbf{E}^0 = \left(-\frac{1}{\sin\theta} \frac{\partial\psi}{\partial\varphi} \mathbf{i}_\theta + \frac{\partial\psi}{\partial\theta} \mathbf{i}_\varphi \right)$$

$$\mathbf{B}^0 = -\frac{i}{\omega} \left[\frac{1}{r\sin\theta} \left(\frac{\partial}{\partial\theta} \sin\theta \frac{\partial\psi}{\partial\theta} + \frac{1}{\sin\theta} \frac{\partial^2\psi}{\partial\varphi^2} \right) \mathbf{i}_r - \frac{1}{r} \frac{\partial}{\partial\theta} \frac{\partial}{\partial r} (r\psi)\mathbf{i}_\theta \right. \qquad (14\text{-}26)$$

$$\left. - \frac{1}{r\sin\theta} \frac{\partial}{\partial\varphi} \frac{\partial}{\partial r} (r\psi)\mathbf{i}_\varphi \right]$$

where ψ is given by (12-19) and (14-22) and satisfies the boundary condition

$$-\frac{1}{\sin\theta} \frac{\partial\psi}{\partial\varphi} \mathbf{i}_\theta + \frac{\partial\psi}{\partial\theta} \mathbf{i}_\varphi \bigg|_{r=a} = 0$$

or

$$\psi \bigg|_{r=a} = 0 \qquad (14\text{-}27)$$

From (14-27) it follows that

$$j_l(ka) = 0$$

or

$$J_{l+\frac{1}{2}}(ka) = 0 \qquad (14\text{-}28)$$

Because of the properties of the Bessel functions there are an infinite number of roots, $k_{l1}a$, $k_{l2}a$, $k_{l3}a$, ... The infinite number of frequencies for the TE waves are then given by

$$\nu_{li} = \frac{v}{2\pi} k_{li} \qquad (14\text{-}29)$$

where the k_{li} satisfy (14-28).

14-6. CYLINDRICAL RESONATORS

The rectangular resonator considered in Sec. 14-2 is a special case of the class of cylindrical resonators. We now consider the general case of the cylindrical resonator which is bounded by the planes $x_3 = 0$ and $x_3 = C$ and whose cross section in any plane $x_3 = $ constant is the same. Again the problem is to find satisfactory solutions of (14-3) and (14-4). It is natural to expect the solutions to depend on x_3 through a $\cos k_3 x_3$

or $\sin k_3 x_3$ $(k_3 = n\pi/C; n = 0, 1, 2, 3, \ldots)$ factor, just as in the case of the rectangular resonator.

In the case of a TM cylindrical wave the solutions of (14-3) and (14-4) are (cf. Secs. 13-2 and 13-3)

$$\mathbf{B}^0 = \left(-\frac{1}{r}\frac{\partial\psi}{\partial\theta}\,\mathbf{i}_r + \frac{\partial\psi}{\partial r}\,\mathbf{i}_\theta \right)$$

$$\mathbf{E}^0 = \frac{iv}{k}\left[-\frac{\partial}{\partial x_3}\frac{\partial\psi}{\partial r}\,\mathbf{i}_r - \frac{1}{r}\frac{\partial}{\partial x_3}\frac{\partial\psi}{\partial\theta}\,\mathbf{i}_\theta + \left(\frac{\partial^2\psi}{\partial r^2} + \frac{1}{r^2}\frac{\partial^2\psi}{\partial\theta^2} \right)\mathbf{i}_3 \right] \tag{14-30}$$

where

$$\psi = \sum_{l,k,k_3} \psi_{l,k,k_3}(r,\theta,x_3) \tag{14-31}$$

with

$$\psi_{l,k,k_3} = Z_l(\kappa r)[c(l)e^{il\theta} + c'(l)e^{-il\theta}][a(k_3)e^{ik_3 x_3} + a'(k_3)e^{-ik_3 x_3}]$$
$$\kappa^2 = k^2 - k_3{}^2 \tag{14-32}$$

and satisfies the boundary conditions

$$\mathbf{E}^0 \times \mathbf{n}\,\Big|_{\text{cylindrical walls}} = 0 \tag{14-33}$$

where $\mathbf{n}$ is the normal to the cylindrical walls, and

$$\frac{\partial\psi}{\partial x_3}\,\Big|_{x_3=0,C} = 0 \tag{14-34}$$

The boundary condition (14-34) requires that (14-32) reduce to

$$\psi_{l,k,k_3} \equiv \psi_{l,k,n} = a_n Z_l(\kappa r)[c(l)e^{il\theta} + c'(l)e^{-il\theta}]\cos\frac{n\pi x_3}{C} \tag{14-35}$$

in which the a_n are constants and $n = 0, 1, 2, \ldots$.

In the case of TE cylindrical waves the solutions of (14-3) and (14-4) are (cf. Secs. 13-2 and 13-4)

$$\mathbf{E}^0 = \left(-\frac{1}{r}\frac{\partial\psi}{\partial\theta}\,\mathbf{i}_r + \frac{\partial\psi}{\partial r}\,\mathbf{i}_\theta \right)$$

$$\mathbf{B}^0 = -\frac{i}{\omega}\left[-\frac{\partial}{\partial x_3}\frac{\partial\psi}{\partial r}\,\mathbf{i}_r - \frac{1}{r}\frac{\partial}{\partial x_3}\frac{\partial\psi}{\partial\theta}\,\mathbf{i}_\theta + \left(\frac{\partial^2\psi}{\partial r^2} + \frac{1}{r^2}\frac{\partial^2\psi}{\partial\theta^2} \right)\mathbf{i}_3 \right] \tag{14-36}$$

where ψ is given by (14-31) and (14-35) and satisfies the boundary conditions

$$\left(-\frac{1}{r}\frac{\partial\psi}{\partial\theta}\,\mathbf{i}_r + \frac{\partial\psi}{\partial r}\,\mathbf{i}_\theta \right) \times \mathbf{n}\,\Big|_{\text{cylindrical walls}} = 0 \tag{14-37}$$

where $\mathbf{n}$ is the normal to the cylindrical walls, and

$$-\frac{1}{r}\frac{\partial\psi}{\partial\theta}\,\mathbf{i}_r + \frac{\partial\psi}{\partial r}\,\mathbf{i}_\theta\,\Big|_{x_3=0,C} = 0$$

or

$$\psi\,\Big|_{x_3=0,C} = 0 \tag{14-38}$$

14-7. THE RIGHT-CIRCULAR-CYLINDER RESONATOR

The right-circular-cylinder resonator is the simplest of the cylindrical resonators. Because of the circular symmetry the fields $\mathbf{B}$ and $\mathbf{E}$ are not functions of the angle θ. Because the resonator includes the line $r = 0$, the radial dependence of the fields must be described by a Bessel function.

The solutions (14-30) for TM waves in a cylindrical resonator reduce, in the present special case, to

$$
\begin{aligned}
\mathbf{B}^0 &= \frac{\partial \psi}{\partial r} \, \mathbf{i}_\theta \\
\mathbf{E}^0 &= \frac{iv}{k} \left(- \frac{\partial}{\partial x_3} \frac{\partial \psi}{\partial r} \, \mathbf{i}_r + \frac{\partial^2 \psi}{\partial r^2} \, \mathbf{i}_3 \right)
\end{aligned}
\tag{14-39}
$$

where the function ψ is given by

$$
\psi = \sum_{k,n} \psi_{0,k,n}(r, x_3)
$$

$$
\psi_{0,k,n} = a_n J_0(\kappa r) \cos \frac{n\pi x_3}{C} \qquad \kappa^2 = k^2 - \left(\frac{n\pi}{C} \right)^2
\tag{14-40}
$$

and satisfies the boundary condition

$$
\frac{\partial^2}{\partial r^2} \psi \bigg|_{r=R} = 0
\tag{14-41}
$$

Substitution of (14-40) into (14-41) yields

$$
\frac{d^2}{dr^2} J_0(\kappa r) \bigg|_{r=R} = 0
$$

or, using the properties of the Bessel functions,

$$
J_0(\kappa R) = 0
\tag{14-42}
$$

Now $J_0(x)$ is zero only for certain values of x, say x_{01}, x_{02}, . . . , of which there are an infinite number. Thus, to satisfy the boundary condition (14-42), κ must have the values x_{01}/R, x_{02}/R, ... Hence

$$
\kappa^2 = \left(\frac{x_{0i}}{R} \right)^2 = k^2 - \left(\frac{n\pi}{C} \right)^2 \qquad i = 1, 2, \ldots
$$

or
$$
k^2 = \frac{\omega^2}{v^2} = \left(\frac{x_{0i}}{R} \right)^2 + \left(\frac{n\pi}{C} \right)^2
\tag{14-43}
$$

There are therefore an infinite number of allowed frequencies

$$
\nu_{0in} = \frac{v}{2\pi} \sqrt{ \left(\frac{x_{0i}}{R} \right)^2 + \left(\frac{n\pi}{C} \right)^2 }
\tag{14-44}
$$

to which belong the modes given by substituting

$$\psi_{0in} = a_n J_0 \left(\frac{x_{0i}r}{R}\right) \cos \frac{n\pi x_3}{C} \qquad (14\text{-}45)$$

into (14-39).

In the case of TE waves in a right-circular-cylinder resonator the solutions (14-36) reduce to

$$\mathbf{E}^0 = \frac{\partial \psi}{\partial r} \mathbf{i}_\theta$$

$$\mathbf{B}^0 = -\frac{i}{\omega}\left(-\frac{\partial}{\partial x_3}\frac{\partial \psi}{\partial r}\mathbf{i}_r + \frac{\partial^2 \psi}{\partial r^2}\mathbf{i}_3\right) \qquad (14\text{-}46)$$

where the function ψ is given by (14-40) and satisfies the boundary condition

$$\left.\frac{\partial \psi}{\partial r}\right|_{r=R} = 0 \qquad (14\text{-}47)$$

Substitution of (14-40) into (14-47) yields

$$\left.\frac{d}{dr}J_0(\kappa r)\right|_{r=R} = -\kappa J_1(\kappa R) = 0 \qquad (14\text{-}48)$$

Now $J_1(x)$ is zero only for certain values of x, say x_{1i}, $i = 1, 2, 3, \ldots$. Consequently, κ must have the values x_{1i}/R and

$$\kappa^2 = \left(\frac{x_{1i}}{R}\right)^2 = k^2 - \left(\frac{n\pi}{C}\right)^2$$

Hence $\qquad k^2 = \frac{\omega^2}{v^2} = \left(\frac{x_{1i}}{R}\right)^2 + \left(\frac{n\pi}{C}\right)^2$

and there are an infinite number of allowed frequencies

$$\nu_{0in} = \frac{v}{2\pi}\sqrt{\left(\frac{x_{1i}}{R}\right)^2 + \left(\frac{n\pi}{C}\right)^2} \qquad (14\text{-}49)$$

to which belong the modes obtained by substituting

$$\psi_{0in} = a_n J_0 \left(\frac{x_{1i}r}{R}\right) \cos \frac{n\pi x_3}{C} \qquad (14\text{-}50)$$

into (14-46).

14-8. THE COAXIAL-CYLINDRICAL RESONATOR

Let a coaxial-cylindrical resonator be defined by two coaxial right cylinders with radii R_1 and R_2, $R_2 > R_1$, and the two planes $x_3 = 0$ and $x_3 = C$.

The solutions for TM waves in such a resonator are still given by (14-39). However, the function ψ is now given by

$$\psi = \sum_{k,n} \psi_{0,k,n}(r,x_3)$$

$$\psi_{0,k,n} = a_n[b_0 J_0(\kappa r) + b_0' N_0(\kappa r)] \cos \frac{n\pi x_3}{C} \qquad \kappa^2 = k^2 - \left(\frac{n\pi}{C}\right)^2 \qquad (14\text{-}51)$$

and satisfies the boundary conditions

$$\left. \frac{\partial^2}{\partial r^2} \psi \right|_{r=R_1} = \left. \frac{\partial^2}{\partial r^2} \psi \right|_{r=R_2} = 0 \qquad (14\text{-}52)$$

Substitution of (14-51) into (14-52) followed by the use of the properties of the cylindrical functions yields the boundary conditions

$$\begin{aligned} b_0 J_0(\kappa R_1) + b_0' N_0(\kappa R_1) &= 0 \\ b_0 J_0(\kappa R_2) + b_0' N_0(\kappa R_2) &= 0 \end{aligned} \qquad (14\text{-}53)$$

which determine the allowed values of κ (and, consequently, the allowed frequencies) as the roots of the equation

$$J_0(\kappa R_1)N_0(\kappa R_2) - N_0(\kappa R_1)J_0(\kappa R_2) = 0 \qquad (14\text{-}54)$$

Similarly, the solutions for TE waves in a coaxial-cylindrical resonator are given by (14-46), where ψ is now given by (14-51) but satisfies the boundary conditions

$$\left. \frac{\partial}{\partial r} \psi \right|_{r=R_1} = \left. \frac{\partial}{\partial r} \psi \right|_{r=R_2} = 0 \qquad (14\text{-}55)$$

Substitution of (14-51) into (14-55) gives the boundary conditions

$$\begin{aligned} b_0 J_1(\kappa R_1) + b_0' N_1(\kappa R_1) &= 0 \\ b_0 J_1(\kappa R_2) + b_0' N_1(\kappa R_2) &= 0 \end{aligned}$$

which determine the allowed values of κ as the roots of the equation

$$J_1(\kappa R_1)N_1(\kappa R_2) - N_1(\kappa R_1)J_1(\kappa R_2) = 0 \qquad (14\text{-}56)$$

EXERCISES

14-1. Find the magnetic induction **B** in a rectangular cavity resonator with perfectly conducting walls.

14-2. A spherical resonator has a 12-cm radius. Find the allowed frequencies for both the TM and TE modes for $l = 1$, 2, 3, 4, and 5.

14-3. Determine the normalized functions $\psi_l{}^m(r,\theta,\varphi)$ for both the TM and TE modes in a spherical resonator.

14-4. Verify that $\left. \dfrac{d^2}{dr^2} J_0(\kappa r) \right|_{r=R} = 0$ is equivalent to $J_0(\kappa R) = 0$.

14-5. Verify that the ψ_{0in} of (14-45) and (14-50) satisfy the orthogonality relation

$$\int_0^R \int^C \psi_{0in}\psi_{0jm}r\,dr\,dx_0 = 0 \qquad i \neq j \text{ or } n \neq m$$

Determine the normalized functions ψ_{0in}.

14-6. A cylindrical resonator is bounded by the planes $x_3 = 0$ and $x_3 = C$ and has for cross section the sector of the circle of radius R bounded by the angles $\theta = 0$ and $\theta = \alpha$, a constant. Determine the solutions for both the TM and TE waves.

14-7. A coaxial-cylindrical resonator is bounded by the planes $x_3 = 0$ and $x_3 = C$ and has for cross section the region bounded by the concentric circles with radii R_1 and R_2, $R_2 > R_1$, and the angles $\theta = 0$ and $\theta = \pi$. Determine the solutions for both the TM and TE waves.

REFERENCES

Condon, E. U.: Principles of Microwave Radio, *Rev. Mod. Phys.*, **14**, 341 (1942).

Morse, P. M., and H. Feshbach: "Methods of Theoretical Physics," chap. 13, McGraw-Hill Book Company, Inc., New York, 1953.

Panofsky, W. K. H., and M. Phillips: "Classical Electricity and Magnetism," chap. 12, Addison-Wesley Publishing Company, Inc., Cambridge, Mass., 1955.

Stratton, J. A.: "Electromagnetic Theory," chap. 9, McGraw-Hill Book Company, Inc., New York, 1941.

CHAPTER 15

Wave Guides

15-1. INTRODUCTION

By the term wave guide we mean a cylindrical pipe bounded by a conductor (of high conductivity) filled with a dielectric (of low loss). It may have arbitrary cross section. The two most common wave guides are those with rectangular and circular cross sections.

As in the case of cavity resonators, the discussion will be limited to wave guides with infinitely conducting walls. The problem is to solve the wave equations

$$\nabla^2 \mathbf{B} - \frac{1}{v^2}\frac{\partial^2}{\partial t^2}\mathbf{B} = 0 \qquad (9\text{-}47)$$

$$\nabla^2 \mathbf{E} - \frac{1}{v^2}\frac{\partial^2}{\partial t^2}\mathbf{E} = 0 \qquad (9\text{-}48)$$

We shall seek solutions of the form

$$\mathbf{B}(\mathbf{r},t) = \mathbf{B}^0 e^{-i(\omega t - k_3 x_3)} \qquad (15\text{-}1)$$
$$\mathbf{E}(\mathbf{r},t) = \mathbf{E}^0 e^{-i(\omega t - k_3 x_3)} \qquad (15\text{-}2)$$

where $\mathbf{B}^0$ and $\mathbf{E}^0$ are vector functions of (x_1,x_2) or (r,θ), the coordinates in the plane of the cross section of the guide, and satisfy the conditions that $\mathbf{E}^0$ is normal and $\mathbf{B}^0$ tangential to the walls of the guide. The constant k_3 can be written

$$k_3 = \frac{2\pi}{\lambda_g} \qquad (15\text{-}3)$$

where λ_g is called the *guide wavelength*. It is the wavelength with which the wave is propagated down the guide.

To determine under what conditions the fields (15-1) and (15-2) satisfy the wave equations (9-47) and (9-48), substitute the former into the latter. Then we find that $\mathbf{B}^0$ and $\mathbf{E}^0$ must satisfy the time-independent wave equations

$$\nabla_s^2 \mathbf{B}^0 + k_s^2 \mathbf{B}^0 = 0 \qquad (15\text{-}4)$$
$$\nabla_s^2 \mathbf{E}^0 + k_s^2 \mathbf{E}^0 = 0 \qquad (15\text{-}5)$$

247

where
$$\nabla_s^2 \equiv \frac{\partial^2}{\partial x_1{}^2} + \frac{\partial^2}{\partial x_2{}^2} \equiv \frac{1}{r}\frac{\partial}{\partial r}\left(r\frac{\partial}{\partial r}\right) + \frac{1}{r^2}\frac{\partial^2}{\partial \theta^2} \tag{15-6}$$

$$k_s{}^2 \equiv k^2 - k_3{}^2 \equiv \left(\frac{2\pi}{\lambda_f}\right)^2 - \left(\frac{2\pi}{\lambda_g}\right)^2 \tag{15-7}$$

$\lambda_f = 2\pi/k = v/(\omega/2\pi)$ is the *free wavelength*, that is, the wavelength which a disturbance of frequency ν $(= \omega/2\pi)$ would have if propagated in a dielectric of infinite extent.

It is convenient to write

$$k_s = \frac{2\pi}{\lambda_c} \tag{15-8}$$

so that (15-7) becomes

$$\frac{1}{\lambda_c{}^2} \equiv \frac{1}{\lambda_f{}^2} - \frac{1}{\lambda_g{}^2} \tag{15-7a}$$

The quantity λ_c so defined is called the *cutoff wavelength*. The reason for this terminology becomes obvious after the following considerations: If the free wavelength λ_f is smaller than the cutoff wavelength λ_c, then $1/\lambda_g{}^2$ is positive and the guide wavelength λ_g is real. On the other hand, if λ_f is greater than λ_c, then $1/\lambda_g{}^2$ is negative and the guide wavelength λ_g is imaginary. Inserting an imaginary k_3 $(= 2\pi/\lambda_g)$ into (15-1) and (15-2), we note that the solutions represent an attenuated wave rather than a propagated one. Thus the wave guide acts like a high-pass filter, only wavelengths shorter (frequencies higher) than the cutoff wavelength (frequency) being propagated.

15-2. THE TE WAVE IN A RECTANGULAR WAVE GUIDE

In the case of a rectangular wave guide with perfectly conducting walls at the ends of the ranges $0 < x_1 < A$ and $0 < x_2 < B$, the solution of (15-5) satisfying the boundary condition that $\mathbf{E}^0$ is normal to the walls is (cf. Sec. 14-2)

$$\mathbf{E}_t{}^0 = \mathbf{E}_1{}^0\mathbf{i}_1 + \mathbf{E}_2{}^0\mathbf{i}_2 \tag{15-9}$$

where
$$E_1{}^0 = E_{01} \cos\frac{l\pi x_1}{A} \sin\frac{m\pi x_2}{B}$$
$$E_2{}^0 = E_{02} \sin\frac{l\pi x_1}{A} \cos\frac{m\pi x_2}{B} \tag{15-10}$$

in which E_{01} and E_{02} are arbitrary constants and l and m are zero or positive integers which satisfy the relation

$$-\left(\frac{l\pi}{A}\right)^2 - \left(\frac{m\pi}{B}\right)^2 + \left(\frac{2\pi}{\lambda_c}\right)^2 = 0$$

or
$$\lambda_c = \left[\left(\frac{l}{2A}\right)^2 + \left(\frac{m}{2B}\right)^2\right]^{-\frac{1}{2}} \tag{15-11}$$

If $A > B$, the longest cutoff wavelength is given by $l = 1$, $m = 0$ and is equal to $2A$.

In the case of a TE wave, $E_3{}^0 = 0$. The magnetic induction field is given by

$$\frac{\partial}{\partial t} \mathbf{B} = - \text{ curl } \mathbf{E} \tag{9-26}$$

or, using (15-1) and (15-2),

$$\mathbf{B} = - \frac{i}{\omega} \text{ curl } \mathbf{E} \tag{15-12}$$

Hence
$$B_3{}^0 = - \frac{i\pi}{\omega} \left(\frac{l}{A} E_{02} - \frac{m}{B} E_{01} \right) \cos \frac{l\pi x_1}{A} \cos \frac{m\pi x_2}{B}$$

$$\mathbf{B}_t{}^0 = - \frac{2\pi}{\omega \lambda_g} E_2{}^0 \mathbf{i}_1 + \frac{2\pi}{\omega \lambda_g} E_1{}^0 \mathbf{i}_2 \tag{15-13}$$

where $E_1{}^0$ and $E_2{}^0$ are given by (15-10).

Note that $\mathbf{B}_t{}^0 \cdot \mathbf{E}_t{}^0 = 0$; that is, the transverse components of $\mathbf{B}$ and $\mathbf{E}$ are at right angles to each other. Note also that

$$|\mathbf{B}_t{}^0| = \frac{2\pi}{\omega \lambda_g} |\mathbf{E}_t{}^0| = \frac{1}{v} \frac{\lambda_f}{\lambda_g} |\mathbf{E}_t{}^0| \tag{15-14}$$

The rate at which energy is transmitted down the wave guide is given by the time average of the x_3 component of the Poynting vector:

$$\bar{N}_3 = \frac{1}{\mu} \frac{1}{v} \frac{\lambda_f}{\lambda_g} |\mathbf{E}_t{}^0|^2 = \sqrt{\frac{\epsilon}{\mu}} \frac{\lambda_f}{\lambda_g} |\mathbf{E}_t{}^0|^2 \tag{15-15}$$

The quantity $\sqrt{(\mu/\epsilon)}\,(\lambda_g/\lambda_f)$ is the *impedance of the wave guide for TE waves* (cf. Sec. 10-4).

Comparison of (15-15) with (10-11) shows that v_g, the velocity with which energy is transmitted down the guide, is given by

$$v_g = v \frac{\lambda_f}{\lambda_g}$$

$$= v \sqrt{1 - \frac{\lambda_f{}^2}{\lambda_c{}^2}}$$

$$= v \sqrt{1 - \lambda_f{}^2 \left[\left(\frac{l}{2A} \right)^2 + \left(\frac{m}{2B} \right)^2 \right]} \tag{15-16}$$

where use has been made of (15-7a) and (15-11). Thus, the guide velocity is less than the free-space velocity.

15-3. THE TM WAVE IN A RECTANGULAR WAVE GUIDE

Consider again the rectangular wave guide with perfectly conducting walls at the ends of the ranges $0 < x_1 < A$ and $0 < x_2 < B$. The solution of (15-14) which satisfies the boundary condition that $\mathbf{B}^0$ is tangential to the walls is

$$B_3{}^0 = B_{03} \cos \frac{l\pi x_1}{A} \cos \frac{m\pi x_2}{B}$$

$$\mathbf{B}_t{}^0 = B_1{}^0 \mathbf{i}_1 + B_2{}^0 \mathbf{i}_2 \tag{15-17}$$

in which
$$B_1{}^0 = B_{01} \sin \frac{l\pi x_1}{A} \cos \frac{m\pi x_2}{B}$$

$$B_2{}^0 = B_{02} \cos \frac{l\pi x_1}{A} \sin \frac{m\pi x_2}{B} \tag{15-18}$$

and B_{01}, B_{02}, and B_{03} are arbitrary constants and l and m are zero or positive integers satisfying (15-11).

For a TM wave, $B_3{}^0 = 0$. The magnetic induction field is then given by $\mathbf{B}_t{}^0$. From

$$\frac{\partial}{\partial t} \mathbf{E} = \frac{1}{\mu\epsilon} \operatorname{curl} \mathbf{B} = v^2 \operatorname{curl} \mathbf{B}$$

or, using (15-1) and (15-2),

$$\mathbf{E} = \frac{i}{\omega} v^2 \operatorname{curl} \mathbf{B} \tag{15-19}$$

we find that the electric field intensity is given by

$$\mathbf{E}_t{}^0 = E_1{}^0 \mathbf{i}_1 + E_2{}^0 \mathbf{i}_2$$

$$E_3{}^0 = -\frac{i\pi}{\mu\epsilon\omega} \left(\frac{l}{A} B_{02} + \frac{m}{B} B_{01} \right) \sin \frac{l\pi x_1}{A} \sin \frac{m\pi x_2}{B} \tag{15-20}$$

where
$$E_1{}^0 = \frac{1}{\sqrt{\mu\epsilon}} \frac{\lambda_f}{\lambda_g} B_{02} \cos \frac{l\pi x_1}{A} \sin \frac{m\pi x_2}{B}$$

$$E_2{}^0 = -\frac{1}{\sqrt{\mu\epsilon}} \frac{\lambda_f}{\lambda_g} B_{01} \sin \frac{l\pi x_1}{A} \cos \frac{m\pi x_2}{B} \tag{15-21}$$

Note that $\mathbf{B}_t{}^0 \cdot \mathbf{E}_t{}^0 = 0$ and that

$$|\mathbf{E}_t{}^0| = \frac{1}{\sqrt{\mu\epsilon}} \frac{\lambda_f}{\lambda_g} |\mathbf{B}_t{}^0| \tag{15-22}$$

Then the rate at which energy is transmitted down the wave guide is

$$\bar{N}_3 = \frac{1}{\mu} \sqrt{\mu\epsilon} \frac{\lambda_g}{\lambda_f} |\mathbf{E}_t{}^0|^2 = \sqrt{\frac{\epsilon}{\mu}} \frac{\lambda_g}{\lambda_f} |\mathbf{E}_t{}^0|^2 \tag{15-23}$$

The quantity $\sqrt{(\mu/\epsilon)}\,(\lambda_f/\lambda_g)$ is the *impedance of the wave guide for TM waves*. From (15-15) and (15-23) we obtain

$$\frac{\text{Impedance for TM waves}}{\text{Impedance for TE waves}} = \frac{\lambda_f{}^2}{\lambda_g{}^2} \tag{15-24}$$

showing that the impedance for TE waves is greater than that for TM waves.

15-4. THE TE WAVE IN A CIRCULAR WAVE GUIDE

In the case of a circular wave guide consisting of a perfectly conducting cylindrical shell of radius R, the solution of (15-5) satisfying the boundary condition that $\mathbf{E}^0$ is normal to the walls is (cf. Sec. 14-7)

$$E_t^0 = E_\theta^0 \mathbf{i}_\theta \tag{15-25}$$

where

$$E_\theta^0 = E_{0\theta} J_1\left(\frac{x_{1i}r}{R}\right) \tag{15-26}$$

in which $E_{0\theta}$ is an arbitrary constant and the x_{1i} are those values of x which make $J_1(x) = 0$. The cutoff wavelength λ_c is then given by

$$k_s^2 \equiv \left(\frac{2\pi}{\lambda_c}\right)^2 = \left(\frac{x_{1i}}{R}\right)^2$$

or

$$\lambda_c = \frac{2\pi R}{x_{1i}} \tag{15-27}$$

The magnetic induction field is obtained from $\mathbf{B} = -(i/\omega)$ curl $\mathbf{E}$:

$$B_3^0 = -\frac{iE_{00}}{\omega}\left[\frac{1}{r} J_1\left(\frac{x_{1i}r}{R}\right) + \frac{\partial}{\partial r} J_1\left(\frac{x_{1i}r}{R}\right)\right] \tag{15-28}$$

$$B_t^0 = B_r^0 = -\frac{2\pi}{\omega\lambda_g} E_{0\theta} J_1\left(\frac{x_{1i}r}{R}\right) \tag{15-29}$$

EXERCISES

15-1. Solve the problem of a TM wave in a circular wave guide.
15-2. Solve the problem of a TE wave in a coaxial line.
15-3. Solve the problem of a TM wave in a coaxial line.

REFERENCES

Barlow, H. M.: "Microwaves and Wave Guides," Dover Publications, Inc., New York, 1949.
Morse, P. M., and H. Feshbach: "Methods of Theoretical Physics," chap. 13, McGraw-Hill Book Company, Inc., New York, 1953.
Stratton, J. A.: "Electromagnetic Theory," chap. 9, McGraw-Hill Book Company, Inc., New York, 1941.

CHAPTER 16

Lagrangian and Hamiltonian Formulations of the Electromagnetic Field

16-1. INTRODUCTION

In this chapter we develop the Lagrangian and Hamiltonian formulations of the electromagnetic field. It is assumed that the reader is familiar with the equations of Lagrange and Hamilton for discrete systems. The transition from a discrete to a continuous (one-dimensional) system is carried out in Sec. 16-3. The extension to a three-dimensional continuum is described in Sec. 16-4. The pure radiation field is then treated in Sec. 16-5. The representation of the pure radiation field by plane waves and as an assembly of independent harmonic oscillators is described in Sec. 16-6. The Lagrangian and Hamiltonian equations for charged particles in an electromagnetic field are derived in Sec. 16-7. Section 16-8 deals with the general electromagnetic field.

It should be noted that the Lagrangian and Hamiltonian formulations of the electromagnetic field do not lead to anything new in classical electrodynamics. The main reason for introducing these formulations is to prepare the reader for quantum electrodynamics.

16-2. THE EQUATIONS OF LAGRANGE AND HAMILTON

For a system with n (finite or at most denumerably infinite) degrees of freedom there are n Lagrange equations of motion

$$\frac{d}{dt}\frac{\partial L}{\partial \dot{q}_i} - \frac{\partial L}{\partial q_i} = 0 \qquad i = 1, 2, \ldots, n \qquad (16\text{-}1)$$

where the Lagrangian $L(q_i, \dot{q}_i, t)$ is defined by the relation

$$L = T - V \qquad (16\text{-}2)$$

252

in which $T(q_i,\dot{q}_i,t)$ and $V(q_i)$ are, respectively, the kinetic and potential energies of the system. The quantities t, q_i, and $\dot{q}_i$ represent, respectively, the time, the generalized coordinates of the system, and the generalized velocities.

The quantity $\partial L/\partial \dot{q}_i$ plays the part of a momentum. For example, in the case of the motion of a particle of mass m, one has in rectangular coordinates, $\partial L/\partial \dot{x}_i = m\dot{x}_i$, exactly the momentum associated with the coordinate x_i. Similarly, in polar coordinates, the quantities associated with r and φ are $m\dot{r}$, the radial momentum, and $mr^2\dot{\varphi}$, the angular momentum, respectively. Consequently, one defines a generalized momentum p_i by

$$p_i = \frac{\partial L}{\partial \dot{q}_i} \qquad (16\text{-}3)$$

Lagrange's equations (16-1) can then be written as

$$\dot{p}_i = \frac{\partial L}{\partial q_i} \qquad i = 1, 2, \ldots, n \qquad (16\text{-}4)$$

The Hamiltonian $H(p_i,q_i,t)$ is defined by the relation

$$H(p_i,q_i,t) = \sum_i p_i\dot{q}_i - L(q_i,\dot{q}_i,t) \qquad (16\text{-}5)$$

Then

$$dH = \sum_i \left(p_i\, d\dot{q}_i + \dot{q}_i\, dp_i - \frac{\partial L}{\partial q_i}\, dq_i - \frac{\partial L}{\partial \dot{q}_i}\, d\dot{q}_i \right) - \frac{\partial L}{\partial t}\, dt$$

$$- \sum_i (\dot{q}_i\, dp_i - \dot{p}_i\, dq_i) - \frac{\partial L}{\partial t}\, dt \qquad (16\text{-}6)$$

by reason of (16-3) and (16-4). On the other hand, consideration of H as a function of p_i, q_i, and t yields

$$dH = \sum_i \left(\frac{\partial H}{\partial p_i}\, dp_i + \frac{\partial H}{\partial q_i}\, dq_i \right) + \frac{\partial H}{\partial t}\, dt \qquad (16\text{-}7)$$

Comparison of (16-7) with (16-6) yields the following set of $2n + 1$ equations:

$$\left.\begin{aligned} \dot{q}_i &= \frac{\partial H}{\partial p_i} \\[2mm] \dot{p}_i &= -\frac{\partial H}{\partial q_i} \end{aligned}\right\} \qquad i = 1, 2, \ldots, n \qquad (16\text{-}8)$$

$$\frac{\partial L}{\partial t} = -\frac{\partial H}{\partial t} \qquad (16\text{-}9)$$

Equations 16-8 are known as Hamilton's canonical equations. The generalized momenta p_i and the coordinates q_i are said to be canonically conjugate.

It is clear from (16-9) that, if the Lagrangian L is not an explicit function of the time t, then the Hamiltonian also is not an explicit function of the time. If the equations which define the generalized coordinates in terms of the cartesian coordinates do not depend explicitly on the time, the Hamiltonian is not only a constant of the motion ($\partial H/\partial t = 0$) but also the total energy $T + V$ of the system.†

16-3. TRANSITION FROM A DISCRETE TO A CONTINUOUS SYSTEM

Since the electromagnetic field is a continuous system with a non-denumerably infinite number of degrees of freedom, it is necessary for us to extend the formulations of the preceding section to such systems. One method for accomplishing this is (1) to approximate the continuous system by one containing discrete units, (2) to study the discrete system, and (3) to examine the changes induced as the continuous limit is approached. As an example of this method we consider the free vibrations of a finite string of length a and constant mass per unit length ρ under tension $\mathfrak{I}$. First replace the actual string by one of negligible mass loaded at n equally spaced points $x_i = ih$ ($i = 1, 2, \ldots, n$) by beads of equal mass m and attached to the x axis at the points $x_0 = 0$ and $x_{n+1} = (n + 1)h = a$. If y_i denotes the displacement of the ith bead from its equilibrium position, the kinetic energy of the set of beads is

$$T = \tfrac{1}{2} \sum_i m\dot{y}_i{}^2 \tag{16-10}$$

and the corresponding potential energy is

$$V = \frac{\mathfrak{I}}{2h} \sum_i (y_{i+1} - y_i)^2 \tag{16-11}$$

where $y_0 = y_{n+1} = 0$.

The Lagrangian for the system is then

$$L = T - V = \frac{1}{2} \sum_i \left[\frac{m}{h} \dot{y}_i{}^2 - \mathfrak{I} \left(\frac{y_{i+1} - y_i}{h} \right)^2 \right] h = \sum_i L_i h \tag{16-12}$$

so that Lagrange's equations of motion are

$$\frac{m}{h} \ddot{y}_i = \frac{\mathfrak{I}}{h} \left(\frac{y_{i+1} - y_i}{h} - \frac{y_i - y_{i-1}}{h} \right) \tag{16-13}$$

---

† See, for instance, H. Goldstein, "Classical Mechanics," p. 54, Addison-Wesley Publishing Company, Inc., Cambridge, Mass., 1950.

The particular forms of L, Eq. (16-12), and of Lagrange's equations, (16-13), were chosen for convenience in going to the limit of a uniform string as $h \to 0$ and $n \to \infty$, such that $(n + 1)h = a$. Clearly,

$$\lim_{h \to 0} \frac{m}{h} = \rho$$

the mass per unit length of the continuous string. Furthermore

$$\lim_{h \to 0} \frac{y_{i+1} - y_i}{h} = \lim_{h \to 0} \frac{y(x + h) - y(x)}{h} = \frac{\partial y}{\partial x}$$

and

$$\lim_{h \to 0} \frac{1}{h} \left(\frac{y_{i+1} - y_i}{h} - \frac{y_i - y_{i-1}}{h} \right) = \lim_{h \to 0} \frac{1}{h} \left[\left(\frac{\partial y}{\partial x} \right) \Big|_x - \left(\frac{\partial y}{\partial x} \right) \Big|_{x-h} \right] = \frac{\partial^2 y}{\partial x^2}$$

Hence, in the limit of a uniform string, (16-12) and (16-13) reduce, respectively, to

$$L = \frac{1}{2} \int_0^a \left[\rho \dot{y}^2 - 3 \left(\frac{\partial y}{\partial x} \right)^2 \right] dx \qquad (16\text{-}14)$$

and

$$\rho \ddot{y} = 3 \frac{\partial^2 y}{\partial x^2}$$

or

$$\frac{\partial^2 y}{\partial x^2} - \frac{1}{v^2} \frac{\partial^2 y}{\partial t^2} = 0 \qquad (16\text{-}15)$$

the wave equation, in which $v = \sqrt{3/\rho}$.

The relation (16-14) can be written

$$L = \int_0^a \mathcal{L} \, dx \qquad (16\text{-}16)$$

where

$$\mathcal{L} \equiv \frac{\rho}{2} \left[\dot{y}^2 - v^2 \left(\frac{\partial y}{\partial x} \right)^2 \right] \qquad (16\text{-}17)$$

corresponds to the continuous limit of the quantity L_i appearing in (16-12) and is known as the *Lagrangian density*. In terms of this Lagrangian density, the equation of motion for the continuous string (16-15) becomes

$$\frac{\partial}{\partial t} \left(\frac{\partial \mathcal{L}}{\partial \dot{y}} \right) + \frac{\partial}{\partial x} \frac{\partial \mathcal{L}}{\partial (\partial y / \partial x)} = 0 \qquad (16\text{-}18)$$

If one defines a generalized momentum density p by

$$p = \frac{\partial \mathcal{L}}{\partial \dot{y}} \qquad (16\text{-}19)$$

the Lagrange equation of motion (16-18) may be rewritten

$$\dot{p} = - \frac{\partial}{\partial x} \frac{\partial \mathcal{L}}{\partial (\partial y / \partial x)} \qquad (16\text{-}20)$$

Note that $y_i(t)$ in the discrete system became $y(x,t)$ in the continuous system.   Thus, the position coordinate x is *not* a generalized coordinate. It is a continuous index which replaces the discrete index i.

Note further that the Lagrangian density for the continuous string is *not* an explicit function of either the displacement y or the time t, that is, $\mathcal{L} = \mathcal{L}(\dot{y}, \partial y/\partial x)$ only.   It is for this reason that the Lagrangian equation of motion has the simple form (16-18).   In the more general case in which $\mathcal{L} = \mathcal{L}(y, \dot{y}, \partial y/\partial x)$, the equation of motion takes the form†

$$\frac{\partial}{\partial t}\left(\frac{\partial \mathcal{L}}{\partial \dot{y}}\right) + \frac{\partial}{\partial x}\frac{\partial \mathcal{L}}{\partial(\partial y/\partial x)} - \frac{\partial \mathcal{L}}{\partial y} = 0 \qquad (16\text{-}21)$$

Consider now the Hamiltonian.   In the case of the discrete system

$$H = \sum_i p_i \dot{y}_i - L$$

$$= \frac{1}{2}\sum_i \left[\frac{p_i^2}{mh} + \mathfrak{z}\left(\frac{y_{i+1} - y_i}{h}\right)^2\right]h = \sum_i H_i h \qquad (16\text{-}22)$$

where we have used (16-12) and

$$p_i = \frac{\partial L}{\partial \dot{y}_i} = m\dot{y}_i \qquad (16\text{-}23)$$

In the limit of the uniform string (16-22) reduces to

$$H = \frac{1}{2}\int_0^a \left[\frac{p^2}{\rho} + \mathfrak{z}\left(\frac{\partial y}{\partial x}\right)^2\right] dx = \int_0^a \mathfrak{IC}\, dx \qquad (16\text{-}24)$$

so that
$$\mathfrak{IC} = \frac{1}{2}\left[\frac{p^2}{\rho} + \mathfrak{z}\left(\frac{\partial y}{\partial x}\right)^2\right]$$

$$= \frac{\rho}{2}\left[\frac{p^2}{\rho^2} + v^2\left(\frac{\partial y}{\partial x}\right)^2\right] \qquad (16\text{-}25)$$

where
$$p = \lim_{h \to 0} \frac{p_i}{h} \qquad (16\text{-}26)$$

The *Hamiltonian density* $\mathfrak{IC}$ can also be determined from the Lagrangian density $\mathcal{L}$.   If a generalized momentum density is defined by (16-19), the Hamiltonian density is defined by

$$\mathfrak{IC}\left(p\,\frac{\partial y}{\partial x}\right) = p\dot{y} - \mathcal{L}\left(\dot{y}\,\frac{\partial y}{\partial x}\right) \qquad (16\text{-}27)$$

† See, for instance, *ibid.*, p. 352, or L. I. Schiff, "Quantum Mechanics," 2d ed., p. 343, McGraw-Hill Book Company, Inc., New York, 1955.

Hamilton's canonical equations in the case of the discrete system are

$$\dot{y}_i = h\frac{\partial H_i}{\partial p_i} = \frac{p_i}{m}$$

$$\dot{p}_i = -h\frac{\partial H_i}{\partial y_i} = \Im\left(\frac{y_{i+1} - y_i}{h} - \frac{y_i - y_{i-1}}{h}\right)$$

(16-28)

In the case of the continuous system they become

$$\dot{y} = \frac{\partial \mathfrak{K}}{\partial p} = \frac{p}{\rho}$$

$$\dot{p} = \frac{\partial}{\partial x}\left[\frac{\partial \mathfrak{K}}{\partial(\partial y/\partial x)}\right] = \Im\frac{\partial^2 y}{\partial x^2}$$

(16-29)

16-4. GENERALIZATION TO A THREE-DIMENSIONAL CONTINUUM

According to the results in the preceding section the Lagrangian density in a one-dimensional continuum is

$$\mathfrak{L}\left(\dot{q}\,\frac{\partial q}{\partial x}\right) = \frac{\rho}{2}\left[\dot{q}^2 - v^2\left(\frac{\partial q}{\partial x}\right)^2\right]$$

(16-30)

in which q is the generalized coordinate of the system, $\dot{q}$ its time derivative, and x is the position index or variable. ρ and v^2 are properties of the system.

The Lagrange equation of motion is

$$\frac{\partial}{\partial t}\left(\frac{\partial \mathfrak{L}}{\partial \dot{q}}\right) + \frac{\partial}{\partial x}\left[\frac{\partial \mathfrak{L}}{\partial(\partial q/\partial x)}\right] = 0$$

(16-31)

Substitution for $\mathfrak{L}$ by means of (16-30) yields the wave equation

$$\frac{\partial^2 q}{\partial x^2} - \frac{1}{v^2}\frac{\partial^2 q}{\partial t^2} = 0$$

(16-32)

A generalized momentum density p can then be defined by

$$p = \frac{\partial \mathfrak{L}}{\partial \dot{q}}$$

(16-33)

so that the equation of motion (16-31) can be written

$$\dot{p} = -\frac{\partial}{\partial x}\left[\frac{\partial \mathfrak{L}}{\partial(\partial q/\partial x)}\right]$$

(16-34)

The Hamiltonian density is defined by the relation

$$\mathfrak{K}\left(p\,\frac{\partial q}{\partial x}\right) = p\dot{q} - \mathfrak{L}\left(\dot{q}\,\frac{\partial q}{\partial x}\right)$$

(16-35)

Using Eqs. (16-30) and (16-33), this becomes

$$\mathcal{H}\left(p\,\frac{\partial q}{\partial x}\right) = \frac{\rho}{2}\left[\frac{p^2}{\rho^2} + v^2\left(\frac{\partial q}{\partial x}\right)^2\right] \tag{16-36}$$

The Hamiltonian equations of motion are

$$\dot{q} = \frac{\partial \mathcal{H}}{\partial p} = \frac{p}{\rho}$$

$$\dot{p} = \frac{\partial}{\partial x}\left[\frac{\partial \mathcal{H}}{\partial(\partial q/\partial x)}\right] = \rho v^2\,\frac{\partial^2 q}{\partial x^2} \tag{16-37}$$

The extension to a three-dimensional continuum proceeds as follows:

$$\left.\begin{array}{l} x \to x_i \\ q \to q_i \\ p \to p_i \end{array}\right\} \qquad i = 1,\,2,\,3$$

Then the Lagrange equation of motion (16-31) becomes

$$\frac{\partial}{\partial t}\left(\frac{\partial \mathcal{L}}{\partial \dot{q}_i}\right) + \sum_{j=1}^{3}\frac{\partial}{\partial x_j}\left[\frac{\partial \mathcal{L}}{\partial(\partial q_i/\partial x_j)}\right] = 0 \qquad i = 1,\,2,\,3 \tag{16-38}$$

Generalized momentum densities p_i can then be defined by

$$p_i = \frac{\partial \mathcal{L}}{\partial \dot{q}_i} \qquad i = 1,\,2,\,3 \tag{16-39}$$

so that the equation of motion (16-38) can be written

$$\dot{p}_i = -\sum_{j=1}^{3}\frac{\partial}{\partial x_j}\left[\frac{\partial \mathcal{L}}{\partial(\partial q_i/\partial x_j)}\right] \qquad i = 1,\,2,\,3 \tag{16-40}$$

If it is agreed that the equations of motion must be linear, then the Lagrangian density cannot contain higher powers than the second of either the $\dot{q}_i$ or the $\partial q_i/\partial x_j$. One possible extension of (16-30) which satisfies these requirements is

$$\mathcal{L} = \frac{\rho}{2}\left[\dot{\mathbf{q}}\cdot\dot{\mathbf{q}} - v^2(\text{curl }\mathbf{q})\cdot(\text{curl }\mathbf{q})\right] \tag{16-41}$$

where $\mathbf{q} = q_1\mathbf{i}_1 + q_2\mathbf{i}_2 + q_3\mathbf{i}_3$.

The Hamiltonian density is given by

$$\mathcal{H} = \mathbf{p}\cdot\dot{\mathbf{q}} - \mathcal{L} \tag{16-42}$$

where $\mathbf{p} = p_1\mathbf{i}_1 + p_2\mathbf{i}_2 + p_3\mathbf{i}_3$.   Thus, if the Lagrangian density is given by (16-41), the corresponding Hamiltonian density is

$$\mathcal{H} = \frac{\rho}{2}\left[\frac{\mathbf{p}\cdot\mathbf{p}}{\rho^2} + v^2(\text{curl }\mathbf{q})\cdot(\text{curl }\mathbf{q})\right] \tag{16-43}$$

The Hamiltonian equations of motion are then

$$\dot{q}_i = \frac{\partial\mathcal{H}}{\partial p_i} = \frac{p_i}{\rho}$$

$$\dot{p}_i = \sum_{j=1}^{3}\frac{\partial}{\partial x_j}\left[\frac{\partial\mathcal{H}}{\partial(\partial q_i/\partial x_j)}\right] = -\rho v^2(\text{curl curl }\mathbf{q})_i \tag{16-44}$$

16-5. THE PURE RADIATION FIELD

Maxwell's equations in a homogeneous isotropic medium containing no charges and no currents are

$$\text{curl }\mathbf{B} = \mu\epsilon\frac{\partial\mathbf{E}}{\partial t} = \frac{1}{v^2}\frac{\partial\mathbf{E}}{\partial t} \tag{16-45}$$

$$\text{curl }\mathbf{E} = -\frac{\partial\mathbf{B}}{\partial t} \tag{16-46}$$

$$\text{div }\mathbf{B} = 0 \tag{16-47}$$

$$\text{div }\mathbf{E} = 0 \tag{16-48}$$

The energy density in the electromagnetic field is

$$w = \tfrac{1}{2}(\epsilon\mathbf{E}\cdot\mathbf{E} + \mu^{-1}\mathbf{B}\cdot\mathbf{B})$$

$$= \frac{\epsilon}{2}(\mathbf{E}\cdot\mathbf{E} + v^2\mathbf{B}\cdot\mathbf{B}) \tag{16-49}$$

The field vectors $\mathbf{E}$ and $\mathbf{B}$ are related to the electrodynamic potentials $\mathbf{A}$ and ϕ by

$$\mathbf{B} = \text{curl }\mathbf{A} \tag{9-49}$$

$$\mathbf{E} = -\frac{\partial\mathbf{A}}{\partial t} - \boldsymbol{\nabla}\phi \tag{9-51}$$

The electrodynamic potentials satisfy the Lorentz condition

$$\text{div }\mathbf{A} + \frac{1}{v^2}\frac{\partial\phi}{\partial t} = 0 \tag{9-53}$$

Substitution for $\mathbf{B}$ and $\mathbf{E}$ in (16-49) by means of (9-49) and (9-51) yields

$$w = \frac{\epsilon}{2}\left[\left(\frac{\partial\mathbf{A}}{\partial t} + \boldsymbol{\nabla}\phi\right)\cdot\left(\frac{\partial\mathbf{A}}{\partial t} + \boldsymbol{\nabla}\phi\right) + v^2(\text{curl }\mathbf{A})\cdot(\text{curl }\mathbf{A})\right] \tag{16-50}$$

We note that, if we think of

$$\frac{\epsilon}{2}\,\mathbf{E}\cdot\mathbf{E} = \frac{\epsilon}{2}\left(\frac{\partial\mathbf{A}}{\partial t} + \boldsymbol{\nabla}\phi\right)\cdot\left(\frac{\partial\mathbf{A}}{\partial t} + \boldsymbol{\nabla}\phi\right)$$

as a kinetic energy density and

$$\frac{\epsilon}{2}\,v^2\mathbf{B}\cdot\mathbf{B} = \frac{\epsilon}{2}\,v^2(\text{curl }\mathbf{A})\cdot(\text{curl }\mathbf{A})$$

as a potential energy density, we can write

$$\mathfrak{L} = \frac{\epsilon}{2}\left[\left(\frac{\partial\mathbf{A}}{\partial t} + \boldsymbol{\nabla}\phi\right)\cdot\left(\frac{\partial\mathbf{A}}{\partial t} + \boldsymbol{\nabla}\phi\right) - v^2(\text{curl }\mathbf{A})\cdot(\text{curl }\mathbf{A})\right] \quad (16\text{-}51)$$

for the Lagrangian density for the pure radiation field. This expression can be brought into precisely the form of (16-41) by transforming to the solenoidal gauge (cf. Secs. 9-10 and 9-11) in which the divergence of the vector potential is zero and the scalar potential is constant. For convenience, the constant value of the scalar potential is taken equal to zero. Then

$$\phi_s = 0 \quad\quad\quad\quad\quad\quad\quad (16\text{-}52)$$
$$\text{div }\mathbf{A}_s = 0 \quad\quad\quad\quad\quad\quad (16\text{-}53)$$
$$\mathbf{B} = \text{curl }\mathbf{A}_s \quad\quad\quad\quad\quad (16\text{-}54)$$
$$\mathbf{E} = -\frac{\partial\mathbf{A}_s}{\partial t} \quad\quad\quad\quad (16\text{-}55)$$

and
$$\mathfrak{L} = \frac{\epsilon}{2}\left[\left(\frac{\partial\mathbf{A}_s}{\partial t}\right)\cdot\left(\frac{\partial\mathbf{A}_s}{\partial t}\right) - v^2(\text{curl }\mathbf{A}_s)\cdot(\text{curl }\mathbf{A}_s)\right] \quad (16\text{-}56)$$

If we regard the components of $\mathbf{A}_s$ as the field variables, application of (16-38) to (16-56) yields

$$\text{curl curl }\mathbf{A}_s + \frac{1}{v^2}\frac{\partial}{\partial t}\left(\frac{\partial\mathbf{A}_s}{\partial t}\right) = 0$$

which is the same as (16-45) and reduces to the wave equation

$$\nabla^2\mathbf{A}_s - \frac{1}{v^2}\frac{\partial^2\mathbf{A}_s}{\partial t^2} = 0$$

because of (16-53). The remaining three Maxwell equations are automatically satisfied by the definitions (16-53), (16-54), and (16-55) for the vector potential $\mathbf{A}_s$.

The generalized momentum densities are obtained from (16-39):

$$p_{si} = \frac{\partial\mathfrak{L}}{\partial(\partial A_{si}/\partial t)} = \epsilon\frac{\partial A_{si}}{\partial t} \quad\quad i = 1, 2, 3 \quad\quad (16\text{-}57)$$

Then the Hamiltonian density for the pure radiation field is [cf. Eq. (16-43)]

$$\mathcal{3C} = \frac{\epsilon}{2}\left[\frac{\mathbf{p}_s \cdot \mathbf{p}_s}{\epsilon^2} + v^2(\text{curl } \mathbf{A}_s) \cdot (\text{curl } \mathbf{A}_s)\right] \tag{16-58}$$

or, substituting for $\mathbf{p}_s$ and curl $\mathbf{A}_s$,

$$\mathcal{3C} = \frac{\epsilon}{2}[\mathbf{E} \cdot \mathbf{E} + v^2\mathbf{B} \cdot \mathbf{B}] = w$$

The transformation to the solenoidal gauge was not necessary. The Lagrangian density can be left in the form (16-51) provided that A_1, A_2, A_3, and ϕ are regarded as the field variables. Application of (16-38) to (16-51) then yields

$$\sum_{j=1}^{3}\frac{\partial}{\partial x_j}\left[\frac{\partial \mathcal{L}}{\partial(\partial\phi/\partial x_j)}\right] = 0$$

or

$$\text{div}\left(\frac{\partial \mathbf{A}}{\partial t} + \boldsymbol{\nabla}\phi\right) = -\text{div } \mathbf{E} = 0$$

and

$$\frac{\partial}{\partial t}\left[\frac{\partial \mathcal{L}}{\partial(\partial A_i/\partial t)}\right] + \sum_{j=1}^{3}\frac{\partial}{\partial x_j}\left[\frac{\partial \mathcal{L}}{\partial(\partial A_i/\partial x_j)}\right] = 0 \quad i = 1, 2, 3 \tag{16-59}$$

or

$$\text{curl curl } \mathbf{A} + \frac{1}{v^2}\frac{\partial}{\partial t}\left(\frac{\partial \mathbf{A}}{\partial t} + \boldsymbol{\nabla}\phi\right) - 0$$

which are the same as the Maxwell equations (16-48) and (16-45), respectively. The definitions (9-49) and (9-51) for the potentials automatically satisfy the other two Maxwell equations.

The generalized momentum densities are obtained from (16-39):

$$p_\phi = \frac{\partial \mathcal{L}}{\partial\dot\phi} = 0$$

since $\dot\phi = \partial\phi/\partial t$ does not occur in the Lagrangian density, and

$$p_i = \frac{\partial \mathcal{L}}{\partial\dot{A}_i} = \epsilon\left(\frac{\partial A_i}{\partial t} + \frac{\partial\phi}{\partial x_i}\right) \quad i = 1, 2, 3 \tag{16-60}$$

or

$$\mathbf{p} = \epsilon\left(\frac{\partial \mathbf{A}}{\partial t} + \boldsymbol{\nabla}\phi\right) \tag{16-60a}$$

The Hamiltonian density is obtained from (16-42):

$$\mathcal{3C} = \mathbf{p} \cdot \frac{\partial \mathbf{A}}{\partial t} - \mathcal{L}$$

$$= \frac{\epsilon}{2}\left[\frac{\mathbf{p} \cdot \mathbf{p}}{\epsilon^2} + v^2(\text{curl } \mathbf{A}) \cdot (\text{curl } \mathbf{A}) - \frac{2\mathbf{p}}{\epsilon} \cdot \boldsymbol{\nabla}\phi\right] \tag{16-61}$$

where use has been made of (16-60a).

The Hamiltonian equations of motion are obtained from (16-44):

$$\left.\begin{aligned} \frac{\partial A_i}{\partial t} &= \frac{\partial \mathcal{K}}{\partial p_i} = \frac{p_i}{\epsilon} - \frac{\partial \phi}{\partial x_i} \\ \dot{p}_i &= \sum_{j=1}^{3} \frac{\partial}{\partial x_j} \left[\frac{\partial \mathcal{K}}{\partial(\partial A_i/\partial x_j)} \right] = -\epsilon v^2 (\text{curl curl } \mathbf{A})_i \end{aligned}\right\} i = 1, 2, 3 \quad (16\text{-}62)$$

The first of these is the same as (16-60). Note that since the Hamiltonian formalism consists only of (16-61) and the canonical variables **A** and **p**, we must make use of this equation to define a quantity **E** that is equal to $-\mathbf{p}/\epsilon$. The second of Eqs. (16-62) then agrees with the Maxwell equation (16-45) provided that we use (9-49) to define a quantity **B** in terms of **A**. The Maxwell equations (16-46) and (16-47) are then satisfied because of the definitions of **E** and **B**.

The Maxwell equation (16-48) cannot be obtained as a Hamiltonian equation based on (16-61). However, from the second of Eqs. (16-62) it follows that

$$\frac{\partial}{\partial t} \text{div } \mathbf{p} = -\epsilon \frac{\partial}{\partial t} \text{div } \mathbf{E} = -\epsilon v^2 \text{ div curl curl } \mathbf{A} = 0$$

Hence div **E** is constant in time. We take the constant equal to zero and so use (16-48) as an equation of constraint. In this way we can specify that we are interested only in those solutions of the Hamiltonian equations which satisfy (16-48).

The Hamiltonian is obtained by integrating the Hamiltonian density over the entire volume of the field:

$$\begin{aligned} H &= \int \mathcal{K} \, d\tau \\ &= \frac{\epsilon}{2} \int \left[\frac{\mathbf{p} \cdot \mathbf{p}}{\epsilon^2} + v^2 (\text{curl } \mathbf{A}) \cdot (\text{curl } \mathbf{A}) - \frac{2\mathbf{p}}{\epsilon} \cdot \nabla \phi \right] d\tau \\ &= \frac{\epsilon}{2} \int \left[\frac{\mathbf{p} \cdot \mathbf{p}}{\epsilon^2} + v^2 (\text{curl } \mathbf{A}) \cdot (\text{curl } \mathbf{A}) \right] d\tau - \iint \phi \mathbf{p} \cdot d\mathbf{S} \quad (16\text{-}63) \end{aligned}$$

where dS is an element of the surface S which bounds the volume τ and use has been made of the condition div **E** = 0. The surface integral in (16-63) vanishes because **p** either vanishes sufficiently rapidly at infinity or obeys suitable boundary conditions at the surface of a finite volume.

The Hamiltonian is then

$$H = \frac{\epsilon}{2} \int \left[\frac{\mathbf{p} \cdot \mathbf{p}}{\epsilon^2} + v^2(\text{curl } \mathbf{A}) \cdot (\text{curl } \mathbf{A}) \right] d\tau$$

$$= \frac{1}{2} \int [\epsilon \mathbf{E} \cdot \mathbf{E} + \mu^{-1}\mathbf{B} \cdot \mathbf{B}] \, d\tau$$

the total energy in the electromagnetic field.

16-6. PLANE-WAVE REPRESENTATION OF THE PURE RADIATION FIELD

According to (16-58) the Hamiltonian density for the pure radiation field is given by

$$\mathcal{3C} = \frac{\epsilon}{2}\left[\frac{\mathbf{p}_s \cdot \mathbf{p}_s}{\epsilon^2} + v^2(\text{curl } \mathbf{A}_s) \cdot (\text{curl } \mathbf{A}_s) \right] \qquad (16\text{-}58)$$

in the solenoidal gauge. The Hamiltonian is then

$$H = \iiint \frac{\epsilon}{2}\left[\frac{\mathbf{p}_s \cdot \mathbf{p}_s}{\epsilon^2} + v^2(\text{curl } \mathbf{A}_s) \cdot (\text{curl } \mathbf{A}_s) \right] d\tau \qquad (16\text{-}64)$$

where the integration is over the entire volume of the field.

For many purposes it is convenient to think of the radiation field as being confined to a large cubical box of volume L^3 and to then require that the field variables $\mathbf{p}_s$ and $\mathbf{A}_s$ satisfy periodic boundary conditions at the walls of the box. This permits the expansion of the field variables in terms of plane waves; i.e.,

$$\mathbf{A}_s(\mathbf{r},t) = \sqrt{\mu} \sum_{\mathbf{k},\lambda} [q_{\mathbf{k}\lambda}(t)\mathbf{u}_{\mathbf{k}\lambda}(\mathbf{r}) + q_{\mathbf{k}\lambda}^*(t)\mathbf{u}_{\mathbf{k}\lambda}^*(\mathbf{r})] \qquad (16\text{-}65)$$

$$\mathbf{p}_s(\mathbf{r},t) = \sqrt{\epsilon} \sum_{\mathbf{k},\lambda} [p_{\mathbf{k}\lambda}(t)\mathbf{u}_{\mathbf{k}\lambda}(\mathbf{r}) + p_{\mathbf{k}\lambda}^*(t)\mathbf{u}_{\mathbf{k}\lambda}^*(\mathbf{r})] \qquad (16\text{-}66)$$

where the $q_{\mathbf{k}\lambda}$ and $p_{\mathbf{k}\lambda}$ are functions of the time alone and the

$$\mathbf{u}_{\mathbf{k}\lambda}(\mathbf{r}) = \frac{1}{L^{3/2}} \mathbf{i}_{\mathbf{k}\lambda} e^{i\mathbf{k}\cdot\mathbf{r}} \qquad (16\text{-}67)$$

depend on the space coordinates only. The summations in (16-65) and (16-66) extend over only half the $\mathbf{k}$ space. The $\mathbf{i}_{\mathbf{k}\lambda}$ are unit vectors, $\mathbf{k}$ is a vector in the direction of propagation and has components

$$k_i = \frac{2\pi n_i}{L} \qquad i = 1, 2, 3 \qquad n_i = 0, \pm 1, \pm 2, \ldots$$

and the asterisks denote complex conjugates. The $\mathbf{u}_{k\lambda}$ satisfy the ortho-normality relation

$$\iiint \mathbf{u}_{k\lambda}^* \cdot \mathbf{u}_{k'\lambda'}\, d\tau \;=\; \delta_{kk'}\delta_{\lambda\lambda'} \tag{16-68}$$

Substitution of (16-65) into the wave equation

$$\nabla^2 \mathbf{A}_s \;-\; \frac{1}{v^2}\frac{\partial^2}{\partial t^2}\,\mathbf{A}_s \;=\; 0$$

gives the equation of harmonic motion

$$\ddot{q}_{k\lambda} + k^2 v^2 q_{k\lambda} = 0$$

with a corresponding equation for $q_{k\lambda}^*$. Hence

$$q_{k\lambda}(t) = q_{k\lambda}(0)e^{-ikvt}$$
$$\dot{q}_{k\lambda}(t) = -ikv q_{k\lambda}(t)$$

Since

$$p_{si} = \epsilon \frac{\partial}{\partial t} A_{si} \qquad i = 1, 2, 3 \tag{16-57}$$

it follows from (16-65) and (16-66) that

$$p_{k\lambda}(t) = \sqrt{\epsilon\mu}\;\dot{q}_{k\lambda}(t) = -ik q_{k\lambda}(t) \tag{16-69}$$

Substitution of (16-65) and (16-67) into

$$\operatorname{div}\mathbf{A}_s = 0 \tag{16-53}$$

gives

$$\operatorname{div}\mathbf{u}_{k\lambda} = \operatorname{div}\mathbf{u}_{k\lambda}^* = 0 \tag{16-70}$$

and

$$\mathbf{k}\cdot\mathbf{u}_{k\lambda} = \mathbf{k}\cdot\mathbf{u}_{k\lambda}^* = 0 \tag{16-71}$$

Thus, to each vector $\mathbf{k}$ there are two vectors $\mathbf{u}_{k1}$ and $\mathbf{u}_{k2}$ (or, equivalently, two unit vectors $\mathbf{i}_{k1}$ and $\mathbf{i}_{k2}$) orthogonal to $\mathbf{k}$ and to each other [by (16-68)].

Substitution of (16-65) and (16-66) into (16-64) gives

$$H = \sum_{k,\lambda} (p_{k\lambda}p_{k\lambda}^* + k^2 q_{k\lambda}q_{k\lambda}^*) \tag{16-72}$$

If we introduce real canonical variables $P_{k\lambda}$ and $Q_{k\lambda}$ by means of the definitions

$$Q_{k\lambda} = q_{k\lambda} + q_{k\lambda}^*$$
$$P_{k\lambda} = p_{k\lambda} + p_{k\lambda}^* = -ik(q_{k\lambda} - q_{k\lambda}^*)$$

(16-72) becomes

$$H = \sum_{k,\lambda} \tfrac{1}{2}(P_{k\lambda}{}^2 + k^2 Q_{k\lambda}{}^2) \tag{16-73}$$

Thus the Hamiltonian for the radiation field can be expressed as the sum of Hamiltonians of harmonic oscillators. In this way the radiation field is represented as an assembly of independent harmonic oscillators.

16-7. CHARGED PARTICLE IN AN ELECTROMAGNETIC FIELD

Consider the motion of a particle of rest mass m_0 and charge q in an arbitrary electromagnetic field. When the velocity of the particle is $\mathbf{u}$, its momentum is (cf. Sec. 7-8)

$$m\mathbf{u} = \frac{m_0}{\sqrt{1 - u^2/c^2}} \, \mathbf{u} \tag{16-74}$$

The force experienced by the particle is the Lorentz force

$$\mathbf{F} = q(\mathbf{E} + \mathbf{u} \times \mathbf{B}) \tag{16-75}$$

where it should be noted that the field whose electric and magnetic vectors are $\mathbf{E}$ and $\mathbf{B}$, respectively, is the sum of the external field and the field produced by the charged particle itself.

The equation of motion is then

$$\frac{d}{dt}(m\mathbf{u}) = q(\mathbf{E} + \mathbf{u} \times \mathbf{B})$$

or, substituting for $\mathbf{B}$ and $\mathbf{E}$ by means of (9-49) and (9-51),

$$\frac{d}{dt}(m\mathbf{u}) - q\left[-\frac{\partial \mathbf{A}}{\partial t} - \boldsymbol{\nabla}\phi + \mathbf{u} \times (\text{curl } \mathbf{A})\right]$$

But

$$\frac{d}{dt}\mathbf{A} = \frac{\partial}{\partial t}\mathbf{A} + (\mathbf{u} \cdot \boldsymbol{\nabla})\mathbf{A}$$

Hence

$$\frac{d}{dt}(m\mathbf{u} + q\mathbf{A}) = q[(\mathbf{u} \cdot \boldsymbol{\nabla})\mathbf{A} - \boldsymbol{\nabla}\phi + \mathbf{u} \times (\text{curl } \mathbf{A})]$$
$$= q\boldsymbol{\nabla}(\phi - \mathbf{u} \cdot \mathbf{A}) \tag{16-76}$$

If this equation of motion is taken as a Lagrange equation of motion [cf. Eq. (16-1)], then the generalized momenta p_i ($i = 1, 2, 3$) must be defined by

$$p_i = \frac{\partial L}{\partial u_i} = mu_i + qA_i \tag{16-77}$$

where L is the as yet undetermined Lagrangian for the particle in the electromagnetic field, and

$$\dot{p}_i = \frac{d}{dt}\left(\frac{\partial L}{\partial u_i}\right) = \frac{\partial L}{\partial x_i} = -q\frac{\partial}{\partial x_i}(\phi - \mathbf{u} \cdot \mathbf{A}) \tag{16-78}$$

Hence the Lagrangian is

$$L = -m_0 c^2 \sqrt{1 - u^2/c^2} - q\phi + q(\mathbf{u} \cdot \mathbf{A}) \tag{16-79}$$

The reader should note that, while the Lagrangian (16-79) satisfies Lagrange's equation of motion (16-1), it is not of the form (16-2) where the potential energy is independent of velocity. Since the kinetic energy of a particle with rest mass m_0 moving with velocity $\mathbf{u}$ is

$$T = m_0c^2 \left(\frac{1}{\sqrt{1 - u^2/c^2}} - 1 \right) \qquad (7\text{-}39)$$

it follows that, if the Lagrangian (16-79) is defined by

$$L = T - V \qquad (16\text{-}2)$$

then the potential energy V must be velocity dependent. Thus one must either allow velocity-dependent potential energies or adopt the point of view that a function $L(q_i, \dot{q}_i, t)$ is to be called a Lagrangian if, when substituted into Lagrange's equation (16-1), the correct equation of motion is produced.

The Hamiltonian is given by

$$\begin{aligned} H &= \mathbf{p} \cdot \mathbf{u} - L \\ &= mu^2 + m_0c^2 \sqrt{1 - \frac{u^2}{c^2}} + q\phi \\ &= \frac{m_0c^2}{\sqrt{1 - u^2/c^2}} + q\phi \end{aligned} \qquad (16\text{-}80)$$

$$H = c\sqrt{m_0^2c^2 + (\mathbf{p} - q\mathbf{A}) \cdot (\mathbf{p} - q\mathbf{A})} + q\phi \qquad (16\text{-}81)$$

where use has been made of (16-77). It is interesting to note that, regardless of the interpretation of the Lagrangian, under certain conditions this Hamiltonian may be equal to the total energy of the particle. The first term in the Hamiltonian expression (16-80) is mc^2, the sum of the rest and kinetic energies of the particle. If the vector potential $\mathbf{A}$ does not depend on the time explicitly, the expression (9-51) for the electric field intensity reduces to $\mathbf{E} = -\nabla\phi$ and, consequently, $q\phi$ is the potential energy of the charged particle.

The Lagrangian and Hamiltonian for a system of n charges q_k with rest masses m_{0k} and velocities $\mathbf{u}_k$ are obtained by summing (16-79) and (16-81), respectively, over all the charges:

$$L = \sum_{k=1}^{n} L_k = \sum_{k=1}^{n} \left[-m_{0k}c^2 \sqrt{1 - \frac{u_k^2}{c^2}} - q_k\phi_k + q_k(\mathbf{u}_k \cdot \mathbf{A}_k) \right] \qquad (16\text{-}82)$$

$$H = \sum_{k=1}^{n} H_k = \sum_{k=1}^{n} \left[c\sqrt{m_{0k}^2c^2 + (\mathbf{p}_k - q_k\mathbf{A}_k) \cdot (\mathbf{p}_k - q_k\mathbf{A}_k)} + q_k\phi_k \right]$$

$$(16\text{-}83)$$

where the subscripts on ϕ and $\mathbf{A}$ indicate that they are to be evaluated at the positions of the particles.

The charge density ρ and current density $\mathbf{j}$ for the system of n charges can now be introduced by use of the Dirac delta function (cf. Sec. 1-14):

$$\rho(\mathbf{r}) = \sum_{k=1}^{n} q_k \delta(\mathbf{r} - \mathbf{r}_k) \tag{16-84}$$

$$\mathbf{j}(\mathbf{r}) = \sum_{k=1}^{n} q_k \mathbf{u}_k \delta(\mathbf{r} - \mathbf{r}_k) \tag{16-85}$$

where $\mathbf{r}_k$ is the position vector for the kth particle.   Then

$$\int \rho(\mathbf{r}) \phi(\mathbf{r}) \, d\tau = \sum_{k=1}^{n} \int q_k \phi(\mathbf{r}) \delta(\mathbf{r} - \mathbf{r}_k) \, d\tau = \sum_{k=1}^{n} q_k \phi_k$$

$$\int \mathbf{j}(\mathbf{r}) \cdot \mathbf{A}(\mathbf{r}) \, d\tau = \sum_{k=1}^{n} \int q_k \mathbf{u}_k \cdot \mathbf{A}(\mathbf{r}) \delta(\mathbf{r} - \mathbf{r}_k) \, d\tau = \sum_{k=1}^{n} q_k \mathbf{u}_k \cdot \mathbf{A}_k$$

where the integration is over the volume of the electromagnetic field. Hence, the relations (16-82) and (16-83) can be written

$$L = - \sum_{k=1}^{n} m_{0k} c^2 \sqrt{1 - \frac{u_k{}^2}{c^2}} - \int [\rho(\mathbf{r}) \phi(\mathbf{r}) - \mathbf{j}(\mathbf{r}) \cdot \mathbf{A}(\mathbf{r})] \, d\tau \tag{16-86}$$

$$H = c \sum_{k=1}^{n} \sqrt{m_{0k}{}^2 c^2 + (\mathbf{p}_k - q_k \mathbf{A}_k) \cdot (\mathbf{p}_k - q_k \mathbf{A}_k)} + \int \rho(\mathbf{r}) \phi(\mathbf{r}) \, d\tau$$

$$\tag{16-87}$$

In the nonrelativistic approximation these relations reduce to

$$L = \tfrac{1}{2} \sum_{k=1}^{n} m_{0k} u_k{}^2 - \int [\rho(\mathbf{r}) \phi(\mathbf{r}) - \mathbf{j}(r) \cdot \mathbf{A}(r)] \, d\tau \tag{16-88}$$

$$H = \tfrac{1}{2} \sum_{k=1}^{n} \frac{1}{m_{0k}} (\mathbf{p}_k - q_k \mathbf{A}_k) \cdot (\mathbf{p}_k - q_k \mathbf{A}_k) + \int \rho(\mathbf{r}) \phi(\mathbf{r}) \, d\tau \tag{16-89}$$

respectively, where we have omitted the constant term $m_{0k} c^2$.

16-8. THE GENERAL ELECTROMAGNETIC FIELD

Maxwell's equations in a homogeneous isotropic medium containing charges and currents with densities ρ and $\mathbf{j}$, respectively, are

$$\operatorname{curl} \mathbf{B} = \mu\left(\mathbf{j} + \frac{\partial}{\partial t}\mathbf{D}\right) = \mu\mathbf{j} + \frac{1}{v^2}\frac{\partial}{\partial t}\mathbf{E} \tag{16-90}$$

$$\operatorname{curl} \mathbf{E} = -\frac{\partial}{\partial t}\mathbf{B} \tag{16-91}$$

$$\operatorname{div} \mathbf{B} = 0 \tag{16-92}$$

$$\operatorname{div} \mathbf{E} = \frac{\rho}{\epsilon} \tag{16-93}$$

We assume that the Lagrangian for the general electromagnetic field consists of two terms, one for the pure radiation field and the other for the interaction of the charges and currents with the field. The first term is obtained by integration of (16-51) over the volume of the field. The second term is given by the second term in the Lagrangian (16-86). Then

$$L = \frac{\epsilon}{2}\int\left[\left(\frac{\partial \mathbf{A}}{\partial t} + \boldsymbol{\nabla}\phi\right)\cdot\left(\frac{\partial \mathbf{A}}{\partial t} + \boldsymbol{\nabla}\phi\right) - v^2(\operatorname{curl} \mathbf{A})\cdot(\operatorname{curl} \mathbf{A})\right]d\tau$$
$$- \int(\rho\phi - \mathbf{j}\cdot\mathbf{A})\,d\tau \tag{16-94}$$

Note that the Lagrangian density

$$\mathfrak{L} = \frac{\epsilon}{2}\left[\left(\frac{\partial \mathbf{A}}{\partial t} + \boldsymbol{\nabla}\phi\right)\cdot\left(\frac{\partial \mathbf{A}}{\partial t} + \boldsymbol{\nabla}\phi\right) - v^2(\operatorname{curl} \mathbf{A})\cdot(\operatorname{curl} \mathbf{A})\right]$$
$$- \rho\phi + \mathbf{j}\cdot\mathbf{A} \tag{16-95}$$

differs from the Lagrangian densities which we have considered thus far in that it is a function of ϕ and $\mathbf{A}$ as well as their derivatives. In such a case the Lagrangian equation of motion is (cf. Sec. 16-3)

$$\frac{\partial}{\partial t}\left(\frac{\partial \mathfrak{L}}{\partial \dot{q}_i}\right) + \sum_{j=1}^{3}\frac{\partial}{\partial x_j}\left[\frac{\partial \mathfrak{L}}{\partial(\partial q_i/\partial x_j)}\right] - \frac{\partial \mathfrak{L}}{\partial q_i} = 0 \tag{16-96}$$

Since

$$\frac{\partial \mathfrak{L}}{\partial \phi} = -\rho \qquad \frac{\partial \mathfrak{L}}{\partial \dot{\phi}} = 0$$

and

$$\sum_{j=1}^{3}\frac{\partial}{\partial x_j}\left[\frac{\partial \mathfrak{L}}{\partial(\partial \phi/\partial x_j)}\right] = \epsilon\operatorname{div}\left(\frac{\partial \mathbf{A}}{\partial t} + \boldsymbol{\nabla}\phi\right) = -\epsilon\operatorname{div}\mathbf{E}$$

the Lagrangian equation of motion corresponding to the field variable ϕ is

$$\text{div } \mathbf{E} = \frac{\rho}{\epsilon}$$

the Maxwell equation (16-93).

The Lagrangian equations of motion corresponding to the field variables A_i are

$$\frac{\partial}{\partial t}\left(\frac{\partial \mathcal{L}}{\partial \dot{A}_i}\right) + \sum_{j=1}^{3}\frac{\partial}{\partial x_j}\left[\frac{\partial \mathcal{L}}{\partial(\partial A_i/\partial x_j)}\right] - \frac{\partial \mathcal{L}}{\partial A_i} = 0 \qquad i = 1, 2, 3$$

or

$$\text{curl curl } \mathbf{A} + \frac{1}{v^2}\frac{\partial}{\partial t}\left(\frac{\partial \mathbf{A}}{\partial t} + \nabla\phi\right) - \frac{1}{\epsilon v^2}\mathbf{j} = 0$$

which is the Maxwell equation (16-90). The Maxwell equations (16-91) and (16-92) are satisfied because of the definitions of $\mathbf{E}$ and $\mathbf{B}$ in terms of ϕ and $\mathbf{A}$.

EXERCISES

16-1. Verify that the total Lagrangian which describes both the mechanical motion of n charged particles q_k with rest masses m_{0k} and velocities $\mathbf{u}_k$ and the electromagnetic field is

$$L = \frac{\epsilon}{2}\int\left[\left(\frac{\partial \mathbf{A}}{\partial t} + \nabla\phi\right)\cdot\left(\frac{\partial \mathbf{A}}{\partial t} + \nabla\phi\right) - v^2\,(\text{curl } \mathbf{A})\cdot(\text{curl } \mathbf{A})\right]d\tau$$

$$- \sum_{k=1}^{n} m_{0k}c^2\sqrt{1 - \frac{u_k^2}{c^2}} - \sum_{k=1}^{n} q_k(\phi_k - \mathbf{u}_k\cdot\mathbf{A}_k) \quad (16\text{-}97)$$

Note that the first term represents the Lagrangian for the field in the absence of the charged particles, the second term the Lagrangian of the particles in the absence of the field, and the third term the mutual interaction between particles and field.

The Lagrangian in the nonrelativistic approximation is obtained from (16-97) by replacing $-m_{0k}c^2\sqrt{1 - u_k^2/c^2}$ by $\frac{1}{2}m_{0k}u_k^2$.

16-2. Verify that the total Hamiltonian corresponding to the total Lagrangian (16-97) is

$$H = \frac{\epsilon}{2}\int\left[\frac{\mathbf{p}\cdot\mathbf{p}}{\epsilon^2} + v^2\,(\text{curl } \mathbf{A})\cdot(\text{curl } \mathbf{A}) - 2\frac{\mathbf{p}}{\epsilon}\cdot\nabla\phi\right]d\tau$$

$$+ \sum_{k} c\sqrt{m_{0k}^2c^2 + (\mathbf{p}_k - q_k\mathbf{A}_k)\cdot(\mathbf{p}_k - q_k\mathbf{A}_k)} + \sum_{k} q_k\phi_k \quad (16\text{-}98)$$

where

$$\mathbf{p} = \epsilon\left(\frac{\partial \mathbf{A}}{\partial t} + \nabla\phi\right)$$

$$\mathbf{p}_k = m_k\mathbf{u}_k + q_k\mathbf{A}_k = \frac{m_{0k}}{\sqrt{1 - u_k^2/c^2}}\mathbf{u}_k + q_k\mathbf{A}_k$$

and that it reduces to

$$H = \frac{\epsilon}{2} \int \left[\frac{\mathbf{p} \cdot \mathbf{p}}{2} + v^2 \, (\text{curl } \mathbf{A}) \cdot (\text{curl } \mathbf{A}) - 2 \frac{\mathbf{p}}{\epsilon} \cdot \nabla \phi \right] d\tau$$
$$+ \frac{1}{2} \sum_k \frac{1}{m_{0k}} \, (\mathbf{p}_k - q_k \mathbf{A}_k) \cdot (\mathbf{p}_k - q_k \mathbf{A}_k) + \sum_k q_k \phi_k$$

where

$$\mathbf{p}_k = m_{0k} \mathbf{u}_k + q_k \mathbf{A}_k$$

in the nonrelativistic approximation.

16-3. In the case of the general electromagnetic field it is still possible to transform to the solenoidal gauge. However, the scalar potential now turns out to be the static Coulomb potential instead of a constant (cf. Sec. 9-11). Verify that the sum of the first and third terms in the Hamiltonian (16-98) can be expressed as the sum of Hamiltonians of harmonic oscillators and the Coulomb energy $\frac{1}{2} \sum_{i,k} \frac{q_i q_k}{r_{ik}}$, where r_{ik} represents the separation of the ith and kth particles.

16-4. Instead of transforming to the solenoidal gauge, use Helmholtz's theorem (cf. Sec. 1-13) to write

$$\mathbf{A} = \mathbf{A}_s + \mathbf{A}_r$$

where div $\mathbf{A}_s = 0$ and curl $\mathbf{A}_r = 0$. Then verify that the sum of the first and third terms in the Hamiltonian (16-98) can be expressed as the sum of Hamiltonians of harmonic oscillators corresponding to transverse ($\mathbf{A}_s$), longitudinal ($\mathbf{A}_r$), and scalar (ϕ) waves.

REFERENCES

Goldstein, H.: "Classical Mechanics," chaps. 1 and 11, Addison-Wesley Publishing Company, Inc., Cambridge, Mass., 1950.
Heitler, W.: "The Quantum Theory of Radiation," 3d ed., chap. 1, Oxford University Press, London, 1954.
Panofsky, W. K. H., and M. Phillips: "Classical Electricity and Magnetism," chap. 24, Addison-Wesley Publishing Company, Inc., Cambridge, Mass., 1955.
Schiff, L. I.: "Quantum Mechanics," 2d ed., chaps. 13 and 14, McGraw-Hill Book Company, Inc., New York, 1955.

CHAPTER 17

Electron Theory

17-1. INTRODUCTION

Except for some minor digressions, primarily in the discussion of polarization, the theory presented thus far has been the macroscopic theory of Maxwell. In this theory the electromagnetic properties of different substances are expressed in terms of three experimentally determined quantities, the permittivity ϵ, the permeability μ, and the conductivity σ. Since these fundamental quantities are experimentally determined, the Maxwell theory cannot explain the dependence of the electromagnetic properties of substances on such variables as temperature, density, crystalline state, etc. The explanation lies in the domain of the microscopic Lorentz theory of electrons which we discuss in the present chapter. In this theory, the electron is taken as the fundamental unit of charge and the principles of mechanics are used to explain the electromagnetic properties of substances.

17-2. RADIATION FROM A MOVING ELECTRON

The electromagnetic field due to a moving charge is easily obtained from the expressions (9-63) and (9-64) for the retarded potentials. In the case of vacuum these can be written

$$\mathbf{A}(\mathbf{r},t) = \frac{\mu_0}{4\pi} \int \frac{\mathbf{j}(\mathbf{r}',t - |\mathbf{r} - \mathbf{r}'|/c)}{|\mathbf{r} - \mathbf{r}'|} \, d\mathbf{r}' \tag{17-1}$$

$$\phi(\mathbf{r},t) = \frac{1}{4\pi\epsilon_0} \int \frac{\rho_F(\mathbf{r}',t - |\mathbf{r} - \mathbf{r}'|/c)}{|\mathbf{r} - \mathbf{r}'|} \, d\mathbf{r}' \tag{17-2}$$

in which

$$\mathbf{r} = x_1\mathbf{i}_i + x_2\mathbf{i}_2 + x_3\mathbf{i}_3 \qquad \mathbf{r}' = x_1'\mathbf{i}_1 + x_2'\mathbf{i}_2 + x_3'\mathbf{i}_3$$
$$d\mathbf{r}' = dx_1' \, dx_2' \, dx_3'$$

and c is the velocity of light in vacuum.

Suppose that at time t_0 the electron is at position $\mathbf{r}_0$ and is moving with

271

a velocity $\mathbf{u}(t_0)$. Then (17-2) can be written

$$\phi(\mathbf{r},t) = \frac{1}{4\pi\epsilon_0} \iint \frac{\rho_F(\mathbf{r}',t_0)\,\delta[t_0 - (t - |\mathbf{r} - \mathbf{r}'|/c)]}{|\mathbf{r} - \mathbf{r}'|} \, dt_0 \, d\mathbf{r}'$$

or, since

$$\rho_F(\mathbf{r}',t_0) = -e\delta(\mathbf{r}' - \mathbf{r}_0)$$

where $-e$ is the charge on the electron

$$\phi(\mathbf{r},t) = \frac{-e}{4\pi\epsilon_0} \int \frac{\delta[t_0 - (t - |\mathbf{r} - \mathbf{r}_0|/c)]}{|\mathbf{r} - \mathbf{r}_0|} \, dt_0 \qquad (17\text{-}3)$$

Now let

$$\xi = t_0 - t + \frac{|\mathbf{r} - \mathbf{r}_0|}{c} \equiv t_0 - t + \frac{R}{c}$$

so that at constant t

$$\frac{\partial\xi}{\partial t_0} = 1 + \frac{1}{c}\frac{\partial R}{\partial t_0} = 1 - \frac{\mathbf{R}\cdot\mathbf{u}}{RC}$$

where $\mathbf{R} = \mathbf{r} - \mathbf{r}_0$. Substitution into (17-3) then gives

$$\phi(\mathbf{r},t) = -\frac{e}{4\pi\epsilon_0} \int \frac{\delta(\xi)\,d\xi}{R - (\mathbf{R}\cdot\mathbf{u})/c}$$

$$= -\frac{e}{4\pi\epsilon_0} \frac{1}{R - \dfrac{\mathbf{R}\cdot\mathbf{u}}{c}}\Bigg|_{t_0 = t - R/c} \qquad (17\text{-}4)$$

In a like manner when $\mathbf{j}$ is replaced by $\rho_F\mathbf{u}$ in (17-1), the expression can be reduced to

$$\mathbf{A}(\mathbf{r},t) = -\frac{e\mu_0}{4\pi} \frac{\mathbf{u}}{R - \dfrac{\mathbf{R}\cdot\mathbf{u}}{c}}\Bigg|_{t_0 = t - R/c} \qquad (17\text{-}5)$$

These expressions for the scalar and vector potentials of a moving point charge were first obtained by Liénard and Wiechart. Particular attention should be paid to the fact that R, $\mathbf{R}$, and $\mathbf{u}$ in (17-4) and (17-5) are functions of the retarded time $t_0 = t - R/c$.

The field vectors $\mathbf{E}$ and $\mathbf{B}$ can be obtained from the relations

$$\mathbf{E} = -\frac{\partial}{\partial t}\mathbf{A} - \nabla\phi \qquad (9\text{-}51)$$

$$\mathbf{B} = \nabla \times \mathbf{A} \qquad (9\text{-}49)$$

However, when these relations are used, it should be noted that $\partial/\partial t$ represents differentiation with respect to t at constant $\mathbf{R}$ and ∇ represents partial differentiation at constant t. In order to apply (9-51) and (9-49) to (17-4) and (17-5), we must therefore first transform $\partial/\partial t$ and ∇. Thus

$$t_0 = t - \frac{R}{c}$$

so that

$$\frac{\partial R}{\partial t} = c\left(1 - \frac{\partial t_0}{\partial t}\right) = \frac{\partial R}{\partial t_0}\frac{\partial t_0}{\partial t}$$

But

$$\frac{\partial R}{\partial t_0} = -\frac{\mathbf{R}\cdot\mathbf{u}}{R}$$

Therefore

$$c\left(1 - \frac{\partial t_0}{\partial t}\right) = -\frac{R}{\mathbf{R}\cdot\mathbf{u}}\frac{\partial t_0}{\partial t}$$

or

$$\frac{\partial t_0}{\partial t} = \frac{1}{1 - (\mathbf{R}\cdot\mathbf{u})/Rc} = \frac{R}{s}$$

where

$$s \equiv R - \frac{\mathbf{R}\cdot\mathbf{u}}{c} \tag{17-6}$$

Hence

$$\frac{\partial}{\partial t} = \frac{\partial t_0}{\partial t}\frac{\partial}{\partial t_0} = \frac{R}{s}\frac{\partial}{\partial t_0} \tag{17-7}$$

Similarly

$$\nabla R = -c\,\nabla t_0 = \nabla_0 R + \frac{\partial R}{\partial t_0}\nabla t_0$$

$$= \frac{\mathbf{R}}{R} - \frac{\mathbf{R}\cdot\mathbf{u}}{R}\nabla t_0$$

where ∇_0 represents the gradient at constant t_0. Hence

$$\nabla t_0 = -\frac{\mathbf{R}}{c[R - (\mathbf{R}\cdot\mathbf{u})/c]} = -\frac{\mathbf{R}}{cs}$$

and

$$\nabla = \nabla_0 - \frac{\mathbf{R}}{cs}\frac{\partial}{\partial t_0} \tag{17-8}$$

Then

$$\mathbf{E}(\mathbf{r},t) = -\frac{e}{4\pi\epsilon_0}\left(\frac{R\dot{s}}{c^2 s^3}\mathbf{u} - \frac{R}{c^2 s^2}\dot{\mathbf{u}} + \frac{1}{s^2}\nabla_0 s - \frac{\dot{s}}{cs^3}\mathbf{R}\right)\Bigg|_{t_0 = t - R/c} \tag{17-9}$$

$$\mathbf{B}(\mathbf{r},t) = -\frac{e}{4\pi\epsilon_0}\frac{1}{Rc}\left(\mathbf{R}\times\frac{R\dot{s}}{c^2 s^3}\mathbf{u} - \mathbf{R}\times\frac{R}{c^2 s^2}\dot{\mathbf{u}}\right.$$

$$\left. + \frac{R}{cs}\nabla_0\times\mathbf{u} - \frac{R}{cs^2}\nabla_0 s\times\mathbf{u}\right)\Bigg|_{t_0 = t - R/c} \tag{17-10}$$

where the dot on s and u denotes $\partial/\partial t_0$.

Since

$$\dot{s} = \dot{R} - \frac{\dot{\mathbf{R}}\cdot\mathbf{u}}{c} - \frac{\mathbf{R}\cdot\dot{\mathbf{u}}}{c}$$

$$= -\frac{\mathbf{R}\cdot\mathbf{u}}{R} + \frac{u^2}{c} - \frac{\mathbf{R}\cdot\mathbf{u}}{c}$$

and

$$\nabla_0 s = \frac{\mathbf{R}}{R} - \frac{1}{c}\nabla_0(\mathbf{R}\cdot\mathbf{u}) = \frac{\mathbf{R}}{R} - \frac{\mathbf{u}}{c}$$

the relations (17-9) and (17-10) reduce to

$$\mathbf{E}(\mathbf{r},t) = -\frac{e}{4\pi\epsilon_0 s^3}\left\{\left(1 - \frac{u^2}{c^2}\right)\left(\mathbf{R} - \frac{\mathbf{u}}{c}R\right)\right.$$

$$\left. + \frac{1}{c^2}\mathbf{R}\times\left[\left(\mathbf{R} - \frac{\mathbf{u}}{c}R\right)\times\dot{\mathbf{u}}\right]\right\}\Bigg|_{t_0 = t - R/c} \tag{17-9a}$$

$$\mathbf{B}(\mathbf{r},t) = \frac{\mathbf{R}\times\mathbf{E}}{Rc}\Bigg|_{t_0 = t - R/c} \tag{17-10a}$$

The vector **B** is always perpendicular to both **E** and **R**, the retarded radius vector. The vector **E**, however, has components both perpendicular to and along **R**.

The two terms in the right-hand member of (17-9a) behave quite differently. For $\mathbf{u} = 0$, the first term reduces to $-e\mathbf{R}/4\pi\epsilon_0 R^3$, the electrostatic field of a point charge $-e$. For arbitrary **u** this term decreases with $1/R^2$ for large distances from the charge. The second term in the right-hand member of (17-9a) is proportional to the acceleration of the charge $\dot{\mathbf{u}}$, is perpendicular to **R**, and decreases only as $1/R$ for large distances from the charge. It represents the *radiation part* of the electric field. The region of space in which this term predominates is known as the *wave zone*.

At large distances from the point charge the fields (17-9a) and (17-10a) reduce to

$$\mathbf{E}(\mathbf{r},t) \simeq -\frac{e}{4\pi\epsilon_0 s^3 c^2}\mathbf{R}\times\left[\left(\mathbf{R} - \frac{R}{c}\mathbf{u}\right)\times\dot{\mathbf{u}}\right]\Bigg|_{t_0 = t - R/c} \tag{17-11}$$

$$\mathbf{B}(\mathbf{r},t) = \frac{\mathbf{R}\times\mathbf{E}}{Rc}\Bigg|_{t_0 = t - R/c} \tag{17-12}$$

Thus at large distances the fields **E** and **B** are both perpendicular to **R**, perpendicular to each other, and of magnitude $|\mathbf{E}| = c|\mathbf{B}|$.

The Poynting vector is then

$$\mathbf{N}(\mathbf{r},t) = \mathbf{E}\times\mathbf{H} = \frac{1}{\mu_0 Rc}\mathbf{E}\times(\mathbf{R}\times\mathbf{E})$$

$$= \frac{E^2}{\mu_0 Rc}R\Bigg|_{t_0 = t - R/c} \tag{17-13}$$

Integration of (17-13) over a sphere of radius R gives

$$\int\mathbf{N}\cdot d\mathbf{S} = \frac{e^2 R^6 \dot{u}^2}{8\pi\epsilon_0 s^6 c^3}\left[\frac{4}{3} + \frac{2}{3}\frac{u^2}{c^2} - 4\frac{(\mathbf{R}\cdot\mathbf{u})}{Rc} + 2\frac{(\mathbf{R}\cdot\mathbf{u})^2}{R^2 c^2}\right]\Bigg|_{t_0 = t - R/c} \tag{17-14}$$

as the rate at which energy is radiated by the charge. In the non-relativistic range of velocities ($u \ll c$), Eq. (17-14) reduces to

$$\int\mathbf{N}\cdot d\mathbf{S} = \frac{e^2\dot{u}^2}{6\pi\epsilon_0 c^3}\Bigg|_{t_0 = t} \tag{17-15}$$

In the case of a single charge $-e$ bound elastically to a center of force and moving with simple harmonic motion of angular frequency ω, we can set

$$\mathbf{p} = +e\mathbf{l} = (\text{real part})\mathbf{p}_0 e^{-i\omega t}$$
$$\dot{\mathbf{p}} = +e\dot{\mathbf{l}} \equiv -e\mathbf{u} = (\text{real part}) - i\omega\mathbf{p}_0 e^{-i\omega t}$$
$$\ddot{\mathbf{p}} = -e\dot{\mathbf{u}} = (\text{real part}) - \omega^2\mathbf{p}_0 e^{-i\omega t}$$

so that

$$e^2\dot{u}^2 = \omega^4 p_0{}^2 \cos^2 \omega t$$

and (17-15) becomes

$$\int \mathbf{N} \cdot d\mathbf{S} = \frac{\omega^2 p_0{}^2}{6\pi\epsilon_0 c^3} \cos^2 \omega t$$

Averaging this expression over a complete period of oscillation yields

$$\mathcal{P}_r \equiv \int \bar{\mathbf{N}} \cdot d\mathbf{S} = \frac{\omega^2 p_0{}^2}{12\pi\epsilon_0 c^3}$$

in complete agreement with (12-34) for the average energy radiated per unit time by an oscillating electric dipole.

17-3. REACTION FORCE OF THE RADIATION

According to (17-15) the energy radiated per unit time by an accelerated electron moving with small velocity is

$$\int \mathbf{N} \cdot d\mathbf{S} = \frac{e^2\dot{u}^2}{6\pi\epsilon_0 c^3}$$

Hence the energy radiated in the time interval $t_2 - t_1$ is

$$W_r = \int_{t_1}^{t_2} \frac{e^2\dot{u}^2}{6\pi\epsilon_0 c^3}\, dt$$
$$= \frac{e^2}{6\pi\epsilon_0 c^3} \left[\int_{t_1}^{t_2} d(\mathbf{u} \cdot \dot{\mathbf{u}}) - \int_{t_1}^{t_2} (\mathbf{u} \cdot \ddot{\mathbf{u}})\, dt \right]$$

If the times t_1 and t_2 are such that the state of motion of the electron is the same at t_2 as at t_1, then

$$W_r = -\frac{e^2}{6\pi\epsilon_0 c^3} \int_{t_1}^{t_2} (\mathbf{u} \cdot \ddot{\mathbf{u}})\, dt \equiv -\int_{t_1}^{t_2} \mathbf{F}_r \cdot d\mathbf{s} \qquad (17\text{-}16)$$

where $d\mathbf{s} \equiv \mathbf{u}\, dt$ and

$$\mathbf{F}_r = \frac{e^2}{6\pi\epsilon_0 c^3} \ddot{\mathbf{u}} \qquad (17\text{-}17)$$

is the *reaction force of the radiation*. It should be noted that there is only an *average* energy balance between the force and the radiation field.

As we shall see in the following section, the use of (17-17) is valid only when the reaction force is small compared with the external forces. Thus if $\mathbf{F}$ denotes the external force acting on an electron of mass m, the equation of nonrelativistic motion

$$m\dot{u} = \mathbf{F} + \frac{e^2}{6\pi\epsilon_0 c^3}\ddot{u} \qquad (17\text{-}18)$$

is valid provided that

$$|\mathbf{F}_r| \ll |\mathbf{F}| \simeq |m\dot{u}| \qquad (17\text{-}19)$$

17-4. ELECTROMAGNETIC MASS OF THE ELECTRON

The total energy W and the momentum $\mathbf{G}$ of an electromagnetic field in free space are defined by the relations

$$W = \tfrac{1}{2} \int (\epsilon_0 E^2 + \mu_0^{-1} B^2)\, d\tau \qquad (17\text{-}20)$$

and
$$\mathbf{G} = \frac{1}{c^2} \int \mathbf{E} \times \mathbf{H}\, d\tau \qquad (17\text{-}21)$$

where the integration is over the entire volume τ of the field.

Consider the electromagnetic field due to an electron at rest. Assume that the electron is a sphere of radius a. For simplicity, assume further that the charge $-e$ of the electron resides entirely on its surface. Then the fields at any point R distant from the center of the sphere are

$$\mathbf{E} = -\frac{e}{4\pi\epsilon_0}\frac{\mathbf{R}}{R^3}$$
$$\mathbf{B} = \mathbf{H} = 0 \qquad (17\text{-}22)$$

for R equal to or greater than a and zero for R less than a.

Substitution of (17-22) into (17-20) gives

$$W = \frac{e^2}{32\pi^2\epsilon_0} \int_a^\infty \int_0^\pi \int_0^{2\pi} \frac{\sin\theta}{R^2}\, dR\, d\theta\, d\varphi$$
$$= \frac{e^2}{8\pi\epsilon_0 a} \qquad (17\text{-}23)$$

for the total energy of the electromagnetic field due to the static electron. The numerical factor $\tfrac{1}{8}$ in (17-23) is a consequence of the assumption that the charge of the electron resided entirely on its surface. Different assumptions as to the distribution of charge will yield different numerical factors. For example, if it is assumed that the electron charge is distributed uniformly over the electron volume,

$$\mathbf{E} = -\frac{e}{4\pi\epsilon_0}\frac{\mathbf{R}}{a^3} \qquad \text{for } R \leq a$$

$$= -\frac{e}{4\pi\epsilon_0}\frac{\mathbf{R}}{R^3} \qquad \text{for } R \geq a \qquad (17\text{-}24)$$

$$\mathbf{B} = \mathbf{H} = 0 \qquad \text{for all } R$$

and substitution into (17-20) yields

$$W = \frac{5}{6}\frac{e^2}{8\pi\epsilon_0 a} \qquad (17\text{-}25)$$

Substitution of (17-22) into (17-21) yields

$$\mathbf{G} = 0 \qquad (17\text{-}26)$$

for the total momentum of the electromagnetic field due to the static electron.

If the rest energy $W_0 = m_0 c^2$ of the electron is of electromagnetic origin, it must be equal to the total energy in the electromagnetic field due to the static electron. Thus, for the case when the charge of the electron resides entirely on its surface,

$$W_0 = m_0 c^2 = \frac{e^2}{8\pi\epsilon_0 a} \qquad (17\text{-}27)$$

and the rest mass of the electron is given by

$$m_0 = \frac{e^2}{8\pi\epsilon_0 a c^2} \qquad (17\text{-}28)$$

The momentum $\mathbf{p}$ of the electron is equal to the total momentum, $\mathbf{G} = 0$, of the electromagnetic field.

Note that according to (17-28) when the electron radius a approaches zero, the rest mass m_0 approaches infinity. This is one of the difficulties in the classical electron theory. We shall meet with another difficulty presently.

Suppose now that the electron is moving with constant velocity $\mathbf{u}$. Its total energy and momentum are (cf. Chap. 7)

$$W = mc^2 = \frac{m_0 c^2}{\sqrt{1 - u^2/c^2}}$$

$$\mathbf{p} = m\mathbf{u} = \frac{m_0 \mathbf{u}}{\sqrt{1 - u^2/c^2}} \qquad (17\text{-}29)$$

For a slowly moving electron ($u \ll c$), these relations reduce to

$$W = m_0 c^2 \left(1 + \frac{1}{2} \frac{u^2}{c^2} \right)$$

$$\mathbf{p} = m_0 \mathbf{u}$$

$(17\text{-}30)$

Let us now see if the results (17-30) can be obtained by use of the definitions (17-20) and (17-21) and the fields for a slowly moving electron. According to the result of Exercise 17-2, the fields at any point R distant from the center of the sphere are

$$\mathbf{E} = - \frac{e}{4\pi\epsilon_0} \frac{\mathbf{R}}{R^3}$$

$$\mathbf{B} = - \frac{\mu_0 e}{4\pi} \frac{\mathbf{u} \times \mathbf{R}}{R^3}$$

$(17\text{-}31)$

for R equal to or greater than a. Substitution into (17-20) yields

$$W = \frac{e^2}{32\pi^2\epsilon_0} \int_a^\infty \int_0^\pi \int_0^{2\pi} \frac{1}{R^2} \left(1 + \frac{u^2}{c^2} \sin^2 \theta \right) \sin \theta \, dR \, d\theta \, d\varphi$$

$$= \frac{e^2}{8\pi\epsilon_0 a} \left(1 + \frac{2}{3} \frac{u^2}{c^2} \right) = m_0 c^2 \left(1 + \frac{2}{3} \frac{u^2}{c^2} \right)$$

$(17\text{-}32)$

where θ is the angle between $\mathbf{u}$ and $\mathbf{R}$. Similarly, substitution into (17-21) yields

$$\mathbf{G} = \frac{e^2}{16\pi^2\epsilon_0 c^2} \int_a^\infty \int_0^\pi \int_0^{2\pi} \frac{1}{R^2} \left(\mathbf{u} - \frac{\mathbf{R}}{R} u \cos \theta \right) \sin \theta \, dR \, d\theta \, d\varphi$$

$$= \tfrac{4}{3} m_0 \mathbf{u}$$

$(17\text{-}33)$

If we assume that the momentum of the electron is equal to the momentum (17-33) of the electromagnetic field or, equivalently, that the kinetic energy of the electron is equal to the velocity-dependent part of the total energy (17-32) of the electromagnetic field, we obtain for the rest mass of the electron

$$m_0' = \frac{4}{3} m_0 = \frac{e^2}{6\pi\epsilon_0 a c^2}$$

$(17\text{-}34)$

Thus, the definitions (17-20) and (17-21) yield the wrong rest mass in the case of the slowly moving electron.

It has been pointed out by Rohrlich[†] that this discrepancy arises because the definitions (17-20) and (17-21) are not Lorentz invariant; i.e., their form changes when a Lorentz transformation is applied. The physical reason behind this lack of invariance is that the surface of the moving electron is not spherical to an observer at rest. Rohrlich has

[†] F. Rohrlich, *Am. J. Phys.*, **28**, 639 (1960).

replaced the definitions (17-20) and (17-21) by Lorentz-invariant ones. In the nonrelativistic limit $(u \ll c)$, his expressions reduce to

$$W = \frac{1}{2} \int (\epsilon_0 E^2 + \mu_0^{-1} B^2) \, d\tau - \frac{1}{c^2} \int (\mathbf{E} \times \mathbf{H}) \cdot \mathbf{u} \, d\tau$$

$$\mathbf{G} = \frac{1}{c^2} \int \mathbf{E} \times \mathbf{H} \, d\tau + \frac{1}{c^2} \int \underline{T}^{(em)} \mathbf{u} \, d\tau$$

where the matrix $\underline{T}^{(em)}$ is the representative of the electromagnetic stress tensor (cf. Sec. 10-5). Substituting for the fields by means of (17-31) and neglecting terms in u^2/c^2, one finds that

$$W = m_0 c^2$$
$$\mathbf{G} = m_0 \mathbf{u}$$

Thus, Rohrlich's treatment yields the correct momentum of the electron. Unfortunately, if one retains the term in u^2/c^2 in the expression for the total energy, one finds that it is not $\frac{1}{2} m_0 u^2$, the kinetic energy of the electron. Rohrlich's definitions only partially resolve the discrepancy in the rest mass of the electron.

In what follows we shall consider the electron as a point charge. However, since the theory does not permit the calculation of the electron mass, we shall use the empirically determined mass. For example, in the equation of nonrelativistic motion

$$m\dot{\mathbf{u}} = \mathbf{F} + \frac{e^2}{6\pi\epsilon_0 c^3} \ddot{\mathbf{u}} \tag{17-18}$$

m is the empirical electron mass and includes the electromagnetic contribution to the mass.

17-5. EMISSION OF RADIATION

The simplest model for a source of light is an oscillating electron. For such a case the external force $\mathbf{F}$ in the nonrelativistic equation of motion (17-18) is given by

$$\mathbf{F} = -k\mathbf{r}_0 \tag{17-35}$$

where k is an appropriate Hooke's constant and $\mathbf{r}_0$ denotes the displacement of the electron from its equilibrium position. Hence, writing $\mathbf{u} = \dot{\mathbf{r}}_0$, the equation of motion (17-18) becomes

$$\dddot{\mathbf{r}}_0 - \gamma \ddot{\mathbf{r}}_0 + \omega_0^2 \mathbf{r}_0 = 0 \tag{17-36}$$

where $\omega_0 = \sqrt{k/m}$ is the (angular) frequency with which the electron would oscillate (forever) in the absence of the radiation reaction force and $\gamma \equiv e^2/6\pi m\epsilon_0 c^3$.

Since the equation of motion is valid only if the reaction force is small compared with the external force, we write in first approximation

$$\ddot{\mathbf{r}}_0 = -\omega_0{}^2\mathbf{r}_0$$

so that
$$\dddot{\mathbf{r}}_0 = -\omega_0{}^2\dot{\mathbf{r}}_0$$

and the equation of motion (17-36) becomes

$$\ddot{\mathbf{r}}_0 + \Gamma\dot{\mathbf{r}}_0 + \omega_0{}^2\mathbf{r}_0 = 0 \tag{17-37}$$

where $\Gamma \equiv \omega_0{}^2\gamma$. If $\mathbf{r}_0 = 0$ for $t < 0$ and $\mathbf{r}_0 = \mathbf{A}$ at $t = 0$, then the solution of (17-37) is

$$\mathbf{r}_0 = \mathbf{A}e^{-\Gamma t/2} \cos \sqrt{\omega_0{}^2 - \left(\frac{\Gamma}{2}\right)^2}\, t \tag{17-38}$$

Since the reaction force is small compared with the external force, $\Gamma \ll \omega_0{}^2$ and (17-38) can be approximated by

$$\begin{aligned}
\mathbf{r}_0 &\doteq \mathbf{A}e^{-\Gamma t/2} \cos \omega_0 t \\
&= (\text{real part})\mathbf{A}e^{-\Gamma t/2}e^{-i\omega_0 t}
\end{aligned} \tag{17-39}$$

Then
$$\dot{\mathbf{r}}_0 = -\left(i\omega_0 + \frac{\Gamma}{2}\right)\mathbf{A}e^{-\Gamma t/2}e^{-i\omega_0 t}$$

$$\ddot{\mathbf{r}}_0 = \left(i\omega_0 + \frac{\Gamma}{2}\right)^2 \mathbf{A}e^{-\Gamma t/2}e^{-i\omega_0 t}$$

The total energy of the oscillator is

$$W = \tfrac{1}{2}(m\dot{r}_0{}^2 + kr_0{}^2)$$

and the average over a period of oscillation is

$$\bar{W} \doteq \tfrac{1}{2}m\omega_0{}^2 A^2 e^{-\Gamma t} \tag{17-40}$$

Thus $1/\Gamma$ is the time required for the average energy of the oscillator to decrease to $1/e$th of its original value.

According to (17-15) the rate at which energy is radiated by the oscillating electron is

$$\frac{e^2\dot{u}^2}{6\pi\epsilon_0 c^3} = \frac{e^2\ddot{r}_0{}^2}{6\pi\epsilon_0 c^3}$$

The total energy radiated by the electron is then

$$W = \frac{e^2}{6\pi\epsilon_0 c^3} \int_{-\infty}^{+\infty} \ddot{r}_0{}^2\, dt \tag{17-41}$$

In order to evaluate (17-41) we shall make use of the *convolution* or *Faltung theorem for Fourier transforms:* If $f(t)$ and $\bar{f}(\omega)$ and $g(t)$ and $\bar{g}(\omega)$ are, respectively, Fourier transforms of one another, then the Fourier transform of the product fg is

$$\int_{-\infty}^{+\infty} f(t)g(t)e^{+i\omega t}\,dt = \int_{-\infty}^{+\infty} \bar{g}(\tau)\bar{f}(\omega - \tau)\,d\tau \qquad (17\text{-}42)$$

To verify (17-42) note that

$$\int_{-\infty}^{+\infty} \bar{g}(\tau)\bar{f}(\omega - \tau)\,d\tau = \frac{1}{\sqrt{2\pi}}\int_{-\infty}^{+\infty} \bar{g}(\tau)\,d\tau \int_{-\infty}^{+\infty} f(t)e^{i(\omega-\tau)t}\,dt$$

$$= \frac{1}{\sqrt{2\pi}}\int_{-\infty}^{+\infty} f(t)e^{i\omega t}\,dt \int_{-\infty}^{+\infty} \bar{g}(\tau)e^{-i t\tau}\,d\tau$$

$$= \int_{-\infty}^{+\infty} f(t)g(t)e^{+i\omega t}\,dt$$

In the special case when $\omega = 0$, (17-42) reduces to

$$\int_{-\infty}^{+\infty} f(t)g(t)\,dt = \int_{-\infty}^{+\infty} \bar{g}(\tau)\bar{f}(-\tau)\,d\tau \qquad (17\text{-}43)$$

Hence (17-41) becomes

$$W = \frac{e^2}{6\pi\epsilon_0 c^3}\int_{-\infty}^{+\infty} |\ddot{\mathbf{r}}_0(\omega)|^2\,d\omega \equiv \int_{-\infty}^{+\infty} I(\omega)\,d\omega \qquad (17\text{-}44)$$

where $\quad \ddot{\mathbf{r}}_0(\omega) = \dfrac{1}{\sqrt{2\pi}}\displaystyle\int_{-\infty}^{+\infty} \ddot{\mathbf{r}}_0(t)e^{i\omega t}\,dt = \dfrac{1}{\sqrt{2\pi}}\displaystyle\int_{0}^{\infty} \ddot{\mathbf{r}}_0(t)e^{i\omega t}\,dt$

$$= \frac{(i\omega_0 + \Gamma/2)^2\mathbf{A}}{i(\omega - \omega_0) + \Gamma/2}$$

where we have substituted for $\ddot{\mathbf{r}}_0(t)$ and used the fact that $\ddot{\mathbf{r}}_0(t) = 0$ for $t < 0$. Then the *spectral energy distribution function* $I(\omega)$ is given by

$$I(\omega) = \frac{e^2}{6\pi\epsilon_0 c^3}|\ddot{\mathbf{r}}_0(\omega)|^2 \doteq \frac{e^2\omega_0^4}{6\pi\epsilon_0 c^3}\frac{A^2}{(\omega - \omega_0)^2 + (\Gamma/2)^2} \qquad (17\text{-}45)$$

Note that $I(\omega)$ has a maximum for the (angular) frequency ω_0 of the undamped oscillator and falls off on either side of ω_0 approximately as $(\omega - \omega_0)^{-2}$. Since $I(\omega) = \frac{1}{2}I(\omega_0)$ when $\omega = \omega_0 \pm \Gamma/2$, Γ is called the *width at half maximum* or simply the width of the spectral line. As we have already seen, Γ is also the reciprocal of the time required for the average energy of the oscillator to decrease to $1/e$th of its initial value. Hence Γ is also known as the *reciprocal lifetime*.

17-6. FORCED OSCILLATION OF A CHARGED HARMONIC OSCILLATOR

Let a volume of dielectric material be placed in an electromagnetic field described by the vectors $\mathbf{E}$ and $\mathbf{B}$. In general, the field at a charge in the dielectric is not $\mathbf{E}$, $\mathbf{B}$ but rather some effective field $\mathbf{E}_{\text{eff}}$, $\mathbf{B}_{\text{eff}}$. In the case of isotropic substances

$$\mathbf{E}_{\text{eff}} = \mathbf{E} + \frac{\mathbf{P}}{3\epsilon_0} \qquad (4\text{-}39)$$

where $\mathbf{P}$ is the polarization of the medium. A similar expression holds for $\mathbf{B}_{\text{eff}}$ in terms of the magnetization $\mathbf{M}$.

Consider now an electron in the dielectric, and let it be bound by a Hooke's-law force $-k\mathbf{r}_0$, where $\mathbf{r}_0$ denotes the displacement of the electron from its equilibrium position. The total force on the electron is

$$\mathbf{F} = -k\mathbf{r}_0 - e(\mathbf{E}_{\text{eff}} + \mathbf{u} \times \mathbf{B}_{\text{eff}})$$

where $\mathbf{u} \equiv \dot{\mathbf{r}}_0$ denotes the velocity of the electron. But for nonrelativistic motion we can neglect the magnetic force in comparison with the electric force. Hence

$$\mathbf{F} = -k\mathbf{r}_0 - e\mathbf{E}_{\text{eff}} = -k\mathbf{r}_0 - e\mathbf{E} - e\frac{\mathbf{P}}{3\epsilon_0} \qquad (17\text{-}46)$$

Writing $\mathbf{u} = \dot{\mathbf{r}}_0$ and using (17-46), the nonrelativistic equation of motion (17-18) becomes

$$\ddot{\mathbf{r}}_0 - \gamma \dddot{\mathbf{r}}_0 + \omega_0^2 \mathbf{r}_0 = -\frac{e}{m}\mathbf{E} - \frac{e}{3m\epsilon_0}\mathbf{P}$$

or, approximately,

$$\ddot{\mathbf{r}}_0 + \Gamma \dot{\mathbf{r}}_0 + \omega_0^2 \mathbf{r}_0 = -\frac{e}{m}\mathbf{E} - \frac{e}{3m\epsilon_0}\mathbf{P} \qquad (17\text{-}47)$$

where γ, Γ, and ω_0^2 are defined as in Sec. 17-5.

If N is the number of electrons per unit volume, then $\mathbf{P} = -Ne\mathbf{r}_0$ (cf. Sec. 4-5) and (17-47) can be written

$$\ddot{\mathbf{P}} + \Gamma\dot{\mathbf{P}} + \omega_1^2\mathbf{P} = \frac{Ne^2}{m}\mathbf{E} \qquad (17\text{-}48)$$

where

$$\omega_1^2 \equiv \omega_0^2 - \frac{Ne^2}{3m\epsilon_0} \qquad (17\text{-}49)$$

ω_1 is called the natural (angular) frequency of oscillation. The problem is to solve (17-48) given that $\mathbf{E} = 0$ when $t < 0$.

We introduce the (infinite) Fourier time transform $\bar{\mathbf{E}}$ of $\mathbf{E}$ which is defined by the relations

$$\mathbf{E}(\mathbf{r}_0, t) = \frac{1}{\sqrt{2\pi}} \int_{-\infty}^{+\infty} \bar{\mathbf{E}}(\mathbf{r}_0, \omega) e^{i\omega t}\, d\omega$$

$$\bar{\mathbf{E}}(\mathbf{r}_0, \omega) = \frac{1}{\sqrt{2\pi}} \int_{0}^{+\infty} \mathbf{E}(\mathbf{r}_0, t) e^{-i\omega t}\, dt \qquad (17\text{-}50)$$

where the lower limit on the last integral is 0 and not $-\infty$ because $E(r_0,t) = 0$ for $t < 0$. Equation (17-48) then becomes

$$\ddot{P} + \Gamma\dot{P} + \omega_1^2 P = \frac{Ne^2}{\sqrt{2\pi}\, m} \int_{-\infty}^{+\infty} \bar{E}(r_0,\omega)e^{-i\omega t}\, d\omega \qquad (17\text{-}51)$$

and has for solution

$$P = \frac{Ne^2}{\sqrt{2\pi}\, m} \int_{-\infty}^{+\infty} \frac{\bar{E}(r_0,\omega)e^{i\omega t}}{\omega_1^2 - \omega^2 + i\omega\Gamma}\, d\omega \qquad (17\text{-}52)$$

Since $P = -Ner_0$, the displacement of the electron is

$$r_0 = -\frac{e}{\sqrt{2\pi}\, m} \int_{-\infty}^{+\infty} \frac{\bar{E}(r_0,\omega)e^{i\omega t}}{\omega_1^2 - \omega^2 + i\omega\Gamma}\, d\omega \qquad (17\text{-}53)$$

Suppose now that the electromagnetic field is due solely to monochromatic radiation of (angular) frequency ω; that is,

$$E(r_0,t) = \frac{1}{\sqrt{2\pi}} \bar{E}(r_0,\omega)e^{i\omega t} \qquad (17\text{-}54)$$

In such a case (17-52) and (17-53) reduce to

$$P = \frac{Ne^2}{m} \frac{E(r_0,t)}{\omega_1^2 - \omega^2 + i\omega\Gamma} \qquad (17\text{-}55)$$

and

$$r_0 = -\frac{e}{m} \frac{E(r_0,t)}{\omega_1^2 - \omega^2 + i\omega\Gamma} \qquad (17\text{-}56)$$

respectively.

If of the N electrons per unit volume there are N_α per unit volume characterized by the constants $\omega_{1\alpha}$ and Γ_α, then (17-52) and (17-55) must be replaced by

$$P = \sum_\alpha \frac{N_\alpha e^2}{\sqrt{2\pi}\, m} \int_{-\infty}^{+\infty} \frac{\bar{E}(r_0,\omega)e^{i\omega t}}{\omega_{1\alpha}^2 - \omega^2 + i\omega\Gamma_\alpha}\, d\omega \qquad (17\text{-}57)$$

and

$$P = E(r_0,t) \sum_\alpha \frac{N_\alpha e^2/m}{\omega_{1\alpha}^2 - \omega^2 + i\omega\Gamma_\alpha} \qquad (17\text{-}58)$$

17-7. DISPERSION

Since

$$D = \epsilon E = \epsilon_0 E + P \qquad (4\text{-}31)$$

so that the dielectric constant K is given by

$$K = \frac{\epsilon}{\epsilon_0} = 1 + \frac{P}{\epsilon_0 E}$$

it follows on using (17-58) that

$$K = \eta^2 = 1 + \frac{e^2}{m\epsilon_0} \sum_\alpha \frac{N_\alpha}{\omega_{1\alpha}^2 - \omega^2 + i\omega\Gamma_\alpha} \tag{17-59}$$

i.e., the dielectric constant and the index of refraction of the dielectric are functions of the frequency ω of the existing radiation. It is clear from (17-59) that, in general, the dielectric constant and the index of refraction are complex quantities. Since the index of refraction is complex, so is the phase velocity of an electromagnetic wave in the medium. Hence the wave will be absorbed as it traverses the medium.

Since the index of refraction is complex, we can write

$$\eta = n - ik \tag{17-60}$$

where both n and k are real. Then (17-59) becomes

$$(n - ik)^2 = 1 + \frac{e^2}{m\epsilon_0} \sum_\alpha \frac{N_\alpha}{\omega_{1\alpha}^2 - \omega^2 + i\omega\Gamma_\alpha} \tag{17-59a}$$

In the case of transparent substances there is no appreciable absorption and the index of refraction must be real. We must then assume that for such substances $\omega\Gamma_\alpha$ is negligible compared with $\omega_{1\alpha}^2 - \omega^2$. This is possible only when the frequency ω of the exciting radiation is considerably different from the natural frequencies $\omega_{1\alpha}$. In this case the index of refraction is given by

$$\eta^2 = n^2 = 1 + \frac{e^2}{m\epsilon_0} \sum_\alpha \frac{N_\alpha}{\omega_{1\alpha}^2 - \omega^2} \tag{17-61}$$

Note that in the limit of very low frequencies ($\omega \ll \omega_{1\alpha}$) the index of refraction becomes independent of frequency:

$$\eta^2 = 1 + \frac{e^2}{m\epsilon_0} \sum_\alpha \frac{N_\alpha}{\omega_{1\alpha}^2} = K_{\text{static}} \tag{17-62}$$

the value of the dielectric constant in an electrostatic field.

In terms of wavelength, $\lambda = 2\pi v/\omega$, where v is the phase velocity of propagation, (17-61) becomes

$$\eta^2 = 1 + \sum_\alpha \frac{\lambda^2 A_\alpha}{\lambda^2 - \lambda_{1\alpha}^2} \tag{17-61a}$$

where $A_\alpha = e^2 N_\alpha / m\epsilon_0 \omega_{1\alpha}^2$.

If the electrons are all of one type (17-61a) reduces to

$$\eta^2 = 1 + \frac{\lambda^2 A}{\lambda^2 - \lambda_1^2} \tag{17-63}$$

This equation is known as *Sellmeier's equation*. For $\lambda > \lambda_1$, η^2 is greater than unity and for $\lambda < \lambda_1$ less than unity. In either case (1) the index of refraction η increases with decreasing wavelength and (2) the dispersion $d\eta/d\lambda$ increases with decreasing wavelength. The first of these agrees with the common observation that in refraction by a transparent material violet light is deviated more than the red; the second with the observation that in the spectrum formed by a prism the violet end of the spectrum is spread out on a much larger scale than the red end. For these reasons the dispersion is called *normal dispersion*.

If $\lambda \gg \lambda_{1\alpha}$, (17-61a) becomes

$$\eta^2 = 1 + \sum_\alpha A_\alpha \left[1 + \left(\frac{\lambda_{1\alpha}}{\lambda}\right)^2 + \left(\frac{\lambda_{1\alpha}}{\lambda}\right)^4 + \cdots \right] \tag{17-64}$$

In the case where there is but one natural frequency of oscillation this relation reduces to

$$\eta^2 = 1 + A_1 + \frac{B_1}{\lambda^2} + \frac{B_2}{\lambda^4} + \cdots \tag{17-65}$$

where $B_n = A_1 \lambda_1^{2n}$. Equation (17-65) is *Cauchy's equation* for the index of refraction.

If $\lambda \ll \lambda_{1\alpha}$, (17-61a) becomes

$$\eta^2 = 1 - \sum_\alpha{}' \frac{\lambda^2 A_\alpha}{\lambda_{1\alpha}^2 [1 - (\lambda/\lambda_{1\alpha})^2]}$$

$$= 1 - \lambda^2 \sum_\alpha C_\alpha \left[1 + \left(\frac{\lambda}{\lambda_{1\alpha}}\right)^2 + \left(\frac{\lambda}{\lambda_{1\alpha}}\right)^4 + \cdots \right] \tag{17-66}$$

If the frequency ω of the exciting radiation is nearly equal to a natural frequency $\omega_{1\alpha}$, the term $\omega_{1\alpha}^2 - \omega^2$ in the denominator of (17-60) becomes very small and the term $i\omega\Gamma_\alpha$ can no longer be neglected. Thus the index of refraction is complex in this region. Separation of (17-60) into real and imaginary parts gives

$$n^2 - k^2 = 1 + \frac{e^2}{m\epsilon_0} \sum_\alpha{}' \frac{N_\alpha(\omega_{1\alpha}^2 - \omega^2)}{(\omega_{1\alpha}^2 - \omega^2)^2 + \omega^2\Gamma_\alpha^2} \tag{17-67}$$

$$2nk = \frac{e^2}{m\epsilon_0} \sum_\alpha \frac{N_\alpha\omega\Gamma_\alpha}{(\omega_{1\alpha}^2 - \omega^2)^2 + \omega^2\Gamma_\alpha^2} \tag{17-68}$$

To obtain approximate solutions of these equations we assume that we can replace n by 1 in (17-68). Then

$$k \simeq \frac{1}{2} \frac{e^2}{m\epsilon_0} \sum_\alpha \frac{N_\alpha \omega \Gamma_\alpha}{(\omega_{1\alpha}^2 - \omega^2)^2 + \omega^2 \Gamma_\alpha^2} \qquad (17\text{-}68a)$$

and

$$n^2 \simeq 1 + \frac{e^2}{m\epsilon_0} \sum_\alpha \frac{N_\alpha(\omega_{1\alpha}^2 - \omega^2)}{(\omega_{1\alpha}^2 - \omega^2)^2 + \omega^2 \Gamma_\alpha^2}$$
$$+ \left(\frac{1}{2} \frac{e^2}{m\epsilon_0} \sum_\alpha \frac{N_\alpha \omega \Gamma_\alpha}{(\omega_{1\alpha}^2 - \omega^2)^2 + \omega^2 \Gamma_\alpha^2} \right)^2 \qquad (17\text{-}67a)$$

so that

$$n \simeq 1 + \frac{1}{2} \frac{e^2}{m\epsilon_0} \sum_\alpha \frac{N_\alpha(\omega_{1\alpha}^2 - \omega^2)}{(\omega_{1\alpha}^2 - \omega^2)^2 + \omega^2 \Gamma_\alpha^2} \qquad (17\text{-}69)$$

It is clear from (17-68a) that, when ω approaches $\omega_{1\alpha}$, the absorption coefficient k becomes large and the radiation is strongly absorbed. The maximum value of k occurs when $\omega = \omega_{1\alpha}$. Consequently the natural frequency of oscillation ω_1 is to be interpreted as an *absorption frequency*. The region in which ω is nearly equal to $\omega_{1\alpha}$ is known as an *absorption band*.

It is seen from (17-69) that n, the real part of the index of refraction, has a maximum when

$$\omega \simeq \omega_{1\alpha} - \frac{\Gamma_\alpha}{2}$$

and a minimum when

$$\omega \simeq \omega_{1\alpha} + \frac{\Gamma_\alpha}{2}$$

Between these two frequencies n decreases with increasing frequency (n decreases with decreasing wavelength). Hence the dispersion is said to be *anomalous*.

17-8. SCATTERING BY A BOUND ELECTRON

Consider again an electron in a dielectric. Let it be bound by a Hooke's-law force $-k\mathbf{r}_0$, where $\mathbf{r}_0$ denotes its displacement from its equilibrium position. If the dielectric is placed in a monochromatic radiation field

$$\mathbf{E}(\mathbf{r}_0, t) = (2\pi)^{-\frac{1}{2}} \bar{\mathbf{E}}(\mathbf{r}_0, \omega) e^{i\omega t} \qquad (17\text{-}70)$$

then, from (17-56),

$$\mathbf{r}_0 = -\frac{e}{\sqrt{2\pi}\, m} \frac{\bar{\mathbf{E}}(\mathbf{r}_0, \omega) e^{i\omega t}}{\omega_1^2 - \omega^2 + i\omega\Gamma}$$

and

$$\ddot{\mathbf{r}}_0 = \frac{e\omega^2}{\sqrt{2\pi}\, m} \frac{\bar{\mathbf{E}}(\mathbf{r}_0, \omega) e^{i\omega t}}{\omega_1^2 - \omega^2 + i\omega\Gamma} \qquad (17\text{-}71)$$

According to (17-15) the rate at which energy is reradiated, i.e., scattered, by the electron is

$$\int \mathbf{N} \cdot d\mathbf{S} = \frac{e^2 \dot{u}^2}{6\pi\epsilon_0 c^3} = \frac{e^2 \ddot{r}_0{}^2}{6\pi\epsilon_0 c^3}$$

$$= \frac{e^4 [\bar{E}(\mathbf{r}_0,\omega)]^2}{12\pi^2 m^2 \epsilon_0 c^3} \frac{\omega^4 \cos^2(\omega t - \delta)}{(\omega_1{}^2 - \omega^2)^2 + \omega^2 \Gamma^2} \qquad (17\text{-}72)$$

where we remembered to use the real part of (17-71) and

$$\tan \delta = \frac{\omega \Gamma}{\omega_1{}^2 - \omega^2}$$

Averaging (17-72) over a complete period of oscillation yields

$$\mathcal{P}_r \equiv \int \check{\mathbf{N}} \cdot d\mathbf{S} = \frac{e^2 [\bar{E}(\mathbf{r}_0,\omega)]^2}{24\pi^2 m^2 \epsilon_0 c^3} \frac{\omega^4}{(\omega_1{}^2 - \omega^2)^2 + \omega^2 \Gamma^2} \qquad (17\text{-}73)$$

for the average energy radiated per unit time.

The average intensity of the exciting radiation is

$$N_0 = \overline{|\mathbf{E} \times \mathbf{H}|} = \sqrt{\frac{\epsilon_0}{\mu_0}}\, \overline{E^2} = \frac{1}{4\pi} \sqrt{\frac{\epsilon_0}{\mu_0}}\, [\bar{E}(\mathbf{r}_0,\omega)]^2 \qquad (17\text{-}74)$$

By definition, the *scattering cross section* σ is given by

$$\sigma = \frac{\mathcal{P}_r}{N_0} \qquad (17\text{-}75)$$

Substitution into (17-75) by means of (17-73) and (17-74) yields

$$\sigma = \sigma_0 \frac{\omega^4}{(\omega_1{}^2 - \omega^2)^2 + \omega^2 \Gamma^2} \qquad (17\text{-}76)$$

where

$$\sigma_0 = \frac{e^4}{6\pi m^2 \epsilon_0{}^2 c^4} = \frac{8\pi}{3} a^2 \qquad (17\text{-}77)$$

is a constant, independent of frequency, and a is the radius of the electron. The scattering cross section is a maximum at resonance when $\omega = \omega_1$:

$$\sigma_{\max} = \sigma_0 \left(\frac{\omega_1}{\Gamma}\right)^2 \qquad (17\text{-}78)$$

This cross section is known as the *resonance scattering cross section*.

When $\omega_1 \gg \omega$, (17-76) reduces to the so-called *Rayleigh scattering cross section*

$$\sigma = \sigma_0 \left(\frac{\omega}{\omega_1}\right)^4 \qquad \omega_1 \gg \omega \qquad (17\text{-}79)$$

When $\omega_1 = 0$ and $\Gamma \ll \omega$, (17-76) reduces to

$$\sigma = \sigma_0 \qquad (17\text{-}80)$$

Thus σ_0 is the cross section for the scattering of radiation by a free electron. It is known as the *Thomson scattering cross section*.

17-9. ABSORPTION BY A BOUND ELECTRON

Let us consider now the energy transferred from the exciting radiation to the oscillating electron. This energy is equal to the work done on the electron by the radiation field; i.e.,

$$W = -e \int_{-\infty}^{+\infty} \mathbf{E} \cdot \dot{\mathbf{r}}_0 \, dt = -e \int_{-\infty}^{+\infty} E \dot{r}_0 \, dt \qquad (17\text{-}81)$$

If the radiation field is given by

$$\mathbf{E}(\mathbf{r}_0, t) = \frac{1}{\sqrt{2\pi}} \int_{-\infty}^{+\infty} \bar{\mathbf{E}}(\mathbf{r}_0, \omega) e^{i\omega t} \, d\omega \qquad (17\text{-}50)$$

then

$$\mathbf{r}_0(t) = -\frac{e}{\sqrt{2\pi}\, m} \int_{-\infty}^{+\infty} \frac{\bar{\mathbf{E}}(\mathbf{r}_0, \omega) e^{i\omega t}}{\omega_1{}^2 - \omega^2 + i\omega\Gamma} \, d\omega \qquad (17\text{-}53)$$

$$\dot{\mathbf{r}}_0(t) = -\frac{e}{\sqrt{2\pi}\, m} \int_{-\infty}^{+\infty} \frac{i\omega \bar{\mathbf{E}}(\mathbf{r}_0, \omega) e^{i\omega t}}{\omega_1{}^2 - \omega^2 + i\omega\Gamma} \, d\omega \qquad (17\text{-}82)$$

and

$$\dot{\bar{\mathbf{r}}}_0(\omega) = -\frac{e}{m} \frac{i\omega \bar{\mathbf{E}}(\mathbf{r}_0, \omega)}{\omega_1{}^2 - \omega^2 + i\omega\Gamma} \qquad (17\text{-}83)$$

Hence, using (17-43) with $E \equiv f$ and $\dot{r}_0 \equiv g$, (17-81) becomes

$$
\begin{aligned}
W &= \frac{e^2}{m} \int_{-\infty}^{+\infty} \frac{i\omega |\bar{\mathbf{E}}(\mathbf{r}_0, \omega)|^2}{\omega_1{}^2 - \omega^2 + i\omega\Gamma} \, d\omega \\
&= \frac{e^2}{m} \int_{-\infty}^{+\infty} \frac{[\omega^2\Gamma + i\omega(\omega_1{}^2 - \omega^2)]}{(\omega_1{}^2 - \omega^2)^2 + \omega^2\Gamma^2} |\bar{\mathbf{E}}(\mathbf{r}_0, \omega)|^2 \, d\omega \\
&= \frac{e^2}{m} \int_{-\infty}^{+\infty} \frac{\omega^2\Gamma |\bar{\mathbf{E}}(\mathbf{r}_0, \omega)|^2}{(\omega_1{}^2 - \omega^2)^2 + \omega^2\Gamma^2} \, d\omega \\
&= \frac{2e^2}{m} \int_{0}^{\infty} \frac{\omega^2\Gamma |\bar{\mathbf{E}}(\mathbf{r}_0, \omega)|^2}{(\omega_1{}^2 - \omega^2)^2 + \omega^2\Gamma^2} \, d\omega \qquad (17\text{-}84)
\end{aligned}
$$

The integral can be approximately evaluated as follows: Since the integrand is large only in the neighborhood of the natural frequency ω_1,

$$
\begin{aligned}
\int_{0}^{\infty} \frac{\omega^2\Gamma |\bar{\mathbf{E}}(\mathbf{r}_0, \omega)|^2}{(\omega_1{}^2 - \omega^2)^2 + \omega^2\Gamma^2} \, d\omega &\doteq \frac{\Gamma}{4} |\bar{\mathbf{E}}(\mathbf{r}_0, \omega_1)|^2 \int_{0}^{\infty} \frac{d\omega}{(\omega_1 - \omega)^2 + \Gamma^2/4} \\
&= \frac{\Gamma}{4} |\bar{\mathbf{E}}(\mathbf{r}_0, \omega_1)|^2 \int_{-\omega_1}^{\infty} \frac{d\eta}{\eta^2 + \Gamma^2/4} \\
&\doteq \frac{\Gamma}{4} |\bar{\mathbf{E}}(\mathbf{r}_0, \omega_1)|^2 \int_{-\infty}^{\infty} \frac{d\eta}{\eta^2 + \Gamma^2/4} \\
&= \frac{\pi}{2} |\bar{\mathbf{E}}(\mathbf{r}_0, \omega_1)|^2
\end{aligned}
$$

Hence the energy transferred from the exciting radiation to the oscillating electron is

$$W \doteq \frac{\pi e^2}{m} |\bar{\mathbf{E}}(\mathbf{r}_0, \omega_1)|^2 \tag{17-85}$$

This result can be expressed in a different form. Since the intensity of the exciting radiation is

$$N = |\mathbf{E} \times \mathbf{H}| = \sqrt{\frac{\epsilon_0}{\mu_0}} E^2$$

the total energy crossing unit area at $\mathbf{r}_0$ normal to the direction of propagation of the incident radiation is

$$W_i = \int_{-\infty}^{+\infty} N(\mathbf{r}_0, t) \, dt = \sqrt{\frac{\epsilon_0}{\mu_0}} \int_{-\infty}^{+\infty} [E(\mathbf{r}_0, t)]^2 \, dt$$

Using (17-43) with $f = g = E$, this gives

$$W_i = \sqrt{\frac{\epsilon_0}{\mu_0}} \int_{-\infty}^{+\infty} |\bar{\mathbf{E}}(\mathbf{r}_0, \omega)|^2 \, d\omega \equiv \int_{-\infty}^{+\infty} I(\omega) \, d\omega$$

where $\bar{\mathbf{E}}(\mathbf{r}_0, -\omega) = \bar{\mathbf{E}}^*(\mathbf{r}_0, \omega)$. Hence (17-85) can be written

$$W \doteq \frac{\pi e^2}{m} \sqrt{\frac{\mu_0}{\epsilon_0}} I(\omega_1) \tag{17-86}$$

in terms of the spectral energy distribution functions.

EXERCISES

17-1. Verify that the electromagnetic field produced by an electron in uniform motion is given by

$$\mathbf{E}(\mathbf{r}, t) = -\frac{e}{4\pi\epsilon_0 s^3} \left(1 - \frac{u^2}{c^2}\right) \left(\mathbf{R} - \frac{R}{c} \mathbf{u}\right) \Big|_{t_0 = t - R/c}$$

$$\mathbf{B}(\mathbf{r}, t) = \frac{\mathbf{R} \times \mathbf{E}}{Rc} \Big|_{t_0 = t - R/c}$$

Obtain these same formulas by applying the transformation equations (9-34a) to the field of a static charge and noting that (9-34a) refers to the observer's time.

17-2. Show that, when $u \ll c$, the fields of Exercise 17-1 reduce to

$$\mathbf{E}(\mathbf{r}, t) = -\frac{e}{4\pi\epsilon_0} \frac{\mathbf{R}}{R^3}$$

$$\mathbf{B}(\mathbf{r}, t) = \frac{\mu_0}{4\pi} \frac{-e\mathbf{u} \times \mathbf{R}}{R^3}$$

respectively, the Coulomb field of a static point charge and the Ampère field for a slowly moving charge.

17-3. Show that Eq. (17-13) is explicitly

$$N = -\frac{e^2 R}{16\pi^2 \epsilon_0 s^6 c^3} \mathbf{R} \left[\left(1 - \frac{u^2}{c^2}\right) R^2 \dot{u}^2 \cos^2 \alpha - \frac{2sR\dot{u}}{c} (\mathbf{u} \cdot \dot{\mathbf{u}}) \cos \alpha - s^2 \dot{u}^2 \right] \Bigg|_{t_0 = t - R/c}$$

where α is the angle between the vectors $\mathbf{R}$ and $\dot{\mathbf{u}}$, and then verify Eq. (17-14). It should be noted that this result refers to the time scale of the observer at rest; that is, N represents the energy flow per unit time t through unit area of the surface of the sphere of radius R. To obtain the amount of energy lost by the electron per unit time t_0, we note that

$$\frac{dt}{dt_0} = \frac{cs}{R}$$

Hence

$$N \frac{dt}{dt_0} = -\frac{e^2}{16\pi^2 \epsilon_0 s^5 c^2} \mathbf{R} \left[\left(1 - \frac{u^2}{c^2}\right) R^2 \dot{u}^2 \cos^2 \alpha \right.$$
$$\left. - \frac{2sR\dot{u}}{c} (\mathbf{u} \cdot \dot{\mathbf{u}}) \cos \alpha - s^2 \dot{u}^2 \right] \Bigg|_{t_0 = t - R/c}$$

17-4. Show that, when $\dot{u}$ is parallel to $\mathbf{u}$, (17-13) reduces to

$$N = \frac{e^2 \dot{u}^2}{16\pi^2 \epsilon_0 c^3} \frac{\sin^2 \theta}{\left(1 - \dfrac{\mu}{c} \cos \theta\right)^6} \frac{\mathbf{R}}{R^3} \Bigg|_{t_0 = t - R/c}$$

where θ is the angle between $\mathbf{u}$ and $\mathbf{R}$, so that the energy flow per unit time t_0 through unit area of the surface of the sphere of radius R is

$$N \frac{dt}{dt_0} = \frac{e^2 \dot{u}^2}{16\pi^2 \epsilon_0 c^2} \frac{\sin^2 \theta}{\left(1 - \dfrac{u}{c} \cos \theta\right)^5} \frac{\mathbf{R}}{R^4} \Bigg|_{t_0 = t - R/c}$$

17-5. Show that, when $\dot{\mathbf{u}}$ and $\mathbf{u}$ are perpendicular to each other,

$$N \frac{dt}{dt_0} = -\frac{e^2 \dot{u}^2}{16\pi^2 \epsilon_0 c^2} \frac{(1 - u^2/c^2) \cos^2 \theta - [1 - (u/c) \cos \theta]^2}{\left(1 - \dfrac{u}{c} \cos \theta\right)^5} \frac{\mathbf{R}}{R^4} \Bigg|_{t_0 = t - R/c}$$

Let φ denote the azimuthal angle between the planes determined by $\mathbf{u}$ and $\dot{\mathbf{u}}$ and by $\mathbf{u}$ and $\mathbf{R}$, and verify that

$$N \frac{dt}{dt_0} = -\frac{e^2 \dot{u}^2}{16\pi^2 \epsilon_0 c^2} \frac{(1 - u^2/c^2) \sin^2 \theta \cos^2 \varphi - [1 - (u/c) \cos \theta]^2}{\left(1 - \dfrac{u}{c} \cos \theta\right)^5} \frac{\mathbf{R}}{R^4} \Bigg|_{t_0 = t - R/c}$$

17-6. Show that the width of the line (17-43) in wavelength units is a constant, independent of the frequency of the oscillator. Determine the magnitude of the constant in terms of the electron radius.

REFERENCES

Becker, R.: "Theorie der Elektrizitat," band II, Secs. B and C III, J. W. Edwards Publisher, Incorporated, Ann Arbor, 1946.
Heitler, W.: "The Quantum Theory of Radiation," 3d ed., chapter 1, Oxford University Press, London, 1954.

Landau, L., and E. Lifshitz: "The Classical Theory of Fields," Addison-Wesley Publishing Company, Inc., Cambridge, Mass., 1951.

Lorentz, H. A.: "Theory of Electrons," 2d ed., Dover Publications, Inc., New York, 1952.

Panofsky, W. K. H., and M. Phillips: "Classical Electricity and Magnetism," chaps. 18, 19, 20, and 21, Addison-Wesley Publishing Company, Inc., Cambridge, Mass., 1955.

Rosenfeld, L.: "Theory of Electrons," North Holland Publishing Company, Amsterdam, 1951.

Smythe, W. R.: "Static and Dynamic Electricity," 2d ed., chap. 14, McGraw-Hill Book Company, Inc., New York, 1950.

Sommerfeld, A.: "Electrodynamics," paragraphs 29, 30, and 36, Academic Press, Inc., New York, 1952.

Stratton, J. A.: "Electromagnetic Theory," chaps. 5 and 8, McGraw-Hill Book Company, Inc., New York, 1941.

APPENDIX I

Evaluation of the Integral

$$I_1 = \iiint\limits_{-\infty}^{+\infty} \frac{e^{i[k_1(x_1-x_1')+k_2(x_2-x_2')+k_3(x_3-x_3')]}}{k_1{}^2 + k_2{}^2 + k_3{}^2} \, dk_1 \, dk_2 \, dk_3$$

This integral can be evaluated by transforming to space polar coordinates. Let

$$\mathbf{k} = k_1\mathbf{i}_1 + k_2\mathbf{i}_2 + k_3\mathbf{i}_3$$
$$\mathbf{r} - \mathbf{r}' = (x_1 - x_1')\mathbf{i}_1 + (x_2 - x_2')\mathbf{i}_2 + (x_3 - x_3')\mathbf{i}_3$$

and take the polar axis in the direction of $(\mathbf{r} - \mathbf{r}')$. Then the integral becomes

$$I_1 = \int_0^\infty \int_0^\pi \int_0^{2\pi} \frac{e^{ik|\mathbf{r}-\mathbf{r}'|\cos\theta}}{k^2} \, k^2 \, dk \, \sin\theta \, d\theta \, d\varphi$$

where θ is the angle between $\mathbf{k}$ and $\mathbf{r} - \mathbf{r}'$, or

$$I_1 = 2\pi \int_0^\infty \int_{-1}^{+1} e^{ik|\mathbf{r}-\mathbf{r}'|\cos\theta} \, dk \, d(\cos\theta)$$

$$= 2\pi \int_0^\infty \left(\frac{e^{ik|\mathbf{r}-\mathbf{r}'|}}{ik|\mathbf{r}-\mathbf{r}'|} - \frac{e^{-ik|\mathbf{r}-\mathbf{r}'|}}{ik|\mathbf{r}-\mathbf{r}'|} \right) dk \tag{I-1}$$

$$I_1 = \frac{2\pi}{i|\mathbf{r}-\mathbf{r}'|} \int_{-\infty}^{+\infty} \frac{e^{ik|\mathbf{r}-\mathbf{r}'|}}{k} \, dk \tag{I-2}$$

Note that the integral (I-2) is, strictly speaking, meaningless, since the integrand diverges when $k = 0$. However, the integral (I-1) is well-defined, since

$$\frac{e^{ik|\mathbf{r}-\mathbf{r}'|}}{ik|\mathbf{r}-\mathbf{r}'|} - \frac{e^{-ik|\mathbf{r}-\mathbf{r}'|}}{ik|\mathbf{r}-\mathbf{r}'|} = 2\frac{\sin k|\mathbf{r}-\mathbf{r}'|}{k|\mathbf{r}-\mathbf{r}'|}$$

and

$$\lim_{k=0} \frac{\sin k|\mathbf{r}-\mathbf{r}'|}{k|\mathbf{r}-\mathbf{r}'|} = 1$$

This means that, when we use contour integration to evaluate I_1 in the form (I-2), we must take the principal value of the integral (see below).

293

The integral in (I-2) is of the form

$$\int_{-\infty}^{+\infty} \frac{e^{itx_1}}{x_1 - \alpha} dx_1 \qquad (I\text{-}3)$$

where α and t are both real and $t > 0$. Since the integrand diverges when $x_1 = \alpha$ the integral is, strictly speaking, meaningless. However, with a prescription as to what is to be done at the pole α, the integral can be defined and can be evaluated by means of contour integration. Different prescriptions, such as taking the principal value of the integral or taking a path going above or below the pole, will yield different results. Consider first the principal value of the integral defined by

$$P \int_{-\infty}^{+\infty} \frac{e^{itx_1}}{x_1 - \alpha} dx_1 = \lim_{\rho=0} \left(\int_{-\infty}^{\alpha-\rho} \frac{e^{itx_1}}{x_1 - \alpha} dx_1 + \int_{\alpha+\rho}^{+\infty} \frac{e^{itx_1}}{x_1 - \alpha} dx_1 \right) \quad (I\text{-}4)$$

To evaluate this we form the integral of $e^{itz}/(z - \alpha)$ along a contour C which extends along (1) the real axis from $-R$ to $\alpha - \rho$, (2) a semicircle with center at α and radius ρ, (3) the real axis from $\alpha + \rho$ to R, and (4) a semicircle with center at the origin and radius R, where $\rho \to 0$ and $R \to \infty$. Along the real axis, $z = x_1$, and along the two semicircles,

$$z = \alpha + \rho e^{i\theta} = \alpha + \rho(\cos\theta + i\sin\theta)$$

and

$$z = Re^{i\theta} = R(\cos\theta + i\sin\theta)$$

respectively. We take both the semicircle of radius ρ and that of radius R as lying in the upper half of the complex plane. Then

$$\int_C \frac{e^{itz}}{z - \alpha} dz = 0 = \int_{-R}^{\alpha-\rho} \frac{e^{itx_1}}{x_1 - \alpha} dx_1 + \int_{\pi}^{0} e^{it\alpha + it(\rho e^{i\theta})} i\, d\theta$$
$$+ \int_{\alpha+\rho}^{R} \frac{e^{itx_1}}{x_1 - \alpha} dx_1 + \int_{0}^{\pi} \frac{e^{it(Re^{i\theta})}}{Re^{i\theta} - \alpha} iRe^{i\theta}\, d\theta$$

since the integrand has no pole inside the contour. In the limits $\rho \to 0$ and $R \to \infty$, the sum of the first and third terms on the right becomes

$$P \int_{-\infty}^{+\infty} \frac{e^{itx_1}}{x_1 - \alpha} dx_1$$

the second integral approaches $-\pi i e^{it\alpha}$, and the fourth integral approaches zero. Hence

$$P \int_{-\infty}^{+\infty} \frac{e^{itx_1}}{x_1 - \alpha} dx_1 = \pi i e^{it\alpha} \qquad (I\text{-}5)$$

If the prescription for evaluating (I-3) is to take a contour which goes under the pole α, we write

$$\int_{-\infty}^{+\infty} \frac{e^{itx_1}}{x_1 - \alpha} dx_1 = \lim_{\rho \to 0} \int_{-\infty}^{+\infty} \frac{e^{itx_1}}{x_1 - (\alpha + i\rho)} dx \qquad \rho > 0 \qquad \text{(I-6)}$$

and form the integral of $e^{itz}/[z - (\alpha + i\rho)]$ along a contour C which extends (1) along the real axis from $-R$ to $+R$ and (2) a semicircle lying in the upper half of the complex plane with center at the origin and radius R, where $R \to \infty$. Then

$$\int_C \frac{e^{itz}}{z - (\alpha + i\rho)} dz = 2\pi i e^{it(\alpha + i\rho)}$$

$$= \int_{-R}^{+R} \frac{e^{itx_1}}{x_1 - (\alpha + i\rho)} dx_1$$

$$+ \int_0^\pi \frac{e^{it(Re^{i\theta})}}{Re^{i\theta} - (\alpha + i\rho)} iRe^{i\theta} d\theta$$

In the limit $R \to \infty$, this reduces to

$$2\pi i e^{it(\alpha + i\rho)} = \int_{-\infty}^{+\infty} \frac{e^{itx_1}}{x_1 - (\alpha + i\rho)} dx_1$$

which becomes, when $\rho \to 0$,

$$2\pi i e^{it\alpha} = \int_{-\infty}^{\infty} \frac{e^{itx_1}}{x_1 - \alpha} dx_1 \qquad \text{(I-7)}$$

If the prescription for evaluating (I-3) is to take a contour which goes over the pole α, we write (I-6) but take $\rho < 0$. With the same contour we find that

$$0 = \int_{-\infty}^{+\infty} \frac{e^{itx_1}}{x_1 - \alpha} dx_1 \qquad \text{(I-8)}$$

since the contour does not include the pole.

Thus

$$\int_{-\infty}^{+\infty} \frac{e^{ik|\mathbf{r}-\mathbf{r}'|}}{k} dk = \pi i, \, 2\pi i, \text{ or } 0$$

corresponding, respectively, to the principal value, a contour which goes under the pole or a contour which goes over the pole.

Using the value corresponding to the principal value we find that

$$I_1 = \frac{2\pi^2}{|\mathbf{r} - \mathbf{r}'|}$$

Solution of the Wave Equations for the Electrodynamic Potentials

To solve the equation

$$\nabla^2\phi(\mathbf{r},t) - \frac{1}{v^2}\frac{\partial^2}{\partial t^2}\phi(\mathbf{r},t) = -\frac{1}{\epsilon}\rho_F(\mathbf{r},t) \qquad (9\text{-}62)$$

we first introduce the Fourier time transforms

$$f(\mathbf{r},t) = \left(\frac{1}{2\pi}\right)^{\frac{1}{2}}\int_{-\infty}^{+\infty}\tilde{f}(\mathbf{r},\omega)e^{i\omega t}\,d\omega \qquad (\text{II-1})$$

$$\tilde{f}(\mathbf{r},\omega) = \left(\frac{1}{2\pi}\right)^{\frac{1}{2}}\int_{-\infty}^{+\infty}f(\mathbf{r},t)e^{-i\omega t}\,dt \qquad (\text{II-2})$$

Equation (9-62) then transforms into

$$\nabla^2\tilde{\phi}(\mathbf{r},\omega) + k^2\tilde{\phi}(\mathbf{r},\omega) = -\frac{1}{\epsilon}\tilde{\rho}_F(\mathbf{r},\omega) \qquad (\text{II-3})$$

where $k^2 = \omega^2/v^2$.

The solution of (II-3) can be written

$$\tilde{\phi}(\mathbf{r},\omega) = -\frac{1}{\epsilon}\int_{-\infty}^{+\infty}\tilde{G}(\mathbf{r},\mathbf{r}';\omega)\tilde{\rho}_F(\mathbf{r}',\omega)\,d\mathbf{r}' \qquad (\text{II-4})$$

where Green's function $G(r,r';\omega)$ is the solution of

$$\nabla^2\tilde{G} + k^2\tilde{G} = \delta(\mathbf{r} - \mathbf{r}') \qquad (\text{II-5})$$

which satisfies the same boundary conditions as on $\tilde{\phi}(\mathbf{r},\omega)$. To find this solution first multiply (II-5) by $(2\pi)^{-\frac{3}{2}}e^{-i\mathbf{\kappa}\cdot\mathbf{r}}\,d\mathbf{r}$ and integrate over all $\mathbf{r}$. Then

$$-\kappa^2\bar{\tilde{G}}(\mathbf{\kappa},\mathbf{r}';\omega) + k^2\bar{\tilde{G}}(\mathbf{\kappa},\mathbf{r}';\omega) = \left(\frac{1}{2\pi}\right)^{\frac{3}{2}}e^{-i\mathbf{\kappa}\cdot\mathbf{r}'}$$

or

$$\bar{\tilde{G}}(\mathbf{\kappa},\mathbf{r}';\omega) = -\left(\frac{1}{2\pi}\right)^{\frac{3}{2}}\frac{e^{-i\mathbf{\kappa}\cdot\mathbf{r}'}}{\kappa^2 - k^2} \qquad (\text{II-6})$$

where $\bar{\tilde{G}}(\mathbf{\kappa},\mathbf{r}';\omega)$ is the Fourier space transform of $\tilde{G}(\mathbf{r},\mathbf{r}';\omega)$ (cf. Sec. 1-14).

Hence

$$
\begin{aligned}
\tilde{G}(\mathbf{r},\mathbf{r}';\omega) &= -\left(\frac{1}{2\pi}\right)^3 \int_{-\infty}^{+\infty} \frac{e^{i\mathbf{\kappa}\cdot(\mathbf{r}-\mathbf{r}')}}{\kappa^2 - k^2}\, d\mathbf{\kappa} \\
&= -\left(\frac{1}{2\pi}\right)^3 \int_0^\infty \int_0^\pi \int_0^{2\pi} \frac{e^{i\kappa|\mathbf{r}-\mathbf{r}'|\cos\theta}}{\kappa^2 - k^2}\, \kappa^2\, d\kappa\, \sin\theta\, d\theta\, d\varphi \\
&= \left(\frac{1}{2\pi}\right)^2 \frac{i}{|r-r'|} \int_{-\infty}^{+\infty} \frac{\kappa e^{i\kappa|\mathbf{r}-\mathbf{r}'|}}{\kappa^2 - k^2}\, d\kappa \\
&= \left(\frac{1}{2\pi}\right)^2 \frac{i}{2|\mathbf{r}-\mathbf{r}'|} \left(\int_{-\infty}^{+\infty} \frac{e^{i\kappa|\mathbf{r}-\mathbf{r}'|}}{\kappa - k}\, d\kappa + \int_{-\infty}^{+\infty} \frac{e^{i\kappa|\mathbf{r}-\mathbf{r}'|}}{\kappa + k}\, d\kappa \right) \quad \text{(II-7)}
\end{aligned}
$$

The integrals in (II-7) can be evaluated by the procedure described in Appendix I. Thus, if we take the principal values of the integrals,

$$
\tilde{G}(\mathbf{r},\mathbf{r}';\omega) = \frac{1}{2}\left(-\frac{1}{4\pi} \frac{e^{ik|\mathbf{r}-\mathbf{r}'|}}{|\mathbf{r}-\mathbf{r}'|} - \frac{1}{4\pi} \frac{e^{-ik|\mathbf{r}-\mathbf{r}'|}}{|\mathbf{r}-\mathbf{r}'|} \right) \tag{II-8}
$$

$$
\tilde{G}(\mathbf{r},\mathbf{r}';\omega) = -\frac{1}{4\pi} \frac{\cos k|\mathbf{r}-\mathbf{r}'|}{|\mathbf{r}-\mathbf{r}'|} \tag{II-8a}
$$

If we take a contour which goes under the pole $\kappa = k$ and above the pole $\kappa = -k$,

$$
\tilde{G}(\mathbf{r},\mathbf{r}';\omega) = -\frac{1}{4\pi} \frac{e^{ik|\mathbf{r}-\mathbf{r}'|}}{|\mathbf{r}-\mathbf{r}'|} \tag{II-9}
$$

while use of the contour which goes above the pole $\kappa = k$ and under the pole $\kappa = -k$ yields

$$
\tilde{G}(\mathbf{r},\mathbf{r}';\omega) = -\frac{1}{4\pi} \frac{e^{-ik|\mathbf{r}-\mathbf{r}'|}}{|\mathbf{r}-\mathbf{r}'|} \tag{II-10}
$$

Substitution of Green's function (II-10) into (II-4) gives

$$
\tilde{\phi}(\mathbf{r},\omega) = \frac{1}{4\pi\epsilon} \int_{-\infty}^{+\infty} \frac{\tilde{\rho}_F(\mathbf{r}',\omega)e^{-ik|\mathbf{r}-\mathbf{r}'|}}{|\mathbf{r}-\mathbf{r}'|}\, d\mathbf{r}'
$$

so that

$$
\begin{aligned}
\phi(\mathbf{r},t) &= \frac{1}{4\pi\epsilon} \int_{-\infty}^{+\infty} \frac{d\mathbf{r}'}{|\mathbf{r}-\mathbf{r}'|} \left[\left(\frac{1}{2\pi}\right)^{1/2} \int_{-\infty}^{+\infty} \tilde{\rho}_F(\mathbf{r}',\omega)e^{i\omega t}e^{-iw|\mathbf{r}-\mathbf{r}'|/v} \right) \right] d\omega \\
&= \frac{1}{4\pi\epsilon} \int_{-\infty}^{+\infty} \frac{\rho_F(\mathbf{r}',t - \omega|\mathbf{r}-\mathbf{r}'|/v)}{|\mathbf{r}-\mathbf{r}'|}\, d\mathbf{r}'
\end{aligned}
$$

the retarded potential. Use of Green's function (II-9) leads to the advanced potential, while use of (II-8) yields a potential which is the arithmetic mean of the advanced and retarded potentials.

APPENDIX III

Fundamental Constants

Entity	Symbol	Value
Permittivity of vacuum	ϵ_0	8.854×10^{-12} farad m^{-1}
Permeability of vacuum	μ_0	$4\pi \times 10^{-7}$ henry m^{-1}
Velocity of light in vacuum	c	2.998×10^8 m sec^{-1}
Charge on the electron	e	1.6008×10^{-19} coulomb
Mass of the electron	m	9.107×10^{-31} kg

Conversion Table for Units†

Entity	Symbol	System of Units			
		mks	esu	emu	Gaussian
Time	t	1 second (sec)	1 sec	1 sec	1 sec
Length	l	1 meter (m)	10^2 cm	10^2 cm	10^2 cm
Mass	m	1 kilogram (kg)	10^3 g	10^3 g	10^3 g
Force	F	1 newton	10^5 dyne	10^5 dyne	10^5 dyne
Energy	W	1 joule	10^7 erg	10^7 erg	10^7 erg
Power	P	1 watt	10^7 erg sec^{-1}	10^7 erg sec^{-1}	10^7 erg sec^{-1}
Capacitance	C	1 farad	$10^{-9}\,c^2$ cm	10^{-9}	$10^{-9}\,c^2$ cm
Charge	q	1 coulomb	$10^{-1}\,c$ statcoulomb	10^{-1}	$10^{-1}\,c$ statcoulomb
Charge density	ρ	1 coulomb m^{-3}	$10^{-7}\,c$ statcoulomb cm^{-3}	10^{-7}	$10^{-7}\,c$ statcoulomb cm^{-3}
Conductivity	σ	1 mho m^{-1}	$10^{-11}\,c^2$	10^{-11}	$10^{-11}\,c^2$
Current	i	1 ampere	$10^{-1}\,c$ statampere	10^{-1} abampere	$10^{-1}\,c$ statampere
Current density	j	1 ampere m^{-2}	$10^{-5}\,c$ statampere cm^{-2}	10^{-5} abampere cm^{-2}	$10^{-5}\,c$ statampere cm^{-2}
Electric displacement	D	1 coulomb m^{-2}	$4\pi \times 10^{-5}\,c$	$4\pi \times 10^{-5}$	$4\pi \times 10^{-5}\,c$
Electric field intensity	E	1 volt m^{-1}	$10^3\,c^{-1}$ statvolt cm^{-1}	10^6	$10^6\,c^{-1}$ statvolt cm^{-1}
Electric potential	$\phi = \int E \cdot ds$	1 volt	$10^3\,c^{-1}$ statvolt	10^8	$10^8\,c^{-1}$ statvolt
Inductance	L	1 henry	$10^{-3}\,c^{-2}$ stathenry	10^9	$10^9\,c^{-2}$ stathenry
Magnetic field intensity	H	1 ampere-turn m^{-1}	$4\pi \times 10^{-3}\,c$	$4\pi \times 10^{-3}$ oersted	$4\pi \times 10^{-3}$ oersted
Magnetic flux	$\phi = \int B \cdot dS$	1 weber		10^8 maxwell	10^8 maxwell
Magnetic induction	B	1 weber m^{-2}	$10^4\,c^{-1}$	10^4 gauss	10^4 gauss
Magnetic potential		1 weber m^{-1}	$10^6\,c^{-1}$	10^6	10^6
Magnetization	$\phi_m = \int B \cdot ds$, M	1 ampere-turn m^{-1}	$10^{-3}\,c$	10^{-3}	10^{-3}
Permeability	μ	1 henry m^{-1}	$\dfrac{1}{4\pi}\,10^7\,c^{-2}$	$\dfrac{1}{4\pi}\,10^7$	$\dfrac{1}{4\pi}\,10^7$
Permittivity	ϵ	1 farad m^{-1}	$4\pi10^{-11}\,c^2$	$4\pi10^{-11}$	$4\pi10^{-11}$
Polarization	P	1 coulomb m^{-2}	$10^{-5}\,c$	10^{-5}	$10^{-5}\,c$
Resistance	R	1 ohm	$10^9\,c^{-2}$ statohm	10^9	$10^9\,c^{-2}$ statohm
Specific resistance		1 ohm m	$10^{11}\,c^{-2}$ statohm cm	10^{11}	$10^{11}\,c^{-2}$ statohm cm
Vector potential	A	1 weber m^{-1}	$10^6\,c^{-1}$	10^6	10^6

† Equality signs are implied across any row; $c = 2.998 \times 10^{10}$.

APPENDIX V

Conversion Table for Symbols in Equations

All equations in the text are in mks units. In order to convert any equation into its equivalent in the Gaussian system of units make the following substitutions:

mks $\longrightarrow$ Gaussian	
A	A/c
B	B/c
C	$C/4\pi$
D	$D/4\pi$
E	E
ϵ_0	$1/4\pi$
ϵ	$K/4\pi$
H	$Hc/4\pi$
i	i
j	j
M	Mc
μ_0	$4\pi/c^2$
μ	$\mu 4\pi/c^2$
P	P
$\phi = \int \mathbf{E} \cdot d\mathbf{s}$	ϕ
$\phi_m = \int \mathbf{B} \cdot d\mathbf{s}$	ϕ_m/c

Index